Student Solutions Manual

for use with

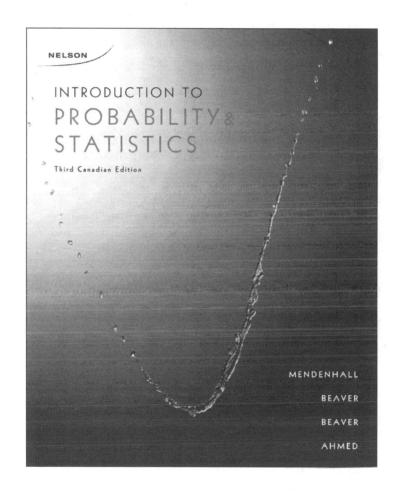

NELSON

INTRODUCTION TO
PROBABILITY &
STATISTICS

Third Canadian Edition

MENDENHALL

BEAVER

BEAVER

AHMED

Updated and revised by SOHAIL KHAN
UNIVERSITY OF WINNIPEG

NELSON / EDUCATION

NELSON EDUCATION

Student Solutions Manual
updated and revised by Sohail Khan

for use with *Introduction to Probability and Statistics,* **Third Canadian Edition**
by William Mendenhall, Robert J. Beaver, Barbara M. Beaver, and S. Ejay Ahmed

Vice President, Editorial Higher Education:
Anne Williams

Publisher:
Paul Fam

Executive Editor:
Jackie Wood

Marketing Manager:
Leanne Newell

Technical Reviewer:
Amy Ching

Senior Developmental Editor:
Mark Grzeskowiak

Content Production Manager:
Jennifer Hare

Copy Editor:
Wendy Yano

Manufacturing Manager:
Joanne McNeil

Design Director:
Ken Phipps

Managing Designer:
Franca Amore

Cover Design:
Courtney Hellam

Cover Image:
Max Schulz/Getty Images

ISBN-13: 978-0-17-666275-2
ISBN-10: 0-17-666275-8

Contents

To the Student

In the tradition of the previous Canadian edition, text exercises in *Introduction to Probability and Statistics*, Third Canadian Edition, are graduated in level of difficulty: some, involving only basic techniques, can be solved by almost all students, while others, involving practical applications and interpretation of results, will challenge students to use more sophisticated statistical reasoning and understanding. The variety and number of real applications in the exercise sets is a major strength of the text. Case studies and projects added throughout the third Canadian edition provide an opportunity for students to build on knowledge gained from previous chapters and apply it to "big picture" projects. Rather than working on problems based only on the individual sections, students will be using almost all of the concepts, definitions, and techniques given in that chapter, thus bolstering students' success rate. More examples and exercises have been added to selected chapters and a number of new and updated real data sets from applications in many interesting fields.

The *Student Solutions Manual* for use with *Introduction to Probability and Statistics*, Third Canadian Edition, was prepared to assist the student in mastering the skills required for an understanding of probability and statistics. The selected questions have been chosen by the authors of your text to allow you to discover the range and depth of your understanding.

This *Student Solutions Manual* contains the worked-out solutions to odd-numbered exercises as well as the solutions to the case studies and projects at the end of each textbook chapter.

Sohail Khan
University of Winnipeg

Chapter 1: Describing Data with Graphs

1.1   **a**   The experimental unit, the individual or object on which a variable is measured, is the student.
         b   The experimental unit on which the number of errors is measured is the exam.
         c   The experimental unit is the patient.
         d   The experimental unit is the azalea plant.
         e   The experimental unit is the car.

1.3   **a**   "Population" is a *discrete* variable because it can take on only integer values.
         b   "Weight" is a *continuous* variable, taking on any values associated with an interval on the real line.
         c   "Time" is a *continuous* variable.
         d   "Number of consumers" is integer-valued and hence *discrete*.

1.5   **a**   The experimental unit, the item or object on which variables are measured, is the vehicle.
         b   Type (qualitative); make (qualitative); carpool (qualitative); one-way commute distance (quantitative continuous); age of vehicle (quantitative continuous)
         c   Since five variables have been measured, the data is *multivariate.*

1.7   The population of interest consists of voter opinions (for or against the candidate) *at the time of the election* for all persons voting in the election. Note that when a sample is taken (at some time prior or the election), we are not actually sampling from the population of interest. As time passes, voter opinions change. Hence, the population of voter opinions changes with time, and the sample may not be representative of the population of interest.

1.9   **a**   The variable "reading score" is a quantitative variable, which is usually integer-valued and hence discrete.
         b   The individual on which the variable is measured is the student.
         c   The population is hypothetical—it does not exist in fact—but consists of the reading scores for all students who could possibly be taught by this method.

1.11   **a–b**   The experimental unit is the pair of jeans, on which the qualitative variable "province" is measured.
         c–d   First, construct a statistical table to summarize the data. The pie chart is shown below; the bar charts is shown on the next page.

Province	Frequency	Fraction of Total	Sector Angle
ON	9	0.36	129.6
QC	8	0.32	115.2
MB	8	0.32	115.2

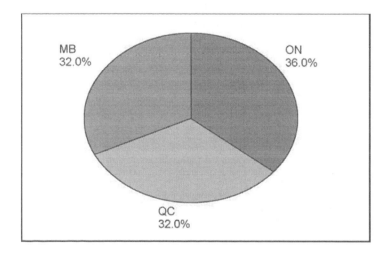

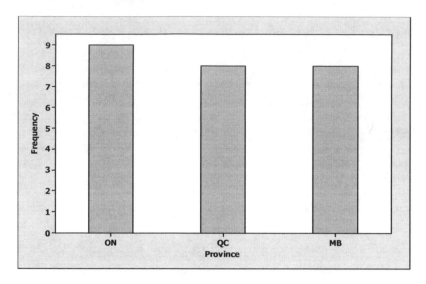

e From the table or the chart, Quebec produced $8/25 = 0.32$ of the jeans.

f The highest bar represents Ontario, which produced the most pairs of jeans.

g Since the bars and the sectors are almost equal in size, the three provinces produced roughly the same number of pairs of jeans.

1.13 **a** No, a few more Islamic countries (Iraq, Pakistan, Afghanistan, Syria, etc.) can be added in the table.

b A bar chart is appropriate.

c

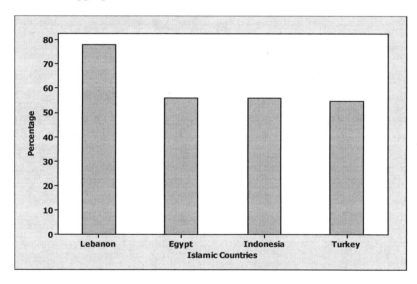

d Answers will vary.

1.15 **a** Yes. The total percentage of education level in each bar graph is 100.

b Yes. There is a significant increase (from 39% to 46%) in the post-secondary education attainment over the years.

c   The pie chart is shown below. The bar chart is probably visually more interesting.

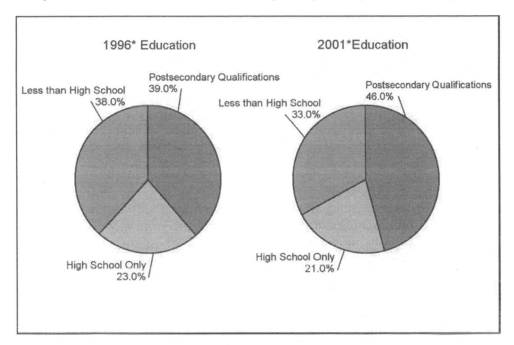

1.17   The most obvious choice of a stem is to use the ones digit. The portion of the observation to the right of the ones digit constitutes the leaf. Observations are classified by row according to stem and also within each stem according to relative magnitude. The stem and leaf display is shown below.

```
1  | 6 8
2  | 1 2 5 5 5 7 8 8 9 9
3  | 1 1 4 5 5 6 6 6 7 7 7 7 8 9 9 9        leaf digit = 0.1
4  | 0 0 0 1 2 2 3 4 5 6 7 8 9 9 9          1 2 represents 1.2
5  | 1 1 6 6 7
6  | 1 2
```

a   The stem and leaf plot has a mound-shaped distribution.
b   From the stem and leaf plot, the smallest observation is 1.6 (1 6).
c   The eight and ninth largest observations are both 4.9 (4 9).

1.19   **a**   As in Exercise 1.17, the stem is chosen as the ones digit, and the portion of the observation to the right of the ones digit is the leaf.

```
3  | 2 3 4 5 5 5 6 6 7 9 9 9              leaf digit = 0.1
4  | 0 0 2 2 3 3 3 4 4 5 8               1 2 represents 1.2
```

b   The stems are split, with the leaf digits 0 to 4 belonging to the first part of the stem and the leaf digits 5 to 9 belonging to the second. The stem and leaf plot shown below improves the presentation of the data.

```
3  | 2 3 4
3  | 5 5 5 6 6 7 9 9 9                    leaf digit = 0.1
3  | 0 0 2 2 3 3 3 4 4                    1 2 represents 1.2
4  | 5 8
```

1.21 **a** The scale is drawn on the horizontal axis and the measurements are represented by dots.

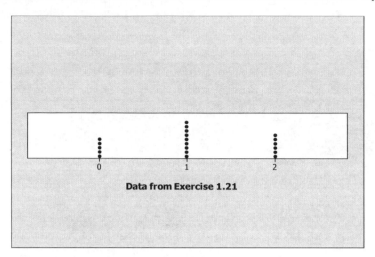

Data from Exercise 1.21

b Since there is only one digit in each measurement, the ones digit must be the stem, and the leaf will be a zero digit for each measurement.

c 0 | 0 0 0 0 0
1 | 0 0 0 0 0 0 0 0 0
2 | 0 0 0 0 0 0

d The two plots convey the same information if the stem and leaf plot is turned 90° and stretched to resemble the dotplot.

1.23 **a–b** The line graph is shown below. Notice the change in y as x increases. The measurements are decreasing over time.

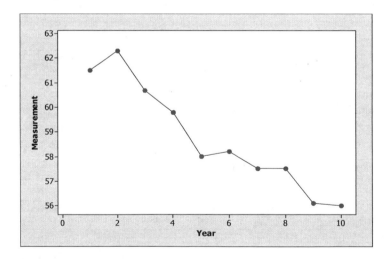

1.25 **a** The range of the data $32.3 - 0.2 = 32.1$. We choose to use eleven class intervals of length 3 ($32.1/11 = 2.9$, which when rounded to the next largest integer is 3). The subintervals 0.1 to < 3.1, 3.1 to < 6.1, 6.1 to < 9.1, and so on, are convenient and the tally is shown below.

Class i	Class Boundaries	Tally	f_i	Relative Frequency, f_i/n
1	0.1 to < 3.1	11111 11111 11111	15	15/50
2	3.1 to < 6.1	11111 1111	9	9/50
3	6.1 to < 9.1	11111 11111	10	10/50
4	9.1 to < 12.1	111	3	3/50
5	12.1 to < 15.1	1111	4	4/50
6	15.1 to < 18.1	111	3	3/50
7	18.1 to < 21.1	11	2	2/50
8	21.1 to < 24.1	11	2	2/50
9	24.1 to < 37.1	1	1	1/50
10	27.1 to < 30.1		0	0/50
11	30.1 to < 33.1	1	1	1/50

The relative frequency histogram is shown below.

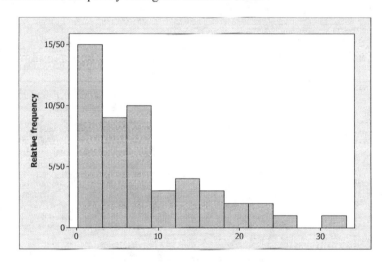

b The data is skewed to the right, with a few unusually large measurements.

c Looking at the data, we see that 36 patients had a disease recurrence within 10 months. Therefore, the fraction of recurrence times less than or equal to 10 is $36/10 = 0.72$.

1.27 **a** Use the tens digit as the stem, and the ones digit as the leaf, dividing each stem into two parts.

```
3 | 0 0 0 1 1 2 2 2 3 3 4 4
3 | 5 5 5 6 6 6 6 7 7 8 8 9 9 9
4 | 0 0 0 0 1 1 1 1 2 2 3 3
4 | 5 5 6 6 6 7 8 8
5 | 0 0
5 | 5
```

b We use class intervals of length 5, beginning with the subinterval 30 to < 35. The tally is shown below.

Class i	Class Boundaries	Tally	f_i	Relative Frequency, f_i/n
1	30 to < 35	11111 11111 11	12	12/50
2	35 to < 40	11111 11111 11111	15	15/50
3	40 to < 45	11111 11111 11	12	12/50
4	45 to < 50	11111 111	8	8/50
5	50 to < 55	11	2	2/50
6	55 to < 60	1	1	1/50

The relative frequency histogram is shown below.

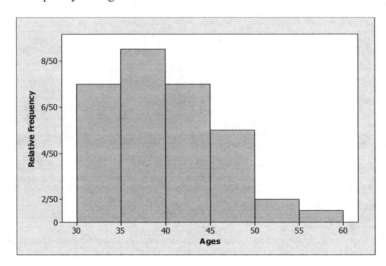

c The two graphs are very similar, with the relative frequency histogram a bit more visually appealing. If the student chose to create the stem and leaf plot without splitting the stems into two parts, the stem and leaf plot would not be very helpful in describing the data set.

d Use either the stem and leaf plot, the table, or the relative frequency histogram. The proportion of children in the interval 35 to < 45 is $(15 + 12)/50 = 0.54$.

e The proportion of children aged less than 50 months is $(12 + 15 + 12 + 8)/50 = 0.94$.

1.29 **a** Use the ones digit as the stem, and the portion to the right of the ones digit as the leaf, dividing each stem into two parts.

```
0 | 2 2 3 3 3 4 4 4
0 | 5 5 6 6 6 6 7 7 7 8 8 8 8 9 9
1 | 0 0 1 1 1 1 1 1 1 2 2 2 3 3 3 4 4
1 | 6 6 7 7 8 8 8 8 9 9
2 | 1 2 3
2 | 5 8                          leaf digit = 0.1
3 | 1 1                          1 2 represents 1.2
3 | 6
4 |
4 | 5
5 | 2
```

b Looking at the original data, we see that 25 customers waited 1 minute or less. Therefore, the fraction of service times less than or equal to 1 is $25/60 = 0.4167$.

c The smallest measurement is 0 2, which is translated as 0.2.

1.31 **a–b** The dotplot and the stem and leaf plot are created using *MINITAB*.

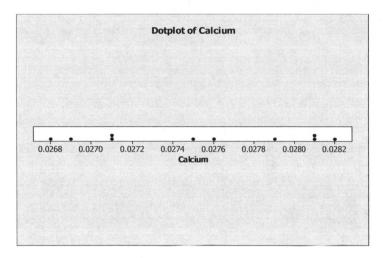

Stem and Leaf Plot: Calcium
```
Stem and leaf of Calcium   N  = 10
Leaf Unit = 0.00010

   2   26   89
   4   27   11
   4   27
   5   27   5
   5   27   6
   4   27   9
   3   28   11
   1   28   2
```

  c The measurements all seem to be within the same range of variability. There do not appear to be any outliers.

1.33 **a** We choose a stem and leaf plot, using the ones and tenths place as the stem, and a zero digit as the leaf. The *MINITAB* printout is shown below.

Stem and Leaf Plot: Cells
```
Stem and leaf of Cells   N  = 15
Leaf Unit = 0.010
   1   49   0
   2   50   0
   3   51   0
  (5)  52   00000
   7   53   000
   4   54   000
   1   55   0
```

  b The data set is relatively mound-shaped, centred at 5.2.
  c The value $x = 5.7$ does not fall within the range of the other cell counts, and would be considered somewhat unusual.

1.35   **a**   The stem and leaf plot is shown below.

Stem and Leaf Plot: Weekend Gross Ticket Sales
```
Stem and leaf of Weekend   N  = 20
Leaf Unit = 0.10

   4    0   3444
   7    0   556
  10    1   024
  10    1   69
   8    2
   8    2   8
   7    3   11
   5    3
   5    4
   5    4
   5    5
   5    5
   5    6   2

HI 155, 201, 405, 593
```

The distribution is skewed to the right, with four outliers, marked by "HI" in the stem and leaf plot.

b   The dotplot of the weekend gross ticket sales is given below.

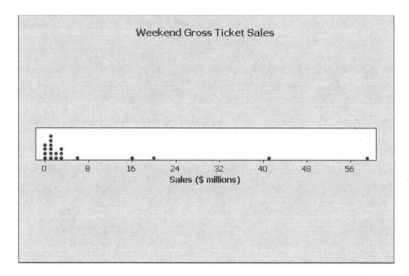

The stem and leaf plot is more informative as compared to the dotplot. We can identify the numerical values of the potential outliers and also original data can be reconstructed from the stem and leaf plot.

1.37 **a** The pie chart is given below.

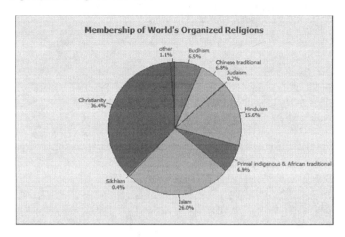

b The bar chart is given below.

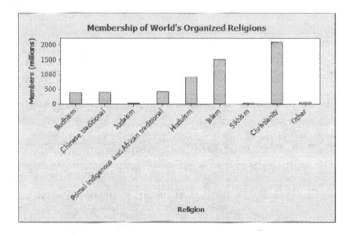

c The Pareto chart is given below.

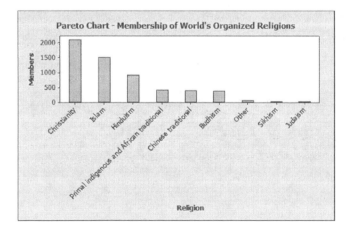

Comparing graphs from parts **a–c**, the Pareto chart seems more effective since it is very easy to compare the relative membership of the organized religions.

1.39   To determine whether a distribution is likely to be skewed, look for the likelihood of observing extremely large or extremely small values of the variable of interest.

    a   The distribution of non-secured loan sizes might be skewed (a few extremely large loans are possible).

    b   The distribution of secured loan sizes is not likely to contain unusually large or small values.

    c   Not likely to be skewed.

    d   Not likely to be skewed.

    e   If a package is dropped, it is likely that all the shells will be broken. Hence, a few large number of broken shells is possible. The distribution will be skewed.

    f   If an animal has one tick, it is likely to have more than one. There will be some "0"s with uninfected rabbits, and then a larger number of large values. The distribution will not be symmetric.

1.41   **a**   Weight is continuous, taking any positive real value.

    b   Body temperature is continuous, taking any real value.

    c   Number of people is discrete, taking the values 0, 1, 2, ...

    d   Number of properties is discrete.

    e   Number of claims is discrete.

1.43   Stem and leaf plots may vary from student to student. The most obvious choice is to use the tens digit as the stem and the ones digit as the leaf.

```
 7  | 8 9
 8  | 0 1 7
 9  | 0 1 2 4 4 5 6 6 6 8 8
10  | 1 7 9
11  | 2
```

The display is fairly mound-shaped, with a large peak in the middle.

1.45   **a–b**   Answers will vary from student to student. Students should notice that the distribution is skewed to the right with a few pennies being unusually old. A typical histogram is shown below.

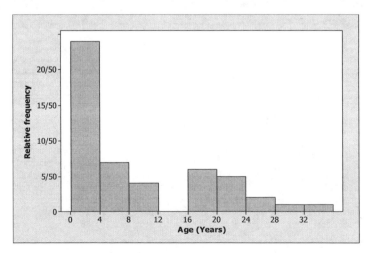

1.47   Answers will vary from student to student. Students should notice that the distribution is mound-shaped (see graph below) with the number of seats won in most of the elections being between 75 and 125. There were an unusually high number of seats won in two of the elections (208 and 211 seats).

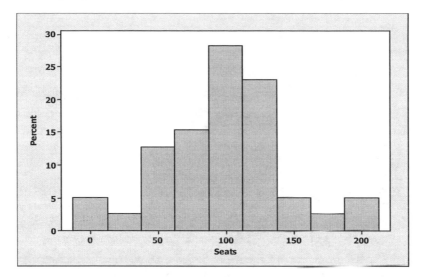

1.49   **a**   The line chart is shown below. The year does not appear to have an effect on his winning time.

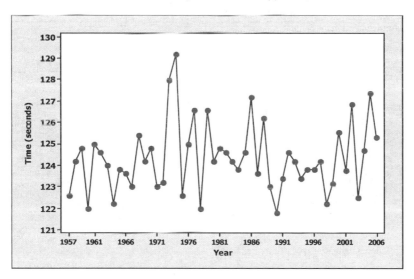

b   Since the year of the race is not important in describing the data set, the distribution can be described using a relative frequency histogram. The distribution is roughly mound-shaped with a few unusually slow ($x = 129.2$, $x = 128.0$) race times (see graph on next page).

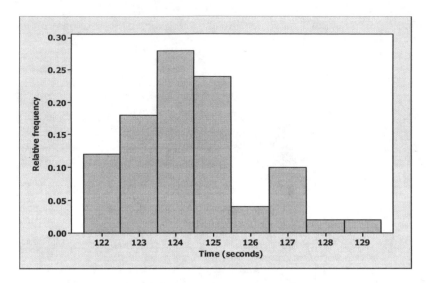

1.51   **a**   Most of the provinces/territories have very few Conservative seats (9 out of 13 have 10 or fewer seats won); the distribution should be skewed to the right.

b–c   Histograms will vary from student to student, but should resemble the histogram generated by *MINITAB* in the figure below. The distribution is indeed skewed to the right, with one outlier: Ontario ($x = 40$).

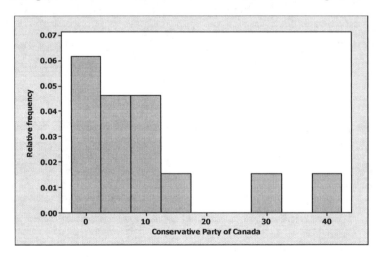

1.53   **Stem and Leaf Plot: Conservative Party of Canada, Liberal Party of Canada**

```
Stem and leaf of                            Stem and leaf of
Conservative Party of Canada   N  = 13      Liberal Party of Canada   N  = 13
Leaf Unit = 1.0                             Leaf Unit = 1.0

(7)   0   0000333                           (8)   0   00112344
 6    0   8                                  5    0   669
 5    1   02                                 2    1   3
 3    1   7                                  1    1
 2    2                                      1    2
 2    2   8                                  1    2
 1    3                                      1    3
 1    3                                      1    3
 1    4   0                                  1    4
                                             1    4
HI  40                                       1    5   4

                                            HI  54
```

a–b As in the case of relative frequency histogram, both the distributions are skewed to the right with one outlier on each (Ontario). When the stem and leaf plots are turned 90°, the shapes are very similar to the histograms.

c Since the total of 308 House of Commons seats are distributed very disproportionately among different provinces and territories, with only four provinces having more than 15 seats, these graphs will be skewed right.

1.55 **a–b** Answers will vary. A typical relative frequency histogram is shown below. The gaps and bimodal nature of the histogram probably is due to the fact that the samples were collected at different locations.

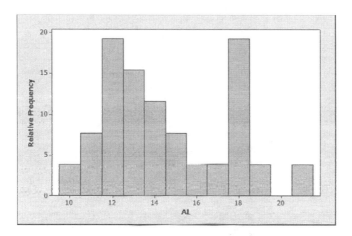

c The dotplot is shown below. The locations seem to be responsible for the unusual gaps and peaks in the relative frequency histogram given in part **b**.

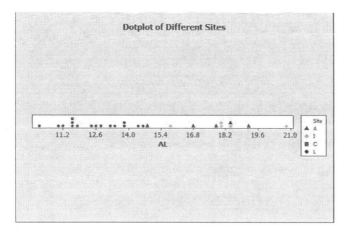

1.57 **a** The measurements are obtained by counting the number of beats for 30 seconds, and then multiplying by 2. Thus, the measurements should all be even numbers.

b The stem and leaf plot is shown below.

Stem and Leaf Plot: Pulse
```
Stem and leaf of Pulse   N  = 50
Leaf Unit = 1.0
   1    4    2
   1    4
   3    5    24
   6    5    688
  10    6    0022
  15    6    66668
  24    7    000222224
  25    7    8
  25    8    0022444444444
  12    8    68888
   7    9    00
   5    9    66
   3   10    04
   1   10
   1   11    0
```

c Answers will vary. A typical histogram, generated by *MINITAB*, is shown below.

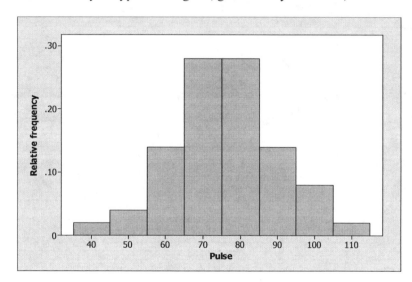

d The distribution of pulse rates is mound-shaped and relatively symmetric around a central location of 75 beats per minute. There are no outliers.

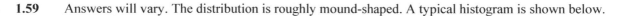

1.59 Answers will vary. The distribution is roughly mound-shaped. A typical histogram is shown below.

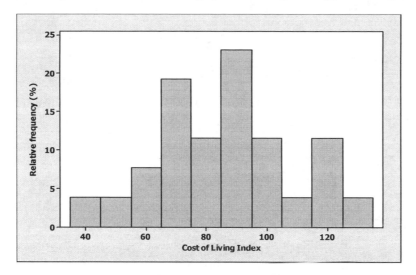

b Answers will vary. The stem and leaf plot generated by *MINITAB* uses the tens place as the stem and the ones place as the leaf.

```
Stem and Leaf Plot: Index
Stem and leaf of Index   N  = 26
Leaf Unit = 1.0

  2     4    28
  2     5
  6     6    2469
  9     7    134
 (6)    8    344568
 11     9    014
  8    10    0119
  4    11    679
  1    12
  1    13    0
```

c Since the data appears in Mercer's site, this global investment consulting agency may have chosen the cities of its business priorities.

1.61 Answers will vary. Students should notice that the first distribution (12:00–1:30) is mound-shaped and the distribution (4:30–6:00) is slightly skewed.

1.63 **a–b** The *MINITAB* stem and leaf plot is shown below. The distribution is slightly skewed to the left.

```
Stem and Leaf Plot: Total Tax Component
Stem and leaf of Total Tax Component   N  - 15
Leaf Unit = 1.0

  1     2    2
  2     2    4
  4     2    66
  4     2
  7     3    000
 (1)    3    3
  7     3
  7     3    667
  4     3    8899
```

c There are no unusually high or low gasoline taxes in the data.

1.65 The data should be displayed with either a bar chart or a pie chart. Because of the large number of categories, the bar chart is probably more effective.

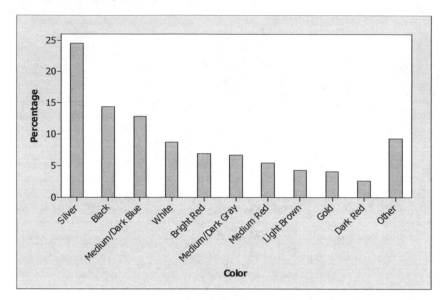

1.67

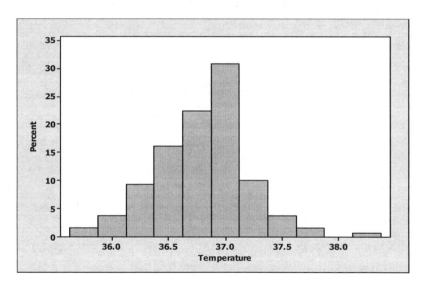

a–b The distribution is approximately mound-shaped, with one unusual measurement, in the class with midpoint at 38.5°C ($x = 38.22$). Perhaps the person whose temperature was 38.22°C had some sort of illness.

c The value 37°C is slightly to the right of centre.

Case Study: How Is Your Blood Pressure?

1   The following variables have been measured on the participants in this study: sex (qualitative); age in years (quantitative discrete); diastolic blood pressure (quantitative continuous, but measured to an integer value); and systolic blood pressure (quantitative continuous, but measured to an integer value). For each person, both systolic and diastolic readings are taken, making the data bivariate.

2   The important variables in this study are diastolic and systolic blood pressure, which can be described singly with histograms in various categories (male vs. female or by age categories). Further, the relationship between systolic and diastolic blood pressure can be displayed together using a scatterplot or a bivariate histogram.

3   Answers will vary, depending on the choice of class boundaries or the software package which is used. The histograms should look fairly mound-shaped. A typical side-by-side histogram generated by *MINITAB* is shown below.

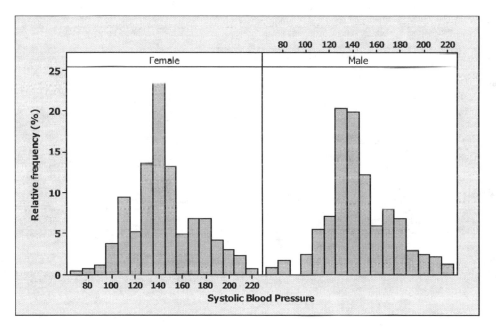

4   Answers will vary.

5   In determining how a student's blood pressure compares to those in a comparable sex and age group, female students (ages 15–20) must compare to the population of females, while male students (ages 15–20) must compare to the population of males. The student should use his or her blood pressure and compare it to the scatterplot generated in part **4**.

Project 1-A: Five Tips for Keeping Your Home Safe This Summer

a   The population is all households in that particular subdivision in the city of North York. The sample is the 300 households in that subdivision that were surveyed.

b   The collected data is based on population, in the sense that the sample taken is randomly selected from the population and meant to be representative of the population.

c   The experimental units are the households.

d   The variable being measured is the type of tip employed.

e   The variable is qualitative.

f   Neither: The variable is qualitative. The counts, however, are discrete.

g   The bar chart is shown below. The chart graphically portrays the counts for each type of tip.

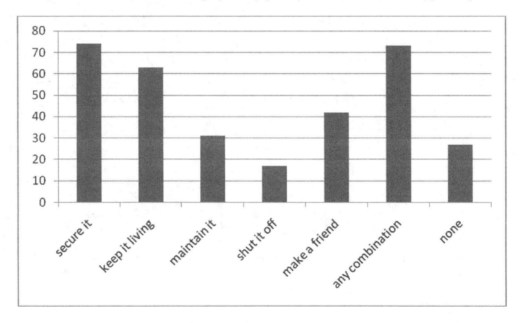

h   The relative frequencies are obtained by dividing the counts by the total sample size (300):

Type of Tips	Number of Households	Relative Frequency
secure it	74	0.246667
keep it living	63	0.210000
maintain it	31	0.103333
shut it off	17	0.056667
make a friend	42	0.140000
any combination	73	0.243333
none	27	0.090000

i   A relative frequency bar chart is shown below.

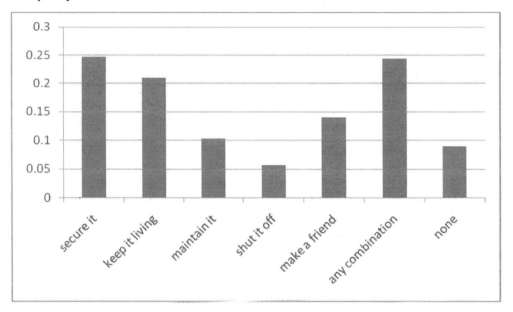

j   A pie chart (by count) is shown below.

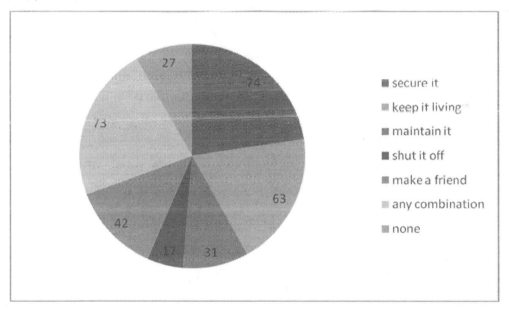

k   The proportion of respondents who chose either "Secure it" or "Make a friend" is the sum of their respective relative frequencies: $0.246667 + 0.140000 = 0.386667$ or 38.67%.

l   Answers will vary.

Project 1-B: Handwashing Saves Lives: It's in Your Hands

a   The experimental units are the students.

b   The variable is the time (in seconds) students take to wash their hands.

c   The variable is quantitative.

d   The variable is discrete because it is only measured to the nearest second.

e   A dotplot is shown below. The value that occurs most often is 5. The range of the data is from 0 to 20. The data is distributed more to the lower values. There are a few gaps in the data as well.

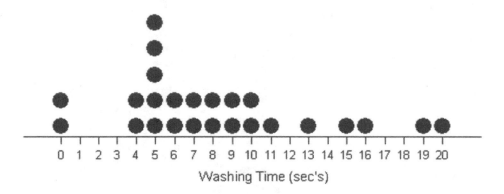

f   The distribution of data is skewed to the lower values, as most students took 10 seconds or less to wash their hands.

g   The line chart was constructed by using the students' numerical order (student 1, 2, ... 25) as the *x*-variable and the amount of time they washed their hands as the *y*-variable.

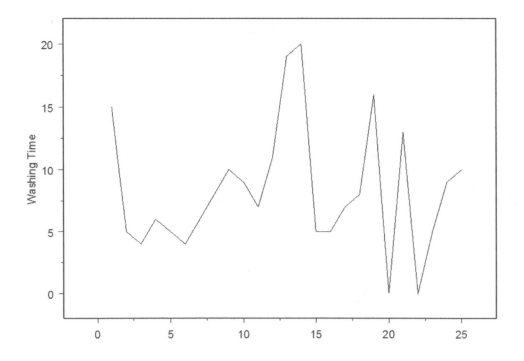

h   The frequency histogram is shown below.

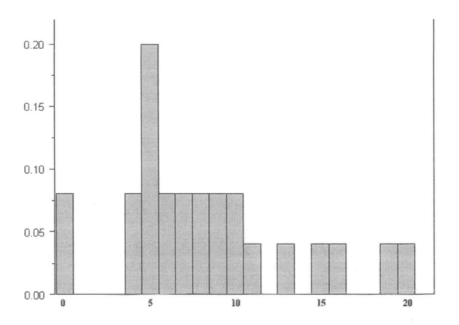

i   We count 17 students that washed their hands for less than 10 seconds, or $17/25 = 68\%$.

j   We count 21 students that washed their hands for at least 5 seconds, or $21/25 = 84\%$.

k   No, we cannot comfortably state that most students wash their hands for 5 seconds or less. This is because only 9 students out of 25 (36%) wash their hands for 5 seconds or less. This leaves the majority of students washing their hands for more than 5 seconds.

l   The stem and leaf plot is below. Note that the colon represents the decimal point in this case.

```
 0 : 00
 1 :
 2 :
 3 :
 4 : 00
 5 : 00000
 6 : 00
 7 : 00
 8 : 00
 9 : 00
10 : 00
11 : 0
12 :
13 : 0
14 :
15 : 0
16 : 0
17 :
18 :
19 : 0
20 : 0
```

m   The data is skewed right, as the tail of the distribution is on the right (i.e., the higher values).

n   Points 0, 19, and 20 appear to be potential outliers.

o   Answers will vary.

Chapter 2: Describing Data with Numerical Measures

2.1   **a**   The dotplot shown below plots the five measurements along the horizontal axis. Since there are two "1"s, the corresponding dots are placed one above the other. The approximate centre of the data appears to be around 1.

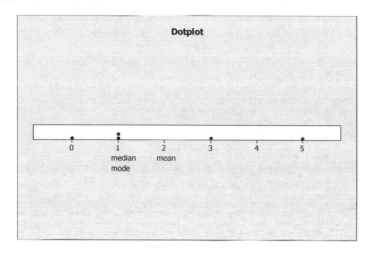

b   The mean is the sum of the measurements divided by the number of measurements, or
$$\bar{x} = \frac{\sum x_i}{n} = \frac{0+5+1+1+3}{5} = \frac{10}{5} = 2.$$
To calculate the median, the observations are first ranked from smallest to largest: 0, 1, 1, 3, 5. Then since $n = 5$, the position of the median is $0.5(n+1) = 3$, and the median is the third ranked measurement, or $m = 1$. The mode is the measurement occurring most frequently, or mode = 1.

c   The three measures in part **b** are located on the dotplot. Since the median and mode are to the left of the mean, we conclude that the measurements are skewed to the right.

2.3   **a** $\bar{x} = \dfrac{\sum x_i}{n} = \dfrac{58}{10} = 5.8$

b   The ranked observations are 2, 3, 4, 5, 5, 6, 6, 8, 9, 10. Since $n = 10$, the median is halfway between the fifth and sixth ordered observations, or $m = (5+6)/2 = 5.5$.

c   There are two measurements, 5 and 6, which both occur twice. Since this is the highest frequency of occurrence for the data set, we say that the set is *bimodal* with modes at 5 and 6.

2.5   **a**   Although there may be a few households who own more than one DVD player, the majority should own either 0 or 1. The distribution should be slightly skewed to the right.

b   Since most households will have only one DVD player, we guess that the mode is 1.

c   The mean is
$$\bar{x} = \frac{\sum x_i}{n} = \frac{1+0+\cdots+1}{25} = \frac{27}{25} = 1.08$$
To calculate the median, the observations are first ranked from smallest to largest: There are six 0s, thirteen 1s, four 2s, and two 3s. Then since $n = 25$, the position of the median is $0.5(n+1) = 13$, which is the thirteenth ranked measurement, or $m = 1$. The mode is the measurement occurring most frequently, or mode = 1.

d The relative frequency histogram is shown below, with the three measures superimposed. Notice that the mean falls slightly to the right of the median and mode, indicating that the measurements are slightly skewed to the right.

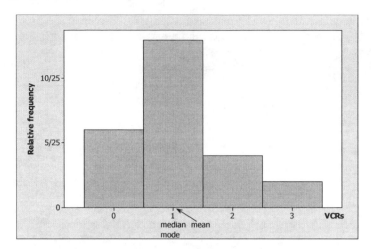

2.7 It is obvious that any one family cannot have 2.5 children, since the number of children per family is a quantitative discrete variable. The researcher is referring to the average number of children per family calculated for all families in the United States during the 1930s. The average does not necessarily have to be integer-valued.

2.9 The distribution of sports salaries will be skewed to the right, because of the very high salaries of some sports figures. Hence, the median salary would be a better measure of centre than the mean.

2.11 **a** This is similar to previous exercises.

$$\bar{x} = \frac{\sum x_i}{n} = \frac{417}{18} = 23.17$$

The ranked observations are shown below:

4	6	7	10	12	16	19	19	20
20	21	22	23	34	39	40	40	65

The median is the average of the 9th and 10th observations or $m = (20 + 20)/2 = 20$ and the mode is the most frequently occurring observation—mode = 19, 20, 40.

b Since the mean is larger than the median, the data are skewed to the right.

c The dotplot is shown below. Yes, the distribution is skewed to the right.

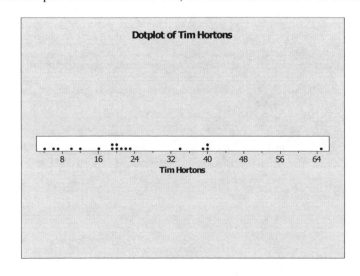

2.13   **a**   The sample mean is
$$\bar{x} = \frac{8+6+3+\dots+8+10}{17} = 6.412$$

   b   We arrange the data in increasing order: $\{0,1,2,2,3,4,5,5,6,6,7,8,8,8,10,11,23\}$. The median is the number in the $0.5(n+1) = $ 9th position, which is 6. The mode is the number that occurs most often, which in this case is 8.

   c   Since the mean and median are only slightly off from each other, there is only slight skewness.

   d   The use of the median is probably better than the mean in this case, as the point with value 23 is likely an outlier (and the median is less sensitive to outliers). The mode is rarely employed in practice.

2.15   **a**   The range is $R = 4 - 1 = 3$.

   b $\bar{x} = \dfrac{\sum x_i}{n} = \dfrac{17}{8} = 2.125$

   c   Calculate $\sum x_i^2 = 4^2 + 1^2 + \dots + 2^2 = 45$. Then
$$s^2 = \frac{\sum x_i^2 - \dfrac{\left(\sum x_i\right)^2}{n}}{n-1} = \frac{45 - \dfrac{(17)^2}{8}}{7} = \frac{8.875}{7} = 1.2679 \text{ and } s = \sqrt{s^2} = \sqrt{1.2679} = 1.126$$

2.17   **a**   The range is $R = 2.39 - 1.28 = 1.11$.

   b   Calculate $\sum x_i^2 = 1.28^2 + 2.39^2 + \dots + 1.51^2 = 15.415$. Then
$$s^2 = \frac{\sum x_i^2 - \dfrac{\left(\sum x_i\right)^2}{n}}{n-1} = \frac{15.451 - \dfrac{(8.56)^2}{5}}{4} = \frac{0.76028}{4} = 0.19007 \text{ and } s = \sqrt{s^2} = \sqrt{0.19007} = 0.436$$

   c   The range, $R = 1.11$, is $1.11/.436 = 2.5$ standard deviations.

2.19   **a**   The range of the data is $R = 6 - 1 = 5$ and the range approximation with $n = 10$ is $s \approx \dfrac{R}{3} = 1.67$.

   b   The standard deviation of the sample is
$$s = \sqrt{s^2} = \sqrt{\frac{\sum x_i^2 - \dfrac{\left(\sum x_i\right)^2}{n}}{n-1}} = \sqrt{\frac{130 - \dfrac{(32)^2}{10}}{9}} = \sqrt{3.0667} = 1.751$$
which is very close to the estimate for part **a**.

   c–e   From the dotplot below, you can see that the data set is not mound-shaped. Hence, you can use Tchebysheff's Theorem, but not the Empirical Rule, to describe the data.

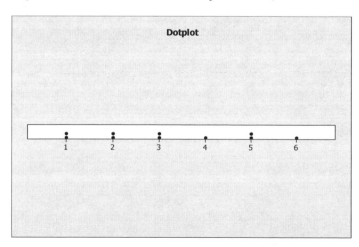

Dotplot

2.21 **a** The interval from 40 to 60 represents $\mu \pm \sigma = 50 \pm 10$. Since the distribution is relatively mound-shaped, the proportion of measurements between 40 and 60 is 68% according to the Empirical Rule and is shown below.

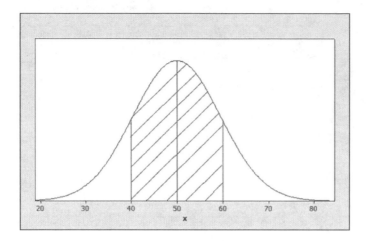

b Again, using the Empirical Rule, the interval $\mu \pm 2\sigma = 50 \pm 2(10)$ or between 30 and 70 contains approximately 95% of the measurements.

c Refer to the figure below.

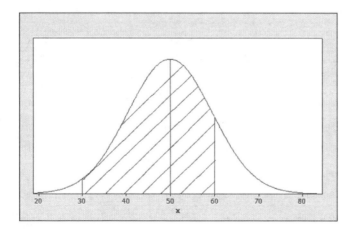

Since approximately 68% of the measurements are between 40 and 60, the symmetry of the distribution implies that 34% of the measurements are between 50 and 60. Similarly, since 95% of the measurements are between 30 and 70, approximately 47.5% are between 30 and 50. Thus, the proportion of measurements between 30 and 60 is $0.34 + 0.475 = 0.815$.

d From the figure in part **a**, the proportion of the measurements between 50 and 60 is 0.34 and the proportion of the measurements which are greater than 50 is 0.50. Therefore, the proportion that are greater than 60 must be $0.5 - 0.34 = 0.16$.

2.23 **a** The range of the data is $R = 1.1 - 0.5 = 0.6$ and the approximate value of s is $s \approx \dfrac{R}{3} = 0.2$.

b Calculate $\sum x_i = 7.6$ and $\sum x_i^2 = 6.02$, the sample mean is $\bar{x} = \dfrac{\sum x_i}{n} = \dfrac{7.6}{10} = 0.76$ and the standard

deviation of the sample is $s = \sqrt{s^2} = \sqrt{\dfrac{\sum x_i^2 - \dfrac{\left(\sum x_i\right)^2}{n}}{n-1}} = \sqrt{\dfrac{6.02 - \dfrac{(7.6)^2}{10}}{9}} = \sqrt{\dfrac{0.244}{9}} = 0.165$

which is very close to the estimate from part **a**.

2.25   According to the Empirical Rule, if a distribution of measurements is approximately mound-shaped,

   a   approximately 68% or 0.68 of the measurements fall in the interval $\mu \pm \sigma = 12 \pm 2.3$ or 9.7 to 14.3

   b   approximately 95% or 0.95 of the measurements fall in the interval $\mu \pm 2\sigma = 12 \pm 4.6$ or 7.4 to 16.6

   c   approximately 99.7% or 0.997 of the measurements fall in the interval
   $\mu \pm 3\sigma = 12 \pm 6.9$ or 5.1 to 18.9

   Therefore, approximately 0.3% or 0.003 will fall outside this interval.

2.27   **a**   The centre of the distribution should be approximately halfway between 0 and 9 or $(0+9)/2 = 4.5$.

   b   The range of the data is $R = 9 - 0 = 9$. Using the range approximation, $s \approx R/4 = 9/4 = 2.25$.

   c   Using the data entry method the students should find $\bar{x} = 4.586$ and $s = 2.892$, which are fairly close to our approximations.

2.29   **a**   Although most of the animals will die at around 32 days, there may be a few animals that survive a very long time, even with the infection. The distribution will probably be skewed right.

   b   Using Tchebysheff's Theorem, at least 3/4 of the measurements should be in the interval
   $\mu \pm \sigma \Rightarrow 32 \pm 72$ or 0 to 104 days.

2.31   **a**   We choose to use 12 classes of length 1.0. The tally and the relative frequency histogram follow.

Class i	Class Boundaries	Tally	f_i	Relative frequency, f_i/n
1	2 to < 3	1	1	1/70
2	3 to < 4	1	1	1/70
3	4 to < 5	111	3	3/70
4	5 to < 6	11111	5	5/70
5	6 to < 7	11111	5	5/70
6	7 to < 8	11111 11111 11	12	12/70
7	8 to < 9	11111 11111 11111 111	18	18/70
8	9 to < 10	11111 11111 11111	15	15/70
9	10 to < 11	11111 1	6	6/70
10	11 to < 12	111	3	3/70
11	12 to < 13		0	0
12	13 to < 14	1	1	1/70

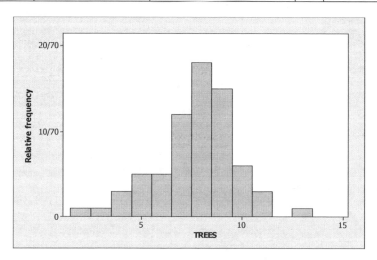

   b   Calculate $n = 70$, $\sum x_i = 541$, and $\sum x_i^2 = 4453$. Then $\bar{x} = \dfrac{\sum x_i}{n} = \dfrac{541}{70} = 7.729$ is an estimate of μ.

   c   The sample standard deviation is

$$s = \sqrt{\frac{\sum x_i^2 - \frac{(\sum x_i)^2}{n}}{n-1}} = \sqrt{\frac{4453 - \frac{(541)^2}{70}}{69}} = \sqrt{3.9398} = 1.985$$

The three intervals, $\bar{x} \pm ks$ for $k = 1, 2, 3$ are calculated below. The table shows the actual percentage of measurements falling in a particular interval as well as the percentage predicted by Tchebysheff's Theorem and the Empirical Rule. Note that the Empirical Rule should be fairly accurate, as indicated by the mound-shape of the histogram in part **a**.

k	$\bar{x} \pm ks$	Interval	Fraction in Interval	Tchebysheff	Empirical Rule
1	7.729 ± 1.985	5.744 to 9.714	$50/70 = 0.71$	at least 0	≈ 0.68
2	7.729 ± 3.970	3.759 to 11.699	$67/70 = 0.96$	at least 0.75	≈ 0.95
3	7.729 ± 5.955	1.774 to 13.684	$70/70 = 1.00$	at least 0.89	≈ 0.997

2.33   **a–b** Calculate $R = 93 - 51 = 42$, so that $s \approx R/4 = 42/4 = 10.5$.

     c   Calculate $n = 30$, $\sum x_i = 2145$, and $\sum x_i^2 = 158,345$. Then

$$s^2 = \frac{\sum x_i^2 - \frac{(\sum x_i)^2}{n}}{n-1} = \frac{158,345 - \frac{(2145)^2}{30}}{29} = 171.6379 \text{ and } s = \sqrt{171.6379} = 13.101$$

which is fairly close to the approximate value of s from part **b**.

     d   The two intervals are calculated below. The proportions agree with Tchebysheff's Theorem, but are not to close to the percentages given by the Empirical Rule. (This is because the distribution is not quite mound-shaped.)

k	$\bar{x} \pm ks$	Interval	Fraction in Interval	Tchebysheff	Empirical Rule
2	71.5 ± 26.20	45.3 to 97.7	$30/30 = 1.00$	at least 0.75	≈ 0.95
3	71.5 ± 39.30	32.2 to 110.80	$30/30 = 1.00$	at least 0.89	≈ 0.997

2.35   **a**   Answers will vary. A typical stem and leaf plot is generated by *MINITAB*.

```
Stem and Leaf Plot: Goals
Stem and leaf of Goals   N  = 21
Leaf Unit = 1.0

   1     0   9
   3     1   16
   6     2   335
   8     3   18
  (4)    4   0016
   9     5   1245
   5     6   2
   4     7   13
   2     8   7
   1     9   2
```

     b   Calculate $n = 21$, $\sum x_i = 940$, and $\sum x_i^2 = 53,036$. Then $\bar{x} = \dfrac{\sum x_i}{n} = \dfrac{940}{21} = 44.76$,

$$s^2 = \frac{\sum x_i^2 - \frac{(\sum x_i)^2}{n}}{n-1} = \frac{53036 - \frac{(940)^2}{21}}{20} = 547.99 \text{ and } s = \sqrt{s^2} = \sqrt{547.99} = 23.41$$

     c   Calculate $\bar{x} \pm 2s \Rightarrow 44.76 \pm 46.82$ or -2.06 to 91.58. From the original data set, 20 of the measurements, or 95.24% fall in this interval.

2.37 **a** Calculate $n = 15$, $\sum x_i = 21$, and $\sum x_i^2 = 49$. Then $\bar{x} = \dfrac{\sum x_i}{n} = \dfrac{21}{15} = 1.4$ and

$$s^2 = \frac{\sum x_i^2 - \dfrac{(\sum x_i)^2}{n}}{n-1} = \frac{49 - \dfrac{(21)^2}{15}}{14} = 1.4$$

b Using the frequency table and the grouped formulas, calculate

$$\sum x_i f_i = 0(4) + 1(5) + 2(2) + 3(4) = 21$$

$$\sum x_i^2 f_i = 0^2(4) + 1^2(5) + 2^2(2) + 3^2(4) = 49$$

Then, as in part **a**,

$$\bar{x} = \frac{\sum x_i f_i}{n} = \frac{21}{15} = 1.4$$

$$s^2 = \frac{\sum x_i^2 f_i - \dfrac{(\sum x_i f_i)^2}{n}}{n-1} = \frac{49 - \dfrac{(21)^2}{15}}{14} = 1.4$$

2.39 **a** The data in this exercise have been arranged in a frequency table.

x_i	0	1	2	3	4	5	6	7	8	9	10
f_i	10	5	3	2	1	0	1	0	0	1	1

Using the frequency table and the grouped formulas, calculate

$$\sum x_i f_i = 0(10) + 1(5) + \cdots + 10(1) = 46$$

$$\sum x_i^2 f_i = 0^2(10) + 1^2(5) + \cdots + 10^2(1) = 268$$

Then

$$\bar{x} = \frac{\sum x_i f_i}{n} = \frac{46}{24} = 1.917$$

$$s^2 = \frac{\sum x_i^2 f_i - \dfrac{(\sum x_i f_i)^2}{n}}{n-1} = \frac{268 - \dfrac{(46)^2}{24}}{23} = 7.819 \text{ and } s = \sqrt{7.819} = 2.796$$

b–c The three intervals $\bar{x} \pm ks$ for $k = 1, 2, 3$ are calculated in the table along with the actual proportion of measurements falling in the intervals. Tchebysheff's Theorem is satisfied and the approximation given by the Empirical Rule are fairly close for $k = 2$ and $k = 3$.

k	$\bar{x} \pm ks$	Interval	Fraction in Interval	Tchebysheff	Empirical Rule
1	1.917 ± 2.796	-0.879 to 4.713	$21/24 = 0.875$	at least 0	≈ 0.68
2	1.917 ± 5.592	-3.675 to 7.509	$22/24 = 0.917$	at least 0.75	≈ 0.95
3	1.917 ± 8.388	-6.471 to 10.305	$24/24 = 1.00$	at least 0.89	≈ 0.997

2.41 The ordered data are 0, 1, 5, 6, 7, 8, 9, 10, 12, 12, 13, 14, 16, 19, 19.

With $n = 15$, the median is in position $0.5(n+1) = 8$, , so that $m = 10$. The lower quartile is in position $0.25(n+1) = 4$ so that $Q_1 = 6$ and the upper quartile is in position $0.75(n+1) = 12$ so that $Q_3 = 14$. Then the five-number summary is

Min	Q_1	Median	Q_3	Max
0	6	10	14	19

and $IQR = Q_3 - Q_1 = 14 - 6 = 8$.

2.43   The ordered data are 2, 3, 4, 5, 6, 6, 6, 7, 8, 9, 9, 10, 22.

For $n = 13$, the position of the median is $0.5(n+1) = 0.5(13+1) = 7$ and $m = 6$. The positions of the quartiles are $0.25(n+1) = 3.5$ and $0.75(n+1) = 10.5$, so that $Q_1 = 4.5$, $Q_3 = 9$, and $IQR = 9 - 4.5 = 4.5$. The *lower and upper fences* are:

$$Q_1 - 1.5IQR = 4.5 - 6.75 = -2.25$$
$$Q_3 + 1.5IQR = 9 + 6.75 = 15.75$$

The value $x = 22$ lies outside the upper fence and is an outlier. The box plot is shown below. The lower whisker connects the box to the smallest value that is not an outlier, which happens to be the minimum value, $x = 2$. The upper whisker connects the box to the largest value that is not an outlier or $x = 10$.

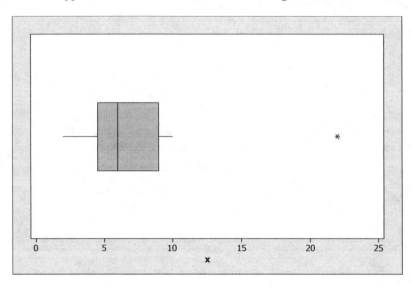

2.45   **a**   The ordered data are shown below:

1.70	101.00	209.00	264.00	316.00	445.00
1.72	118.00	218.00	278.00	318.00	481.00
5.90	168.00	221.00	286.00	329.00	485.00
8.80	180.00	241.00	314.00	397.00	
85.40	183.00	252.00	315.00	406.00	

For $n = 28$, the position of the median is $0.5(n+1) = 14.5$ and the positions of the quartiles are $0.25(n+1) = 7.25$ and $0.75(n+1) = 21.75$. The lower quartile is one-fourth the way between the seventh and eighth measurements or $Q_1 = 118 + 0.25(168 - 118) = 130.5$ and the upper quartile is three-fourths the way between the 21st and 22nd measurements or $Q_3 = 316 + 0.75(318 - 316) = 317.5$. Then the five-number summary is

Min	Q_1	Median	Q_3	Max
1.70	130.5	246.5	317.5	485

b   Calculate $IQR = Q_3 - Q_1 = 317.5 - 130.5 = 187$. Then the *lower and upper fences* are

$$Q_1 - 1.5IQR = 130.5 - 280.5 = -150$$
$$Q_3 + 1.5IQR = 317.5 + 280.5 = 598$$

The box plot is shown on the next page. Since there are no outliers, the whiskers connect the box to the minimum and maximum values in the ordered set.

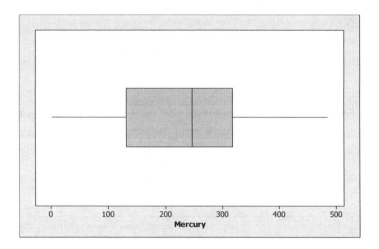

c–d The boxplot does not identify any of the measurements as outliers, mainly because the large variation in the measurements cause the IQR to be large. However, students should notice the extreme difference in the magnitude of the first four observations taken on young dolphins. These animals have not been alive long enough to accumulate a large amount of mercury in their bodies.

2.47   **a**   For $n = 15$, the position of the median is $0.5(n+1) = 8$ and the positions of the quartiles are $0.25(n+1) = 4$ and $0.75(n+1) = 12$. The sorted measurements are shown below.

        Lemieux: 1, 6, 7, 17, 19, 28, 35, 44, 45, 50, 54, 69, 69, 70, 85
        Hull: 0, 1, 25, 29, 30, 32, 37, 39, 41, 42, 54, 57, 70, 72, 86

For Mario Lemieux, $m = 44$, $Q_1 = 17$, $Q_3 = 69$
For Brett Hull, $m = 39$, $Q_1 = 29$, $Q_3 = 57$
Then the five-number summaries are

	Min	Q_1	Median	Q_3	Max
Lemieux	1	17	44	69	85
Hull	0	29	39	57	86

b   For Mario Lemieux, calculate $IQR = Q_3 - Q_1 = 69 - 17 = 52$. Then the *lower and upper fences* are:
        $Q_1 - 1.5IQR = 17 - 78 = -61$
        $Q_3 + 1.5IQR = 69 + 78 = 147$
For Brett Hull, $IQR = Q_3 - Q_1 = 57 - 29 = 28$. Then the *lower and upper fences* are:
        $Q_1 - 1.5IQR = 29 - 42 = -13$
        $Q_3 + 1.5IQR = 57 + 42 = 99$
There are no outliers, and the box plots are shown on the next page.

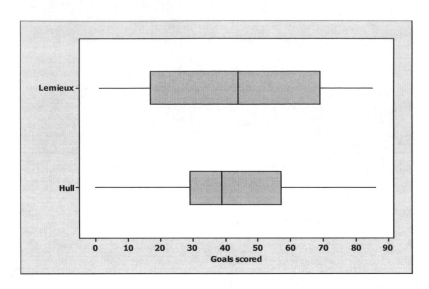

c   Answers will vary. The Lemieux distribution is roughly symmetric, while the Hull distribution seems little skewed. The Lemieux distribution is slightly more variable; it has a higher *IQR* and a higher median number of goals scored.

2.49   **a**   Just by scanning through the 25 measurements, it seems that there are a few unusually large measurements, which would indicate a distribution that is skewed to the right.

b   The position of the median is $0.5(n+1) = 0.5(25+1) = 13$ and $m = 24.4$. The mean is

$$\bar{x} = \frac{\sum x_i}{n} = \frac{960}{25} = 38.4$$

which is larger than the median, indicating a distribution skewed to the right.

c   The positions of the quartiles are $0.25(n+1) = 6.5$ and $0.75(n+1) = 19.5$, so that $Q_1 = 18.7$, $Q_3 = 48.9$, and $IQR = 48.9 - 18.7 = 30.2$. The *lower and upper fences* are

$$Q_1 - 1.5IQR = 18.7 - 45.3 = -26.6$$
$$Q_3 + 1.5IQR = 48.9 + 45.3 = 94.2$$

The box plot is shown below. There are three outliers in the upper tail of the distribution, so the upper whisker is connected to the point $x = 69.2$. The long right whisker and the median line located to the left of the centre of the box indicates that the distribution that is skewed to the right.

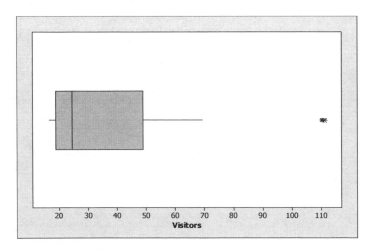

2.51   Answers will vary. Students should notice the outliers in the female group, that the median female temperature is higher than the median male temperature.

2.53   **a**   Calculate $n = 14$, $\sum x_i = 367$, and $\sum x_i^2 = 9641$. Then $\bar{x} = \dfrac{\sum x_i}{n} = \dfrac{367}{14} = 26.214$ and

$$s = \sqrt{\dfrac{\sum x_i^2 - \dfrac{\left(\sum x_i\right)^2}{n}}{n-1}} = \sqrt{\dfrac{9641 - \dfrac{\left(367\right)^2}{14}}{13}} = 1.251$$

b   Calculate $n = 14$, $\sum x_i = 366$, and $\sum x_i^2 = 9644$. Then $\bar{x} = \dfrac{\sum x_i}{n} = \dfrac{366}{14} = 26.143$ and

$$s = \sqrt{\dfrac{\sum x_i^2 - \dfrac{\left(\sum x_i\right)^2}{n}}{n-1}} = \sqrt{\dfrac{9644 - \dfrac{\left(366\right)^2}{14}}{13}} = 2.413$$

c   The centres are roughly the same; the Sunmaid raisins appear slightly more variable.

2.55   **a**   The largest observation found in the data from Exercise 1.25 is 32.3, while the smallest is 0.2. Therefore, the range is $R = 32.3 - 0.2 = 32.1$.

b   Using the range, the approximate value for s is $s \approx R/4 = 32.1/4 = 8.025$.

c   Calculate $n = 50$, $\sum x_i = 418.4$, and $\sum x_i^2 = 6384.34$. Then

$$s = \sqrt{\dfrac{\sum x_i^2 - \dfrac{\left(\sum x_i\right)^2}{n}}{n-1}} = \sqrt{\dfrac{6384.34 - \dfrac{\left(418.4\right)^2}{50}}{49}} = 7.671$$

2.57   The ordered data are shown below.

0.2	2.0	4.3	8.2	14.7
0.2	2.1	4.4	8.3	16.7
0.3	2.4	5.6	8.7	18.0
0.4	2.4	5.8	9.0	18.0
1.0	2.7	6.1	9.6	18.4
1.2	3.3	6.6	9.9	19.2
1.3	3.5	6.9	11.4	23.1
1.4	3.7	7.4	12.6	24.0
1.6	3.9	7.4	13.5	26.7
1.6	4.1	8.2	14.1	32.3

Since $n = 50$, the position of the median is $0.5(n+1) = 25.5$ and the positions of the lower and upper quartiles are $0.25(n+1) = 12.75$ and $0.75(n+1) = 38.25$.

Then $m = (6.1 + 6.6)/2 = 6.35$, $Q_1 = 2.1 + 0.75(2.4 - 2.1) = 2.325$, and

$Q_3 = 12.6 + 0.25(13.5 - 12.6) = 12.825$. Then $IQR = 12.825 - 2.325 = 10.5$.

The *lower and upper fences* are

$$Q_1 - 1.5IQR = 2.325 - 15.75 = -13.425$$
$$Q_3 + 1.5IQR = 12.825 + 15.75 = 28.575$$

and the box plot is shown on the next page. There is one outlier, $x = 32.3$. The distribution is skewed to the right.

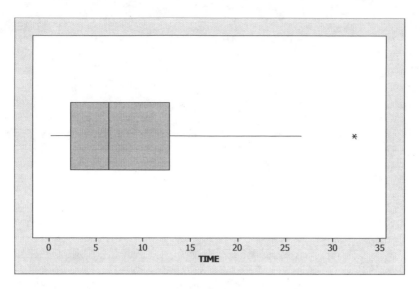

2.59 First calculate the intervals:

$$\bar{x} \pm s = 0.17 \pm 0.01 \qquad \text{or} \qquad 0.16 \text{ to } 0.18$$
$$\bar{x} \pm 2s = 0.17 \pm 0.02 \qquad \text{or} \qquad 0.15 \text{ to } 0.19$$
$$\bar{x} \pm 3s = 0.17 \pm 0.03 \qquad \text{or} \qquad 0.14 \text{ to } 0.20$$

a If no prior information as to the shape of the distribution is available, we use Tchebysheff's Theorem. We would expect at least $(1 - 1/1^2) = 0$ of the measurements to fall in the interval 0.16 to 0.18; at least $(1 - 1/2^2) = 3/4$ of the measurements to fall in the interval 0.15 to 0.19; and at least $(1 - 1/3^2) = 8/9$ of the measurements to fall in the interval 0.14 to 0.20.

b According to the Empirical Rule, approximately 68% of the measurements will fall in the interval 0.16 to 0.18; approximately 95% of the measurements will fall between 0.15 to 0.19; and approximately 99.7% of the measurements will fall between 0.14 and 0.20. Since mound-shaped distributions are so frequent, if we do have a sample size of 30 or greater, we expect the sample distribution to be mound-shaped. Therefore, in this exercise, we would expect the Empirical Rule to be suitable for describing the set of data.

c If the chemist had used a sample size of four for this experiment, the distribution would not be mound-shaped. Any possible histogram we could construct would be non-mound-shaped. We can use at most four classes, each with frequency 1, and we will not obtain a histogram that is even close to mound-shaped. Therefore, the Empirical Rule would not be suitable for describing $n = 4$ measurements.

2.61 The following information is available:

$$n = 400, \ \bar{x} = 600, \ s^2 = 4900$$

The standard deviation of these scores is then 70, and the results of Tchebysheff's Theorem follow:

k	$\bar{x} \pm ks$	Interval	Tchebysheff
1	600 ± 70	530 to 670	at least 0
2	600 ± 140	460 to 740	at least 0.75
3	600 ± 210	390 to 810	at least 0.89

If the distribution of scores is mound-shaped, we use the Empirical Rule, and conclude that approximately 68% of the scores would lie in the interval 530 to 670 (which is $\bar{x} \pm s$). Approximately 95% of the scores would lie in the interval 460 to 740.

2.63 **a** Answers will vary. A typical histogram is shown below. The distribution is slightly skewed to the left.

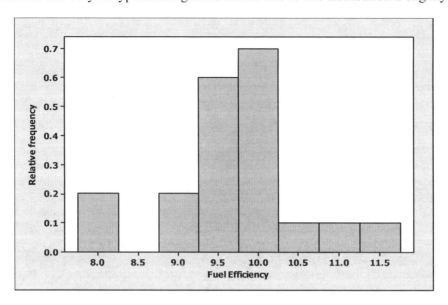

b Calculate $n = 20$, $\sum x_i = 193.1$, $\sum x_i^2 = 1876.65$. Then

$$\overline{x} = \frac{\sum x_i}{n} = 9.655$$

$$s = \sqrt{\frac{\sum x_i^2 - \frac{(\sum x_i)^2}{n}}{n-1}} = \sqrt{\frac{1876.65 - \frac{(193.1)^2}{20}}{19}} = \sqrt{0.646} = 0.804$$

c The sorted data is shown below:

```
7.9      8.1      8.9      8.9      9.4      9.4      9.5      9.5      9.6      9.7
9.8      9.8      9.9      9.9      10.0     10.1     10.2     10.3     10.9     11.3
```

The z-scores for $x = 7.9$ and $x = 11.3$ are

$$z = \frac{x - \overline{x}}{s} = \frac{7.9 - 9.655}{0.804} = -2.18 \text{ and } z = \frac{x - \overline{x}}{s} = \frac{11.3 - 9.655}{0.804} = 2.05$$

Since neither of the z-scores are greater than 3 in absolute value, the measurements are not judged to be outliers.

d The position of the median is $0.5(n+1) = 10.5$ and the median is $m = (9.7 + 9.8)/2 = 9.75$.

e The positions of the quartiles are $0.25(n+1) = 5.25$ and $0.75(n+1) = 15.75$. Then
$Q_1 = 9.4 + 0.25(9.4 - 9.4) = 9.4$ and $Q_3 = 10.0 + 0.75(10.1 - 10.0) = 10.075$.

2.65 **a** The range is $R = 71 - 40 = 31$ and the range approximation is $s \approx R/4 = 31/4 = 7.75$.

b Calculate $n = 10$, $\sum x_i = 592$, $\sum x_i^2 = 36,014$. Then

$$\overline{x} = \frac{\sum x_i}{n} = \frac{592}{10} = 59.2$$

$$s = \sqrt{\frac{\sum x_i^2 - \frac{(\sum x_i)^2}{n}}{n-1}} = \sqrt{\frac{36,014 - \frac{(592)^2}{10}}{9}} = \sqrt{107.5111} = 10.369$$

The sample standard deviation calculated above is of the same order as the approximated value found in part **a**.

   c   The ordered set is 40, 49, 52, 54, 59, 61, 67, 69, 70, 71.

Since $n = 10$, the positions of m, Q_1, and Q_3 are 5.5, 2.75, and 8.25, respectively, and

$$m = (59 + 61)/2 = 60, \quad Q_1 = 49 + 0.75(52 - 49) = 51.25, \quad Q_3 = 69.25, \quad \text{and} \quad IQR = 69.25 - 51.25 = 18.0.$$

The *lower and upper fences* are

$$Q_1 - 1.5IQR = 51.25 - 27.00 = 24.25$$

$$Q_3 + 1.5IQR = 69.25 + 27.00 = 96.25$$

and the box plot is shown below. There are no outliers and the data set is slightly skewed left.

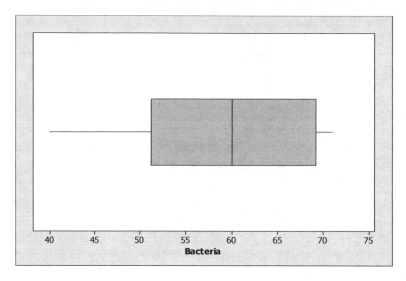

2.67   If the distribution is mound-shaped with mean μ, then almost all of the measurements will fall in the interval $\mu \pm 3\sigma$, which is an interval 6σ in length. That is, the range of the measurements should be approximately 6σ. In this case, the range is $800 - 200 = 600$, so that $\sigma \approx 600/6 = 100$.

2.69   **a**   The range is $R = 172 - 108 = 64$ and the range approximation is $s \approx R/4 = 64/4 = 16$.

        b   Calculate $n = 15$, $\sum x_i = 2041$, $\sum x_i^2 = 281,807$. Then

$$\bar{x} = \frac{\sum x_i}{n} = \frac{2041}{15} = 136.07$$

$$s = \sqrt{\frac{\sum x_i^2 - \frac{\left(\sum x_i\right)^2}{n}}{n-1}} = \sqrt{\frac{281,807 - \frac{(2041)^2}{15}}{14}} = \sqrt{292.495238} = 17.102$$

        c   According to Tchebysheff's Theorem, with $k = 2$, at least 3/4 or 75% of the measurements will lie within $k = 2$ standard deviations of the mean. For this data, the two values, a and b, are calculated as

$$\bar{x} \pm 2s \Rightarrow 136.07 \pm 2(17.10) \Rightarrow 136.07 \pm 34.20 \text{ or } a = 101.87 \text{ and } b = 170.27$$

2.71   **a**   The range is $R = 19 - 4 = 15$ and the range approximation is $s \approx R/4 = 15/4 = 3.75$.

        b   Calculate $n = 15$, $\sum x_i = 175$, $\sum x_i^2 = 2237$. Then

$$\bar{x} = \frac{\sum x_i}{n} = \frac{175}{15} = 11.67$$

$$s = \sqrt{\frac{\sum x_i^2 - \frac{\left(\sum x_i\right)^2}{n}}{n-1}} = \sqrt{\frac{2237 - \frac{(175)^2}{15}}{14}} = \sqrt{13.95238} = 3.735$$

        c   Calculate the interval $\bar{x} \pm 2s \Rightarrow 11.67 \pm 2(3.735) \Rightarrow 11.67 \pm 7.47$ or 4.20 to 19.14. Referring to the original data set, the fraction of measurements in this interval is $14/15 = 0.93$.

2.73 **a** The relative frequency histogram for these data is shown below.

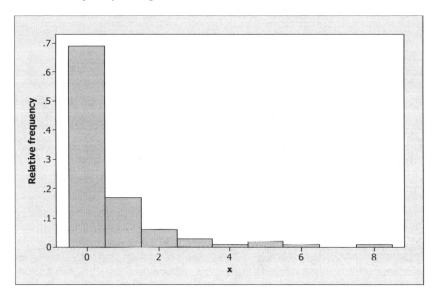

b Refer to the formulas given in Exercise 2.37. Using the frequency table and the grouped formulas, calculate $n = 100$, $\sum x_i f_i = 66$, $\sum x_i^2 f_i = 234$. Then

$$\bar{x} = \frac{\sum x_i f_i}{n} = \frac{66}{100} = 0.66$$

$$s^2 = \frac{\sum x_i^2 f_i - \frac{\left(\sum x_i f_i\right)^2}{n}}{n-1} = \frac{234 - \frac{(66)^2}{100}}{99} = 1.9236 \text{ and } s = \sqrt{1.9236} = 1.39$$

c The three intervals, $\bar{x} \pm ks$ for $k = 2,3$ are calculated in the table along with the actual proportion of measurements falling in the intervals. Tchebysheff's Theorem is satisfied and the approximation given by the Empirical Rule are fairly close for $k = 2$ and $k = 3$.

k	$\bar{x} \pm ks$	Interval	Fraction in Interval	Tchebysheff	Empirical Rule
2	0.66 ± 2.78	-2.12 to 3.44	$95/100 = 0.95$	at least 0.75	≈ 0.95
3	0.66 ± 4.17	-3.51 to 4.83	$96/100 = 0.96$	at least 0.89	≈ 0.997

2.75 We must estimate s and compare with the student's value of 0.263. In this case, $n = 20$ and the range is $R = 17.4 - 16.9 = 0.5$. The estimated value for s is then $s \approx R/4 = 0.5/4 = 0.125$, which is less than 0.263. It is important to consider the magnitude of the difference between the "rule of thumb" and the calculated value. For example, if we were working with a standard deviation of 100, a difference of 0.142 would not be great. However, the student's calculation is twice as large as the estimated value. Moreover, two standard deviations, or $2(0.263) = 0.526$, already exceeds the range. Thus, the value $s = 0.263$ is probably incorrect. The correct value of s is

$$s = \sqrt{\frac{\sum x_i^2 - \frac{\left(\sum x_i\right)^2}{n}}{n-1}} = \sqrt{\frac{5,851.95 - \frac{117,032.41}{20}}{19}} = \sqrt{0.0173} = 0.132$$

2.77 **a** Use the information in the exercise. For $1957 - 80$, $IQR = 21$, and the upper fence is

$$Q_3 + 1.5IQR = 52 + 1.5(21) = 83.5$$

For $1957 - 75$, $IQR = 16$, and the upper fence is

$$Q_3 + 1.5IQR = 52.25 + 1.5(16) = 76.25$$

b   Although the maximum number of goals in both distribution is the same (77 goals), the upper fence is different in 1957 – 80, so that the record number of goals, $x = 77$ is no longer an outlier.

2.79   The variable of interest is the environmental factor in terms of the threat it poses to Canada. Each bulleted statement produces a percentile.
  - $x =$ toxic chemicals is the 61st percentile.
  - $x =$ air pollution and smog is the 55th percentile.
  - $x =$ global warming is the 52nd percentile.

2.81   **a**   Calculate $n = 25$, $\sum x_i = 104.9$, $\sum x_i^2 = 454.810$. Then

$$\bar{x} = \frac{\sum x_i}{n} = \frac{104.9}{25} = 4.196$$

$$s = \sqrt{\frac{\sum x_i^2 - \frac{(\sum x_i)^2}{n}}{n-1}} = \sqrt{\frac{454.810 - \frac{(104.9)^2}{25}}{24}} = \sqrt{0.610} = 0.781$$

b   The ordered data set is shown below:

```
2.5   3.0   3.1   3.3   3.6
3.7   3.8   3.8   3.9   3.9
4.1   4.2   4.2   4.2   4.3
4.3   4.4   4.7   4.7   4.8
4.8   5.2   5.3   5.4   5.7
```

c   The z-scores for $x = 2.5$ and $x = 5.7$ are

$$z = \frac{x - \bar{x}}{s} = \frac{2.5 - 4.196}{0.781} = -2.17 \text{ and } z = \frac{x - \bar{x}}{s} = \frac{5.7 - 4.196}{0.781} = 1.93$$

Since neither of the z-scores are greater than 3 in absolute value, the measurements are not judged to be unusually large or small.

Case Study: The Boys of Winter

1   The *MINITAB* computer package was used to analyze the data. In the printout below, various descriptive statistics as well as histograms and box plots are shown.

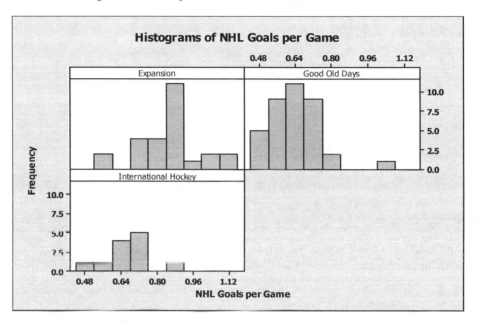

Descriptive Statistics: Average

Variable	Era	Total Count	Mean	SE Mean	StDev	Minimum	Q1	Median	Q3
Average	1	37	0.6345	0.0180	0.1095	0.4667	0.5423	0.6286	0.7113
	2	26	0.8505	0.0280	0.1426	0.5658	0.7594	0.8562	0.9067
	3	12	0.6633	0.0249	0.0864	0.5000	0.6159	0.6585	0.7128

Variable	Era	Maximum	Range	IQR
Average	1	1.0000	0.5333	0.1690
	2	1.1500	0.5842	0.1473
	3	0.8415	0.3415	0.0969

2   Notice that the average goals per game is the least in the Good Old Days era (1 = 1931–1967) and the highest in the Expansion era (2 = 1968–1993). The Expansion era is the most variable. Although the International Hockey era (3 = 1994–2006) has slightly higher average goals per game than Good Old Days era, it is noticeably less variable.

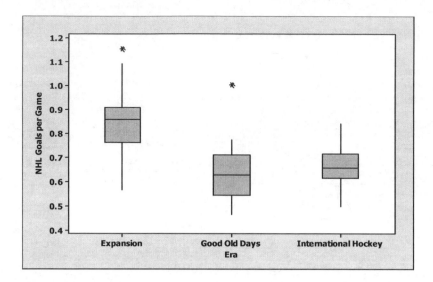

3   The box plot shows that each of the Expansion and Good Old Days eras has one outlier. There is no outlier in the International Hockey era, the least variable era.

4   In summary, the Expansion era is quite different than the other two eras; it has higher mean and median number of goals per game. The outlier in the Expansion era indicates the season with the record-high goals per game. Notice that there is very little difference between the Good Old Days and International Hockey eras.

Project 2: Ignorance Is Not Bliss (Project 1-B continued)

a   The sample mean is $\overline{x} = \dfrac{\Sigma x_i}{n}$. For this example, we have

$$\overline{X} = \frac{22+19+21+\cdots+27+33}{25} = \frac{544}{25} = 21.76$$

The sample mode is the value that occurs most often. For our data set, there are two: at 19 and at 22. Thus, there are two modes.

To find the median, first put the data into increasing order, as follows:

0	10	14	15	16	17	17	18	19	19	19	20
20	21	21	22	22	22	23	27	29	30	33	35
55											

The median is the value that is found in the middle position. For 25 data points, the middle value is the thirteenth largest, which in this case is 20.

From the histogram below, it can be concluded that the data is essentially mound-shaped.

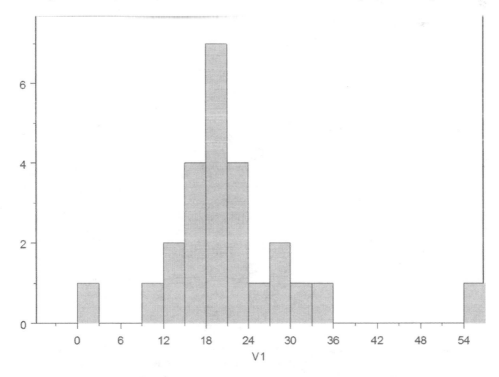

b   Since we have a small data set with a large outlier, the median would be the best choice in this situation. The sample median is less sensitive to outliers and thus gives a more accurate representation of the centre of this distribution. The mean of small samples, such as this one, is heavily influenced by outliers, such as the point $x = 55$ here, and therefore does not give an accurate representation of centre.

c   The sample standard deviation can be calculated as follows:

$$s = \sqrt{\frac{\Sigma\left(x_i^2\right) - \frac{\left(\Sigma x_i\right)^2}{n}}{n-1}} = \sqrt{\frac{14,234 - \frac{(544)^2}{25}}{25-1}} = \sqrt{\frac{2,396.56}{24}} = 9.992831$$

The range (R) is simply the difference between the maximum value and the minimum value. For our data set, $R = 55 - 0 = 55$. The approximation for s based on R (as espoused in Section 2.5 of the text) is $s \approx \dfrac{R}{4}$ or $55/4 = 13.75$, which is a decent approximation, but certainly not very good.

d   If all data points were increased by 4%, the mean would also increase by 4%, or be multiplied by 1.04. This can be proven as follows. Assume that c is a constant. Then, we obtain:

$$\bar{x} = \frac{\Sigma x_i}{n} = \frac{\Sigma c x_i}{n} = \frac{c \Sigma x_i}{n} = c\bar{x}$$

Thus, the result follows if we let c equal 1.04.

e   If all data points were raised by 5%, the standard deviation would also be raised by 5%. Recall the formula for the standard deviation and let c be a constant. Then

$$s = \sqrt{\frac{\Sigma\left(x_i^2\right) - \frac{\left(\Sigma x_i\right)^2}{n}}{n-1}}$$

$$\Rightarrow \sqrt{\frac{\Sigma\left(\left[c x_i\right]^2\right) - \frac{\left(\Sigma c x_i\right)^2}{n}}{n-1}} = \sqrt{\frac{\Sigma\left(c^2 x_i^2\right) - \frac{\left(c \Sigma x_i\right)^2}{n}}{n-1}} = \sqrt{\frac{c^2 \Sigma\left(x_i^2\right) - \frac{c^2\left(\Sigma x_i\right)^2}{n}}{n-1}}$$

$$\Rightarrow \sqrt{\frac{c^2\left\{\Sigma\left(x_i^2\right) - \frac{\left(\Sigma x_i\right)^2}{n}\right\}}{n-1}} = \sqrt{c^2}\sqrt{\frac{\Sigma\left(x_i^2\right) - \frac{\left(\Sigma x_i\right)^2}{n}}{n-1}} = c \cdot s$$

Thus, we see that the standard deviation will be multiplied by the constant multiple c, in this case, 1.05.

f   From part **a**, it was calculated that $\bar{x} = 21.76$ and $s = 9.992831$. Then, the interval $\bar{x} \pm s$ becomes $x \in \left[11.767169, 31.752831\right]$. Counting the number of x values between 12 and 31 (inclusive), there are 20 entries. Thus, $\dfrac{20}{25} = 80\%$ of the entries are within the interval $\bar{x} \pm s$. Now, computing the domain of the interval $\bar{x} \pm 2s$, it can be seen that $x \in \left[1.774338, 41.745662\right]$. There are 23 values of x between 2 and 41 (inclusive), thus, $\dfrac{23}{25} = 92\%$. Comparing to the Empirical Rule, normal distributions should have approximately 68% of the total values of x within $\bar{x} \pm s$ and 95% of the total values within $\bar{x} \pm 2s$. Thus, it can be seen that there are more measurements than predicted for the first interval and slightly less than predicted for the second interval. This discrepancy can be accounted for by the non-normal behaviour in the distribution and the small amount of data points in the sample. Finally, Tchebysheff's Theorem predicts that at least 0% of the measurements are within $\bar{x} \pm s$ and that at least 75% of the measurements are within $\bar{x} \pm 2s$. As such, this sample follows Tchebysheff's Theorem.

g   Yes, Tchebysheff's Theorem can be used to describe this data set, since it can be used for *any* distribution.

h   The Empirical Rule has a limited use in describing this sample. The data is relatively mound-shaped, and so the Empirical Rule is somewhat appropriate. However, due to the outliers in the data set, the Empirical Rule fails to accurately predict the percentage of measurements within the interval $\bar{x} \pm s$. It provides a better approximation for the interval $\bar{x} \pm 2s$.

i   Referring to plot made in part **a**, it seems as though points 0 and 55 could be outliers, as these are far from the bulk of the data in the centre.

j   Given that $n = 25$, the 25th percentile is found at $x = 0.25(n+1) = 0.25(26) = 6.5$. Thus, the 25th percentile is the average of the sixth and seventh measurements when they are arranged in increasing order, $Q_1 = \dfrac{17+17}{2} = 17$. Likewise, $x = 0.50(26) = 13$ and thus $Q_2 = 20$. Lastly, $x = 0.75(26) = 19.5$, thus $Q_3 = \dfrac{23+27}{2} = 25$. The interquartile range is therefore $IQR = Q_3 - Q_1 = 25 - 17 = 8$.

k   The range is 55 as calculated in part **c**, whereas the $IQR = 8$. Thus, about 50% of the data can be found in a very narrow middle area of the data range, suggesting that a mound-shaped distribution is likely.

l   A box plot is shown below. The box plot shows four outliers, as indicated by the points beyond the whiskers.

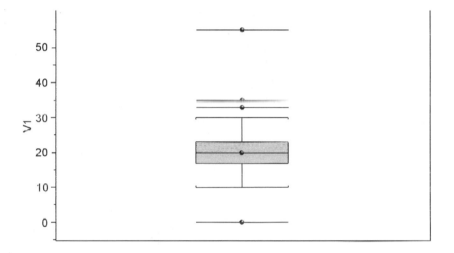

m   The side-by-side box plots for the Hand Washing Time after (box 1) and before (box 2) the training session are given below:

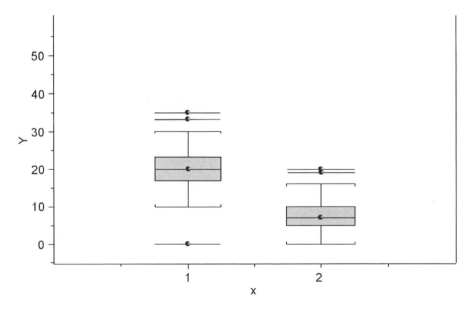

n   It is clear from the box plots that the average time spent washing hands improved after the training session.

o   Yes, we can conclude that the session was useful, and that the conjecture was true. A difference in median times of 20 seconds and 7 seconds is substantial.

p   The histogram for the both data sets taken together is shown below. There is clear evidence of two distinct peaks, suggesting that the data comprises of two distinct populations (which we know is true).

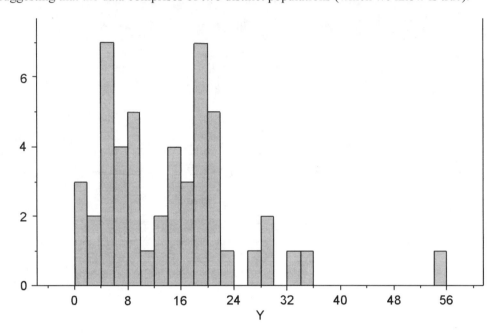

Chapter 3: Describing Bivariate Data

3.1   **a**   The side-by-side pie charts are constructed as in Chapter 1 for each of the two groups (men and women) and are displayed below using the percentages shown in the table below.

	Group 1	Group 2	Group 3	Total
Men	23%	31%	46%	100%
Women	8%	57%	35%	100%

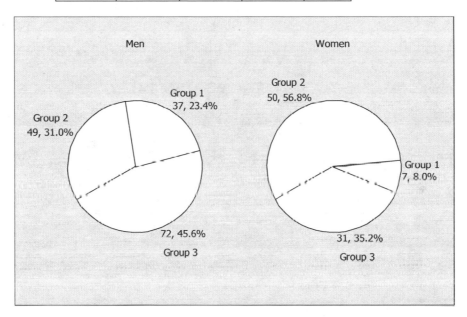

b–c   The side-by-side and stacked bar charts in the next two figures measure the frequency of occurrence for each of the three groups. A separate bar (or portion of a bar) is used for men and women.

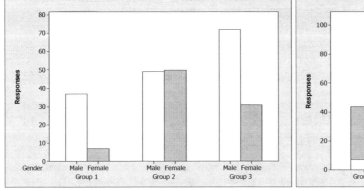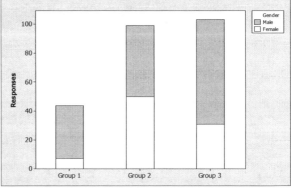

d   The differences in the proportions of men and women in the three groups is most graphically portrayed by the pie charts, since the unequal number of men and women tend to confuse the interpretation of the bar charts. However, the bar charts are useful in retaining the actual frequencies of occurrence in each group, which is lost in the pie chart.

3.3 **a** This is similar to Exercises 3.1 and 3.2. Any of the comparative charts (side-by-side pie charts, stacked or side-by-side bar charts) can be used.

   b–c The two types of comparative bar charts are shown below. The amounts spent in each of the four categories seem to be quite different for men and women, except in category C. In category C, which involves the largest dollar amount of purchase, there is little difference between the genders.

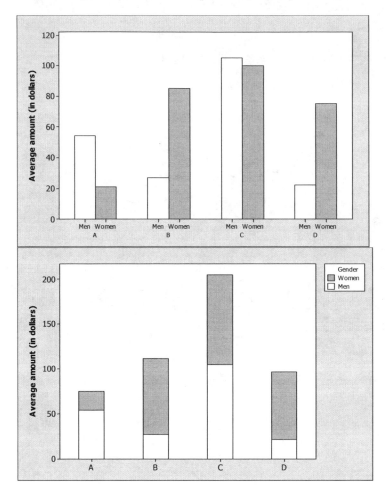

   d Although it is really a matter of preference, the only advantage to the stacked chart is that the reader can easily see the total dollar amount for each category. For comparison purposes, the side-by-side chart may be better.

3.5 **a** The population of interest is the population of responses to the question about free time for all parents and children in the United States. The sample is the set of responses generated for the 198 parents and 200 children in the survey.

   b The data can be considered bivariate if, for each person interviewed, we record the person's relationship (parent or child) and their response to the question (just the right amount, not enough, too much, don't know). Since the measurements are not numerical in nature, the variables are qualitative.

   c The entry in a cell represents the number of people who fell into that relationship–opinion category.

d A pie chart is shown below for both the "parents" and the "children" categories. The size of each sector angle is proportional to the fraction of measurements falling into that category.

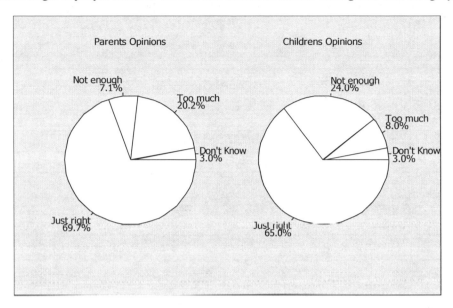

e Either stacked or comparative bar charts could be used, but since the height of the bar represents the frequency of occurrence (and hence is tied to the sample size), this type of chart would be misleading. The comparative pie charts are the best choice.

3.7 **a** The side-by-side bar chart is shown below.

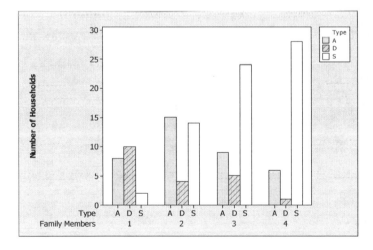

b–c The stacked bar chart is shown below. Both charts indicate that the more family members there are, the more likely it is that the family lives in a duplex or a single residence. The fewer the number of family members, the more likely it is that the family lives in an apartment.

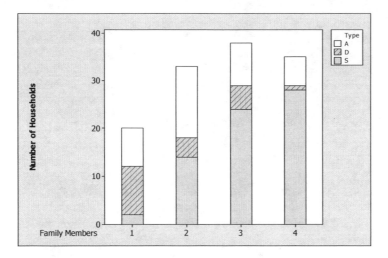

3.9   **a**   A stacked bar chart is given below.

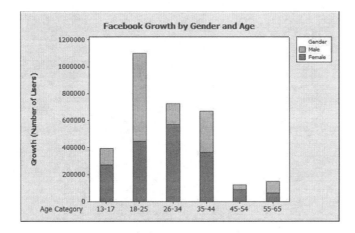

  b   A comparative pie chart of Facebook growth by gender and age is given below.

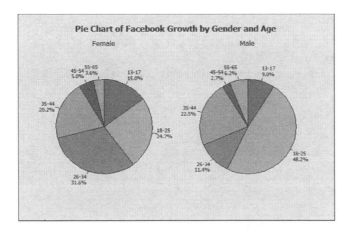

  c   Conclusions will vary from student to student.

3.11   Answers will vary from student to student.

3.13   **a–b**   The scatterplot is shown below. Notice that there is a negative relationship between y and x. The measurements are decreasing over time.

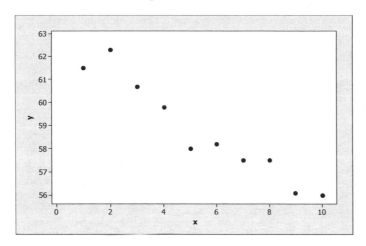

   c   From the *MINITAB* printout, $s_{xy} = -6.42222$, $s_x = \sqrt{9.16667}$, and $s_y = \sqrt{4.84933}$ so that

$$r = \frac{s_{xy}}{s_x s_y} = \frac{-6.42222}{\sqrt{(9.16667)(4.84933)}} = -0.9632$$

   d   The slope and y-intercept of the regression line are

$$b = r\frac{s_y}{s_x} = -0.9632\left(\frac{2.2021}{3.0277}\right) = -0.700 \text{ and } a = \bar{y} - b\bar{x} = \frac{587.6}{10} - (-0.700)\left(\frac{55}{10}\right) = 62.61$$

and the equation of the regression line is $y = 62.61 - 0.70x$.

   e   The graph of the data points and the best fitting line is shown below. The line fits through the points very well.

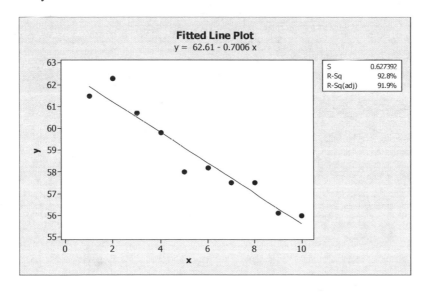

3.15 This is similar to previous exercises. Calculate $n = 12$; $\sum x_i = 1,949$; $\sum y_i = 2843.5$; $\sum x_i^2 = 324,076.86$;

$\sum y_i^2 = 713,073.75$; $\sum x_i y_i = 477,722$.

Then the covariance is

$$s_{xy} = \frac{\sum x_i y_i - \dfrac{(\sum x_i)(\sum y_i)}{n}}{n-1} = 1,444.5644$$

The sample standard deviations are $s_x = 26.16$ and $s_y = 59.76$ so that $r = 0.924$.

Then $b = r\dfrac{s_y}{s_x} = 2.1108$ and $a = \bar{y} - b\bar{x} = 236.96 - 2.1108(162.42) = -105.88$

and the equation of the regression line is $y = -105.88 + 2.11x$.

The graph of the data points and the best fitting line is shown below.

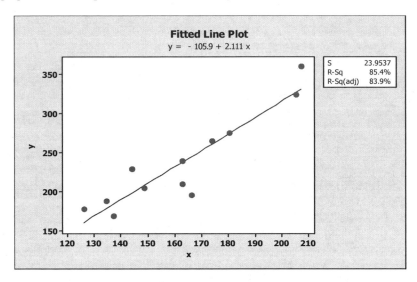

3.17 a The scatterplot is shown below. If we exclude the unusual observation (production in the year 1996), there appears to be a positive linear trend.

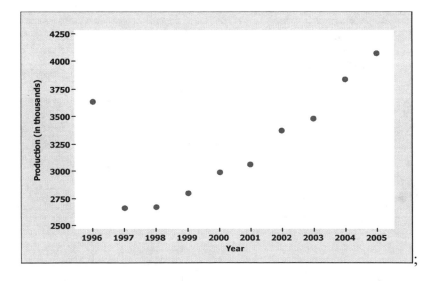

b Calculate $n = 10$; $\sum x_i = 20005$; $\sum y_i = 32614$; $\sum x_i^2 = 40,020,085$; $\sum y_i^2 = 108,612,152$;

$\sum x_i y_i = 65,253,338$.

Then the covariance is

$$s_{xy} = \frac{\sum x_i y_i - \dfrac{(\sum x_i)(\sum y_i)}{n}}{n-1} = 1003.44444444444$$

The sample standard deviations are $s_x = 3.02765035409749$ and $s_y = 499.42771693654$ so that $r = 0.6636131330417$. Then

$$b = r\frac{s_y}{s_x} - 109.466666666667 \text{ and}$$

$$a = \overline{y} - b\overline{x} = 3261.4 - 109.466666666667\,(2000.5) = -215726.666666667$$

and the equation of the regression line is $y = -215726.667 + 109.467x$.

c   The prediction may not be very accurate, since you are predicting outside of the range of values for which you have collected data. This is called *extrapolation*.

3.19 **a**   Since we would be interested in predicting the price of a TV based on its size, the price is the dependent variable (y) and size is the independent variable (x).

b   The scatterplot is shown below. The relationship is somewhat linear, but has a bit of a curve to it. The relationship may in fact be slightly curvilinear.

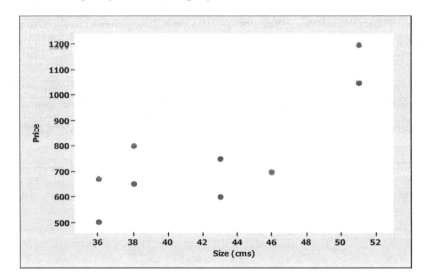

3.21 **a–b**   The data is graphed as a scatterplot in the figure on the next page, with the time in months plotted on the horizontal axis and the number of books on the vertical axis. The data points are then connected to form a line graph. There is a very distinct pattern in this data, with the number of books increasing with time, a response which might be modeled by a quadratic equation. The professor's productivity appears to increase, with less time required to write later books.

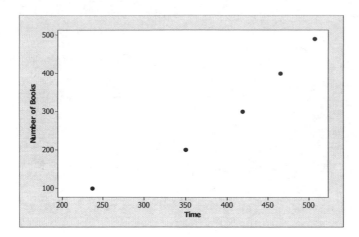

3.23 **a** The following variables are recorded: automobiles sold or produced year (quantitative), the number of sales or production (quantitative), and the automobile brand or type (foreign vs. Japanese, passenger cars vs. trucks/buses, qualitative).

   b The populations of interest are the populations of all import sales of automobiles and domestic automobile production in Japan. Although the source of this data is not given, it is probably based on census information, in which case the data represents the entire population.

   c A comparative (side-by-side) bar chart has been used. An alternative presentation can be obtained by using comparative pie charts.

   d Since there are not much change in both sales and production over the period 1998–2005, there seems to be very little pattern between total sales and total production.

3.25 The scatterplot for these two quantitative variables is shown below. Notice the almost perfect positive correlation. The correlation coefficient and best fitting line can be calculated for descriptive purposes.

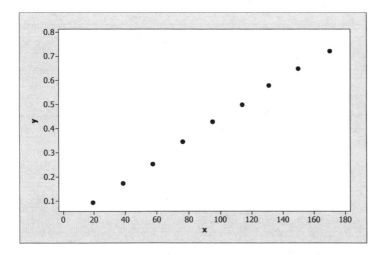

Calculate $n = 9$; $\sum x_i = 850.8$; $\sum y_i = 3.755$; $\sum x_i^2 = 101,495.78$; $\sum y_i^2 = 1.941467$; $\sum x_i y_i = 443.7727$.

Then the covariance is $s_{xy} = \dfrac{\sum x_i y_i - \dfrac{(\sum x_i)(\sum y_i)}{n}}{n-1} = 11.10000417$

The sample standard deviations are $s_x = 51.31620$ and $s_y = 0.216448$, so that $r = 0.999$. Then

$$b = r\frac{s_y}{s_x} = 0.004215 \text{ and } a = \bar{y} - b\bar{x} = 0.417222 - 0.004215(94.5333) = 0.0187$$

and the equation of the regression line is $y = 0.0187 + 0.0042x$.

3.27   **a**   Using the *MINITAB* output, calculate

$$r = \frac{s_{xy}}{s_x s_y} = \frac{1232.231}{\sqrt{(412.528)(4437.109)}} = 0.9108$$

b   Since the first weekend's gross would tend to explain the total gross, we could consider $x =$ first weekend's gross to be the independent variable, and $y =$ total gross to be the dependent variable.

c   Using $r = 0.9108$, $s_x = \sqrt{412.528}$, and $s_y = \sqrt{4437.109}$, calculate

$$b = r\frac{s_y}{s_x} = 2.987 \text{ and } a = \bar{y} - b\bar{x} = 86.71 - 2.987(25.66) = 10.06$$

and the equation of the regression line is $y = 10.06 + 2.987x$.

d   Answers will vary slightly depending on rounding. For the regression line $y = 10.06 + 2.987x$, the predicted value of y when $x = 30$ will be $y = 10.06 + 2.987(30) = 99.67$ or 99.67 million dollars.

3.29   **a**   The scatterplot is shown below.

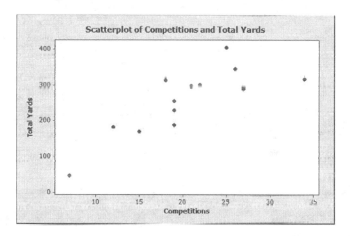

b   The relationship is positive and linear. There are no outliers to the linear trend. Aaron, however, threw unusually low number of passed in week 4.

c $n = 16$; $\Sigma x_i = 312$; $\Sigma y_i = 3{,}922$; $\Sigma x_i^2 = 7{,}106$; $\Sigma y_i^2 = 1{,}131{,}764$; $\Sigma x_i y_i = 88{,}023$

Then the covariance is

$$s_{xy} = \frac{\Sigma x_i y_i - \dfrac{(\Sigma x_i)(\Sigma y_i)}{n}}{n-1} = 460.3857$$

The sample standard deviations are $s_x = 6.6354$ and $s_y = 87.1336$. Thus,

$$r = \frac{s_{xy}}{s_x s_y} = \frac{460.3857}{6.6354(87.1336)} = 0.7963$$

d $b = r\dfrac{s_y}{s_x} = 0.7963\left(\dfrac{87.1336}{6.6354}\right) = 10.4567$ and

$a = \bar{y} - b\bar{x} = 261.4667 - 10.14567(20.8) = 43.971$

and the equation of the regression line is $y = a + bx = 43.971 + 10.4567x$.

e   Use the regression line from part **d.** When $x = 20$, $y = 43.971 + 10.4567(20) = 253.105$.

3.31 **a** The calculations for the correlation coefficients are the same as used in previous exercises. The *MINITAB* printout shows the three correlation coefficients in a 2×2 matrix.

```
Correlations: Al, Fe, Mg
          Al        Fe
Fe    -0.617

Mg    -0.189    0.626
```

b There is a strong positive relationship between iron and magnesium oxide, while there is a strong negative relationship between aluminum and iron oxide. There is very little relationship between aluminum and magnesium oxide.

3.33 **a** The variables are categories of ideological groups (qualitative), classification by religion (Catholics, Protestants; qualitative), and the number of people in each category (quantitative).

b–c The side-by-side bar chart and comparative line charts are shown below.

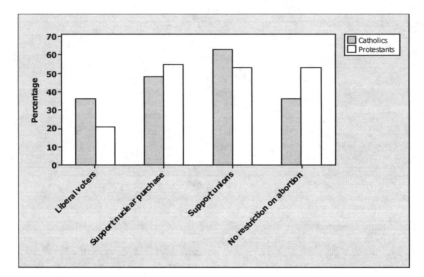

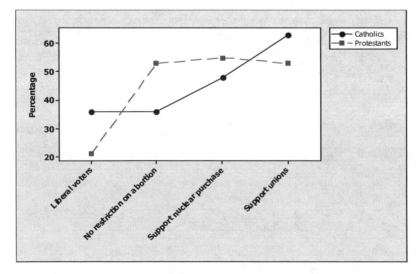

d The line chart is the most effective method of presentation; you can compare both the percentage figures and the patterns for Catholics and Protestants.

3.35 **a–b** The scatterplot is shown below. Most of the data points are clustered together in the lower region. However, we can see a strong positive linear relationship between *x* and *y*.

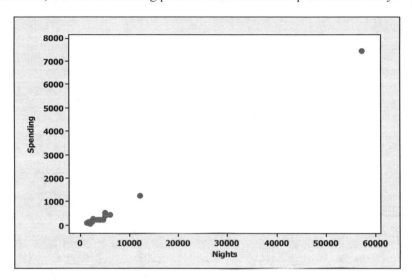

c Calculate $n = 15$; $\sum x_i = 108,277$; $\sum y_i = 11,864$; $\sum x_i^2 = 3,574,990,411$; $\sum y_i^2 = 58,284,922$; $\sum x_i y_i = 454,622,291$ Then the covariance is

$$s_{xy} = \frac{\sum x_i y_i - \dfrac{(\sum x_i)(\sum y_i)}{n}}{n-1} = 26,355,886$$

The sample standard deviations are $s_x = 14,125$ and $s_y = 1,869$, so that $r = 0.998$ (very strong positive correlation).

3.37 **a** Calculate $n = 8$; $\sum x_i = 634$; $\sum y_i = 386$; $\sum x_i^2 = 52270$; $\sum y_i^2 = 19876$; $\sum x_i y_i = 32136$. Then the covariance is

$$s_{xy} = \frac{\sum x_i y_i - \dfrac{(\sum x_i)(\sum y_i)}{n}}{n-1} = 220.78571$$

The sample standard deviations are $s_x = 17.010501$ and $s_y = 13.3710775$ so that $r = 0.971$.

b Since the correlation coefficient is so close to 1, the strong correlation indicates that the second and quicker test could be used in place of the longer test-interview.

3.39 **a** The scatterplot is shown below and the relationship seems positive, linear, and moderate.

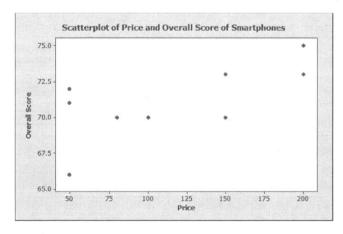

b $n = 9; \Sigma x_i = 1030; \Sigma y_i = 640; \Sigma x_i^2 = 148,900; \Sigma y_i^2 = 45,564; \Sigma x_i y_i = 74,100.$

Then the covariance is

$$s_{xy} = \frac{\Sigma x_i y_i - \dfrac{(\Sigma x_i)(\Sigma y_i)}{n}}{n-1} = 106.9444$$

The sample standard deviations are $s_x = 62.2718$ and $s_y = 2.5712$. Thus,

$$r = \frac{s_{xy}}{s_x s_y} = \frac{106.9444}{62.2718(2.5712)} = 0.6679.$$

c $b = r\dfrac{s_y}{s_x} = 0.6679\left(\dfrac{2.5712}{62.2718}\right) = 0.0276$ and $a = \bar{y} - b\bar{x} = 71.1111 - 0.0276(114.4444) = 67.9524$

and the equation of the regression line is $y = a + bx = 67.9524 + 0.0276x.$

Case Study: Paying for Players

1   Almost all the variables are approximately symmetric. Payroll and Points maybe slightly skewed to the left. On the other hand, overtime loss is slightly skewed right. There are two unusually low Wins ($x = 21$, $x = 22$); and one of the teams has extremely high "Goals for" ($x = 314$).

2   Although the correlations are not very strong, as you can expect, payroll is positively correlated with Points, Wins, and Goals for, and is negatively correlated with Losses, Overtime Losses, and Goals Against.

Correlations: Payroll, Points, Wins, Losses, Goals For, Goals Against, OT Losses

	Payroll	Points	Wins	Losses	Goals For	Goals A.
Points	0.568					
Wins	0.554	0.987				
Losses	-0.566	-0.983	-0.940			
Goals For	0.390	0.767	0.760	-0.749		
Goals Against	-0.451	-0.806	-0.774	0.818	-0.387	
OT Losses	-0.176	-0.375	-0.519	0.197	-0.307	0.176

3   Answers will vary. Yes, the price of the NHL team does convey something about its quality—higher priced teams are in general performed slightly better than poorly priced teams. One way to find this would be to compare the relation between the variables payroll and points or payroll and wins.

Project 3-A: Child Safety Seat Survey

a   Some of the variables measured in this survey are Type of Restraint (i.e., Rear-facing Infant Seat, Forward-facing Infant Seat, Booster Seat, and Seat Belt Only) and Age Group (Infants, Toddlers, School-Aged: 4–9 years, and Older than 9 years). The Restraint Type category consists of qualitative variables, whereas the Age Group category consists of quantitative variables.

b   The side-by-side bar chart is shown below.

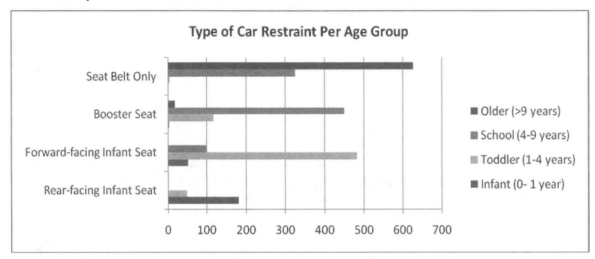

The stacked bar chart is shown below.

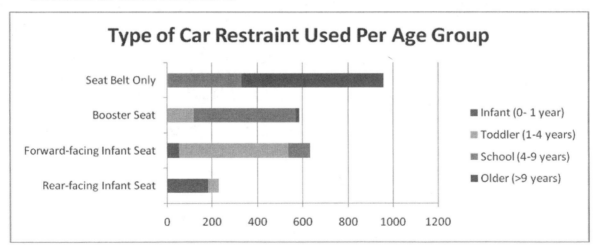

c   Pie charts for each age group are shown below.

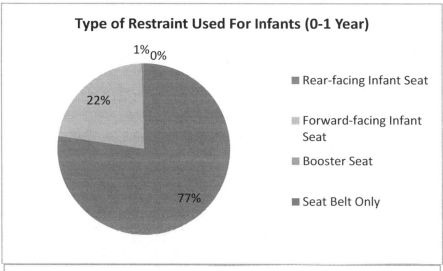

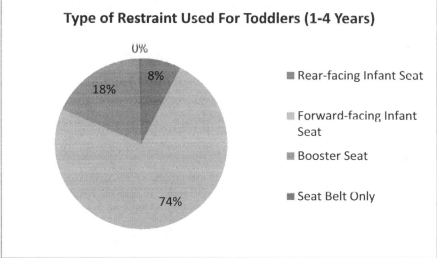

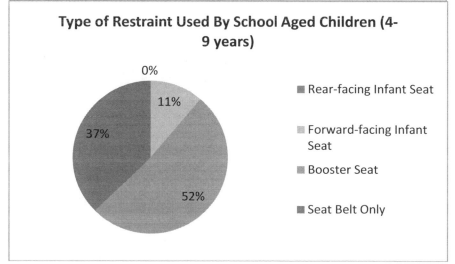

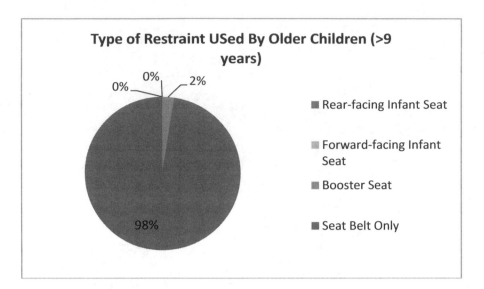

The pie chart titled **"Type of Restraint Used For Toddlers (1–4 Years)"** best depicts the differences and similarities of use for toddler restraint types. It can be clearly seen that approximately three-quarters of the seat restraints used for this age category are forward-facing infant seats, while the other quarter consists of mainly of booster seats, and under half as many rear-facing infant seats. Although we judge the pie chart to be visually more informative, the bar chart does an adequate job as well.

d   By looking at these graphs, one can ascertain information such as which restraints were used the most, least, and so on, as well as which age groups tended to use which types of restraints, and differences and similarities in use of the restraints between age groups. The bar graph is more effective in this case than the pie graph, because it can graphically portray all of the variables in one chart, while many charts are needed if pie graphs are used. By combining all of these variables, bar graphs make it easy to compare them. The stacked bar chart is the more effective of the two bar graphs. It combines the best features of the other two graph types, by containing all of the information that the side-by-side bar graph does, while portraying it in a more compact manner. However, if we take "effective" to refer to visual impact, we might say that the pie charts, although more cumbersome, are somewhat more revealing than the bar charts.

e   Other graphical techniques that could be used to display this data include histograms, dot diagrams, box plots, and stem-and-leaf plots. Each type of graphical representation has its own advantages and disadvantages. It is difficult to say which would be most effective.

Project 3-B: Child Safety Seat Survey, continued

a   A scatterplot of female weight against height is shown below.

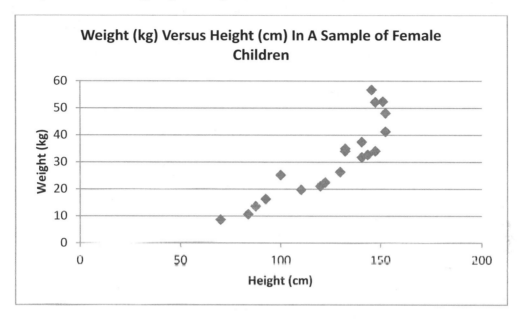

There is evidence of a positive relationship between the variables weight and height. The relationship, however, is not perfectly linear, but somewhat curvilinear.

b   Based on the scatterplot from part **a**, there do not seem to be any outliers.

c   A scatterplot of male weight against height is shown below.

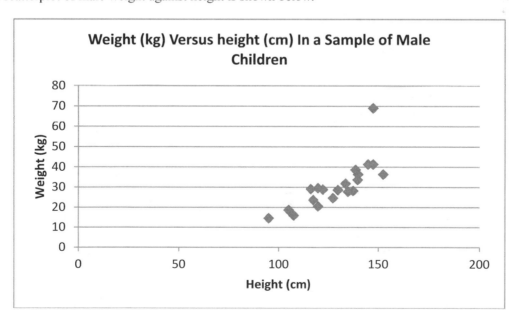

Once again, there is evidence of a positive relationship, this time, more linear. Due to the fact that the points are clustered closer to a straight line (apart from the one outlier), there is a much stronger linear relationship with the males than with the females.

d   In the scatterplot for males, there is a strong linear correlation, with one very clear outlier. The data is also clustered tightly within a smaller range (95.00 to 152.50 cm for height, and 14.51 to 41.28 kg), with the exception of the outlier. The scatterplot for female children, however, is more spread out. It has a larger range for its data values (70.00 to 152.50 cm for height, and 8.62 to 52.39 kg for weight), and is less linear in its distribution, although the values for weight tend to still increase with the values for height. Aside from the females having a larger variance in their weight, many of them tend to have a larger weight than the males of the same height.

e   Side-by-side box plots for height are shown below.

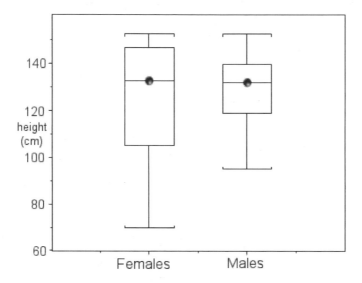

Clearly as you can see from the box plots, the variability of height in females is higher than that of males. Also, the median height for females is slightly larger than for males.

f   The correlation coefficient is $r = \dfrac{S_{xy}}{s_x s_y} = 0.881546$. The value is relatively high, indicating a rather strong linear association between female height and weight.

g   This correlation coefficient reinforces the earlier assertions made based on the scatterplot. It is a positive value (0.881546), indicating that the relationship is positive. As well, since it is close to 1, it indicates a relatively strong correlation, as was evident in the scatterplot (close clustering around a straight line relationship). The slope of the regression line can be found by multiplying the correlation coefficient, r, by s_y, and then dividing by s_x.

h   The regression line can be found using any statistical software package. Alternately, one could use the formulas from the textbook. In either case, the fitted line is $y = -29.648 + 0.4842x$, where x represents female height and y represents female weight.

i   When the female has a height of 160 cm, we can predict her weight by plugging in $x=160$ into the regression equation and finding y. That is, $y = -29.648 + 0.4842(160) = 47.824$ kg as the predicted weight.

j   No. A new regression line for males should be fitted because the weight and height relationship is different for the two sexes (as was seen in the preceding parts of this question).

k   No. The two sexes exhibit different weight–height relationships. Although ignoring the sex category might not produce very unreliable projections, there does not seem to be any compelling reason to do so. More formally, we would be ignoring a lurking variable (sex) for no good reason.

Chapter 4: Probability and Probability Distributions

4.1   **a**   This experiment involves tossing a single die and observing the outcome. The sample space for this experiment consists of the following simple events:

E_1: Observe a 1 E_4: Observe a 4
E_2: Observe a 2 E_5: Observe a 5
E_3: Observe a 3 E_6: Observe a 6

b   Events A through F are composed of the simple events in the following manner:

A: (E_2) D: (E_2)
B: (E_2, E_4, E_6) E: (E_2, E_4, E_6)
C: (E_3, E_4, E_5, E_6) F: contains no simple events

c   Since the simple events E_i, $i = 1, 2, 3, \ldots, 6$ are equally likely, $P(E_i) = 1/6$.

d   To find the probability of an event, we sum the probabilities assigned to the simple events in that event. For example,

$$P(A) = P(E_2) = \frac{1}{6}$$

Similarly, $P(D) = 1/6$; $P(B) = P(E) = P(E_2) + P(E_4) + P(E_6) = \frac{3}{6} = \frac{1}{2}$; and $P(C) = \frac{4}{6} = \frac{2}{3}$. Since

event F contains no simple events, $P(F) = 0$.

4.3   It is given that $P(E_1) = 0.45$ and that $3P(E_2) = 0.45$, so that $P(E_2) = 0.15$. Since $\sum_S P(E_i) = 1$, the

remaining 8 simple events must have probabilities whose sum is
$$P(E_3) + P(E_4) + \ldots + P(E_{10}) = 1 - 0.45 - 0.15 = 0.4$$

Since it is given that they are equiprobable, $P(E_i) = \frac{0.4}{8} = 0.05$ for $i = 3, 4, \ldots, 10$

4.5   **a**   The experiment consists of choosing three coins at random from four. The order in which the coins are drawn is unimportant. Hence, each simple event consists of a triplet, indicating the three coins drawn. Using the letters N, D, Q, and L to represent the nickel, dime, quarter, and loonie, respectively, the four possible simple events are listed below.

E_1: (NDQ) E_2: (NDL) E_3: (NQL) E_4: (DQL)

b   The event that a loonie is chosen is associated with the simple events E_2, E_3, and E_4. Hence,

$$P(\text{choose a loonie}) = P(E_2) + P(E_3) + P(E_4) = \frac{1}{4} + \frac{1}{4} + \frac{1}{4} = \frac{3}{4} \text{ since each simple event is equally likely.}$$

c   The simple events along with their monetary values follow:

E_1 NDQ $0.40
E_2 NDL $1.15
E_3 NQL $1.30
E_4 DQL $1.35

Hence, $P(\text{total amount is \$1.10 or more}) = P(E_2) + P(E_3) + P(E_4) = 3/4$.

4.7   Label the five balls as R_1, R_2, R_3, Y_1, and Y_2. The selection of two balls is accomplished in two stages to produce the simple events in the tree diagram below.

First Ball	Second Ball	Simple Events		First Ball	Second Ball	Simple Events
R_1	R_2	R_1R_2		Y_1	R_1	Y_1R_1
	R_3	R_1R_3			R_2	Y_1R_2
	Y_1	R_1Y_1			R_3	Y_1R_3
	Y_2	R_1Y_2			Y_2	Y_1Y_2
R_2	R_1	R_2R_1		Y_2	R_1	Y_2R_1
	R_3	R_2R_3			R_2	Y_2R_2
	Y_1	R_2Y_1			R_3	Y_2R_3
	Y_2	R_2Y_2			Y_1	Y_2Y_1
R_3	R_1	R_3R_1				
	R_2	R_3R_2				
	Y_1	R_3Y_1				
	Y_2	R_3Y_2				

4.9   The four possible outcomes of the experiment, or simple events, are represented as the cells of a 2×2 table, and have probabilities as given in the table.
  a $P(\text{adult judged to need glasses}) = 0.44 + 0.14 = 0.58$
  b $P(\text{adult needs glasses but does not use them}) = 0.14$
  c $P(\text{adult uses glasses}) = 0.44 + 0.02 = 0.46$

4.11   **a**   *Experiment*: Select three people and record their gender (M or F).
  b   Extend the tree diagram in Figure 4.3 of the text to include one more coin toss (a total of $n = 3$). Then replace the H and T by M and F to obtain the 8 possible simple events shown below:

  FFF   FMM   MFM   MMF
  MFF   FMF   FFM   MMM

  c   Since there are $N = 8$ equally likely simple events, each is assigned probability, $P(E_i) = 1/N = 1/8$.
  d–e   Sum the probabilities of the appropriate simple events:

$$P(\text{only one man}) = P(MFF) + P(FMF) + P(FFM) = 3\left(\frac{1}{8}\right) = \frac{3}{8}$$

$$P(\text{all three are women}) = P(FFF) = \frac{1}{8}$$

4.13   **a**   *Experiment*: A taster tastes and ranks three varieties of tea A, B, and C, according to preference.
  b   Simple events in *S* are in triplet form.

  $E_1 : (1,2,3)$ $E_4 : (2,3,1)$

  $E_2 : (1,3,2)$ $E_5 : (3,2,1)$

  $E_3 : (2,1,3)$ $E_6 : (3,1,2)$

  Here 1 is assigned to the most desirable, 2 to the next most desirable, and 3 to the least desirable.
  c   Define the events   D: variety A is ranked first
                          F: variety A is ranked third
  Then $P(D) = P(E_1) + P(E_2) = 1/6 + 1/6 = 1/3$
  The probability that A is least desirable is $P(F) = P(E_5) + P(E_6) = 1/6 + 1/6 = 1/3$

4.15   Similar to Exercise 4.9. The four possible outcomes of the experiment, or simple events, are represented as the cells of a 2×2 table, and have probabilities (when divided by 300) as given in the table.
  a $P(\text{normal eyes and normal wing size}) = 140/300 = 0.467$
  b $P(\text{vermillion eyes}) = (3 + 151)/300 = 154/300 = 0.513$
  c $P(\text{either vermillion eyes or miniature wings or both}) = (3 + 151 + 6)/300 = 160/300 = 0.533$

4.17   Use the *mn* Rule. There are $10(8) = 80$ possible pairs.

4.19   **a** $P_3^5 = \dfrac{5!}{2!} = 5(4)(3) = 60$

b $P_9^{10} = \dfrac{10!}{1!} = 3,628,800$

c $P_6^6 = \dfrac{6!}{0!} = 6! = 720$

d $P_1^{20} = \dfrac{20!}{19!} = 20$

4.21   Since order is important, you use *permutations* and $P_5^8 = \dfrac{8!}{3!} = 8(7)(6)(5)(4) = 6720$.

4.23   Use the extended *mn* Rule. The first die can fall in 1 of 6 ways, *and* the second and third die can each fall in 1 of 6 ways. The total number of simple events is $6(6)(6) = 216$.

4.25   Since order is unimportant, you use *combinations* and $C_3^{10} = \dfrac{10!}{3!7!} = \dfrac{10(9)(8)}{3(2)(1)} = 120$.

4.27   This exercise involves the arrangement of six different cities in all possible orders. Each city will be visited once and only once. Hence, order is important and elements are being chosen from a single set.
Permutations are used and the number of arrangements is $P_6^6 = \dfrac{6!}{0!} = 6! = 6(5)(4)(3)(2)(1) = 720$.

4.29   **a**   Each student has a choice of 52 cards, since the cards are replaced between selections. The *mn* Rule allows you to find the total number of configurations for three students as $52(52)(52) = 140,608$.

b   Now each student must pick a different card. That is, the first student has 52 choices, but the second and third students have only 51 and 50 choices, respectively. The total number of configurations is found using the *mn* Rule or the rule for permutations:
$$mnt = 52(51)(50) = 132,600 \quad \text{or} \quad P_3^{52} = \dfrac{52!}{49!} = 132,600$$

c   Let A be the event of interest. Since there are 52 different cards in the deck, there are 52 configurations in which all three students pick the same card (one for each card). That is, there are $n_A = 52$ ways for the event A to occur, out of a total of $N = 140,608$ possible configurations from part **a**. The probability of interest is $P(A) = \dfrac{n_A}{N} = \dfrac{52}{140,608} = 0.00037$.

d   Again, let A be the event of interest. There are $n_A = 132,600$ ways (from part **b**) for the event A to occur, out of a total of $N = 140,608$ possible configurations from part **a**, and the probability of interest is $P(A) = \dfrac{n_A}{N} = \dfrac{132,600}{140,608} = 0.943$.

4.31   **a**   Since the order of selection for the five-card hand is unimportant, use *combinations* to find the number of possible hands as $N = C_5^{52} = \dfrac{52!}{5!47!} = \dfrac{52(51)(50)(49)(48)}{5(4)(3)(2)(1)} = 2,598,960$.

b   Since there are only four different suits, there are $n_A = 4$ ways to get a royal flush.

c   From parts **a** and **b**, $P(\text{royal flush}) = \dfrac{n_A}{N} = \dfrac{4}{2,598,960} = 0.000001539$.

4.33   Notice that a sample of 10 nurses will be the same no matter in which order they were selected. Hence, order is unimportant and combinations are used. The number of samples of 10 selected from a total of 90 is

$$C_{10}^{90} = \frac{90!}{10!80!} = \frac{2.0759076\left(10^{19}\right)}{3.6288\left(10^6\right)} = 5.720645\left(10^{12}\right)$$

4.35   **a**   Use the *mn* Rule. The Group I team can be chosen in 1 of $m = 10$ ways, while there are 5 ways to choose the Group II team, for a total of $N = mn = 10(5) = 50$ possible pairings.

      b   You must choose Calgary from the first group and Ottawa from the second group, so that $n_A = (1)(1) = 1$ and the probability is $n_A/N = 1/50$.

      c   Since there are two New York teams in the Group I, there are two choices for the first team and five choices for the second team. Hence $n_A = (2)(5) = 10$ and the probability is $n_A/N = 10/50 = 1/5$.

4.37   The situation presented here is analogous to drawing five items from a jar (the five members voting in favour of the plaintiff). If the jar contains five red and three white items (five women and three men), what is the probability that all five items are red? That is, if there is no sex bias, five of the eight members are randomly chosen to be those voting for the plaintiff. What is the probability that all five are women? There are

$$N = C_5^8 = \frac{8!}{5!3!} = 56 \text{ simple events in the experiment, only one of which results in choosing five women.}$$

Hence, $P(\text{five women}) = \dfrac{1}{56}$.

4.39   The monkey can place the twelve blocks in any order. Each arrangement will yield a simple event, and hence, the total number of simple events (arrangements) is $P_{12}^{12} = 12!$ It is necessary to determine the number of simple events in the event of interest (that he draws three of each kind, in order). First, he may draw the four different <u>types</u> of blocks in any order. Thus, we need the number of ways of arranging these four items, which is $P_4^4 = 4!$ Once this order has been chosen, the three squares can be arranged in $P_3^3 = 3!$ ways, the three triangles can be arranged in $P_3^3 = 3!$ ways, and so on. Thus, the total number of simple events in the event of interest is $P_4^4\left(P_3^3\right)^4$ and the associated probability is

$$\frac{P_4^4\left(P_3^3\right)^4}{P_{12}^{12}} = \frac{4!(3!)^4}{12!}$$

4.41   **a** $P\left(A^C\right) = 1 - P\left(A\right) = 1 - \dfrac{2}{5} = \dfrac{3}{5}$

      b $P\left(A \cap B\right)^C = 1 - P\left(A \cup B\right) = 1 - \dfrac{1}{5} = \dfrac{4}{5}$

4.43   **a** $P\left(A \cup B\right) = P(A) + P(B) - P(A \cap B) = 2/5 + 4/5 - 1/5 = 5/5 = 1$

      b $P(A \cap B) = P(A \mid B)P(B) = (1/4)(4/5) = 1/5$

      c $P(B \cap C) = P(B \mid C)P(C) = (1/2)(2/5) = 1/5$

4.45 Refer to the solution to Exercise 4.1 where the six simple events in the experiment are given, with $P(E_i) = 1/6$.

    a $S = \{E_1, E_2, E_3, E_4, E_5, E_6\}$ and $P(S) = 6/6 = 1$

    b $P(A \mid B) = \dfrac{P(A \cap B)}{P(B)} = \dfrac{1/3}{1/3} = 1$

    c $B = \{E_1, E_2\}$ and $P(B) = 2/6 = 1/3$

    d $A \cap B \cap C$ contains no simple events, and $P(A \cap B \cap C) = 0$

    e $P(A \cap B) = P(A \mid B)P(B) = 1(1/3) = 1/3$

    f $A \cap C$ contains no simple events, and $P(A \cap C) = 0$

    g $B \cap C$ contains no simple events, and $P(B \cap C) = 0$

    h $A \cup C = S$ and $P(A \cup C) = 1$

    i $B \cup C = \{E_1, E_2, E_4, E_5, E_6\}$ and $P(B \cup C) = 5/6$

4.47   **a**   Since A and B are independent, $P(A \cap B) = P(A)P(B) = 0.4(0.2) = 0.08$.

    b $P(A \cup B) = P(A) + P(B) - P(A \cap B) = 0.4 + 0.2 - (0.4)(0.2) = 0.52$

4.49   **a**   Use the definition of conditional probability to find
$$P(B \mid A) = \frac{P(A \cap B)}{P(A)} = \frac{0.12}{0.4} = 0.3$$

    b   Since $P(A \cap B) \neq 0$, A and B are not mutually exclusive.

    c   If $P(B) = 0.3$, then $P(B) = P(B \mid A)$, which means that A and B are independent.

4.51   **a**   From Exercise 4.50, since $P(A \cap B) = 0.34$, the two events are not mutually exclusive.

    b   From Exercise 4.50, $P(A \mid B) = 0.425$ and $P(A) = 0.49$. The two events are not independent.

4.53 Define the following events:
    A: project is approved for funding
    D: project is disapproved for funding
For the first group, $P(A_1) = 0.2$ and $P(D_1) = 0.8$. For the second group,
$P(\text{same decision as first group}) = 0.7$ and $P(\text{reversal}) = 0.3$. That is, $P(A_2 \mid A_1) = P(D_2 \mid D_1) = 0.7$ and $P(A_2 \mid D_1) = P(D_2 \mid A_1) = 0.3$.

    a $P(A_1 \cap A_2) = P(A_1)P(A_2 \mid A_1) = 0.2(0.7) = 0.14$

    b $P(D_1 \cap D_2) = P(D_1)P(D_2 \mid D_1) = 0.8(0.7) = 0.56$

    c $P(D_1 \cap A_2) + P(A_1 \cap D_2) = P(D_1)P(A_2 \mid D_1) + P(A_1)P(D_2 \mid A_1) = 0.8(0.3) + 0.2(0.3) = 0.30$

4.55 Refer to Exercise 4.54.

    a   From the table, $P(A \cap B) = 0.1$, while $P(A)P(B \mid A) = (0.4)(0.25) = 0.1$.

    b   From the table, $P(A \cap B) = 0.1$, while $P(B)P(A \mid B) = (0.37)(0.1/0.37) = 0.1$.

    c   From the table, $P(A \cup B) = 0.1 + 0.27 + 0.30 = 0.67$, while
$$P(A) + P(B) - P(A \cap B) = 0.4 + 0.37 - 0.10 = 0.67.$$

4.57   Fix the birthdate of the first person entering the room. Then define the following events:

A_2: second person's birthday differs from the first
A_3: third person's birthday differs from the first and second
A_4: fourth person's birthday differs from all preceding
$\vdots$
A_n: n^{th} person's birthday differs from all preceding

Then $P(A) = P(A_2)P(A_3)\cdots P(A_n) = \left(\dfrac{364}{365}\right)\left(\dfrac{363}{365}\right)\cdots\left(\dfrac{365-n+1}{365}\right)$

since at each step, one less birthdate is available for selection. Since event B is the complement of event A,

$P(B) = 1 - P(A)$

a   For $n = 3$, $P(A) = \dfrac{(364)(363)}{(365)^2} = 0.9918$ and $P(B) = 1 - 0.9918 = 0.0082$

b   For $n = 4$, $P(A) = \dfrac{(364)(363)(362)}{(365)^3} = 0.9836$ and $P(B) = 1 - 0.9836 = 0.0164$

4.59   The probability table is as follows:

Alcohol Consumption Habits	Smoking Habits		
	Smoker (S)	Non-smoker (N)	Total
No	0.03	0.14	0.17
Yes	0.06	0.77	0.83
Total	0.09	0.91	1.00

The above probability table is constructed using the frequencies given in the question. For example,

$P(S) = \dfrac{3}{100} = 0.03$

Define the following events: S: student smokes
                               A: student consumed alcohol

a $P(A) = 0.83$. This probability is consistent with the survey results, which estimate this around 83%.

b $P(S) = 0.09$. This probability is very close to the survey results, which estimate this around 6%.

c $P(S \cap A^c) = 0.03$

d $P(A^c) = 0.17$

e $P(A \cap S) = 0.06$

f $P(A \mid S) = \dfrac{0.06}{0.09} = 0.667$

g $P(S^c \mid A) = \dfrac{0.77}{0.83} = 0.928$

4.61   Define the events: D: person dies
                               S: person smokes

It is given that $P(S) = 0.2$, $P(D) = 0.006$, and $P(D \mid S) = 10 P(D \mid S^C)$. The probability of interest is $P(D \mid S)$. The event D, whose probability is given, can be written as the union of two mutually exclusive intersections. That is, $D = (D \cap S) \cup (D \cap S^C)$.

Then, using the Addition and Multiplication Rules,

$P(D) = P(D \cap S) + P(D \cap S^C) = P(D \mid S)P(S) + P(D \mid S^C)P(S^C) = P(D \mid S)(0.2) + \left[(1/10)P(D \mid S)\right](0.8)$

Since $P(D) = 0.006$, the above equation can be solved for $P(D \mid S)$

$P(D \mid S)(0.2 + 0.08) = 0.006$

$P(D \mid S) = 0.006/0.28 = 0.0214$

4.63 Define   A: smoke is detected by device A
                         B: smoke is detected by device B

If it is given that $P(A) = 0.95$, $P(B) = 0.98$, and $P(A \cap B) = 0.94$

a $P(A \cup B) = P(A) + P(B) - P(A \cap B) = 0.95 + 0.98 - 0.94 = 0.99$

b $P(A^c \cap B^c) = 1 - P(A \cup B) = 1 - 0.99 = 0.01$

4.65 **a**   Each of the four cell events is equally likely with $P(E_i) = 1/4$. Hence, the probability of at least one

dominate allele is $P(rR) + P(Rr) + P(RR) = \dfrac{3}{4}$.

b   Similar to part **a**. The probability of at least one recessive allele is $P(rR) + P(Rr) + P(rr) = \dfrac{3}{4}$.

c   Define the events: A: plant has red flowers
                              B: plant has one recessive allele

Then $P(B \mid A) = \dfrac{P(A \cap B)}{P(A)} = \dfrac{P(rR) + P(Rr)}{P(rR) + P(Rr) + P(RR)} = \dfrac{2/4}{3/4} = \dfrac{2}{3}$.

4.67   Similar to Exercise 4.54.

a $P(A) = \dfrac{54}{1029}$

b $P(F) = \dfrac{517}{1029}$

c $P(A \cap F) = \dfrac{37}{1029}$

d $P(F \mid A) = \dfrac{P(F \cap A)}{P(A)} = \dfrac{37/1029}{54/1029} = \dfrac{37}{54}$

e $P(F \mid B) = \dfrac{P(F \cap B)}{P(B)} = \dfrac{64/1029}{99/1029} = \dfrac{64}{99}$

f $P(F \mid C) = \dfrac{P(F \cap C)}{P(C)} = \dfrac{138/1029}{241/1029} = \dfrac{138}{241}$

g $P(C \mid M) = \dfrac{P(C \cap M)}{P(M)} = \dfrac{103/1029}{512/1029} = \dfrac{103}{512}$

h $P(B^c) = 1 - P(B) = 1 - \dfrac{99}{1029} = \dfrac{930}{1029} = \dfrac{310}{343}$

4.69   Define A_i: i^{th} working mother in Canada re-enter the workforce:

a $P(A_1^c \cap A_2 \cap A_3) = P(A_1^c)P(A_2)P(A_3) = (0.19)(0.81)(0.81) = 0.1247$

b $P(A_1 \cap A_2 \cap A_3) = P(A_1)P(A_2)P(A_3) = (0.81)(0.81)(0.81) = 0.5314$

c $P(A_1^c \cap A_2^c \cap A_3^c) = P(A_1^c)P(A_2^c)P(A_3^c) = (0.19)(0.19)(0.19) = 0.0069$

d $P(A_1 \cap A_2 \cap A_3^c) + P(A_1 \cap A_2^c \cap A_3) + P(A_1^c \cap A_2 \cap A_3) + P(A_1 \cap A_2 \cap A_3) =$
      $(0.81)(0.81)(0.19) + (0.81)(0.19)(0.81) + (0.19)(0.81)(0.81) + (0.81) = 0.9054$

4.71   Define the following events: A: player A wins the tournament

B: player B enters the tournament

It is given that $P(A \mid B) = 1/6; P(A \mid B^C) = 3/4;$ and $P(B) = 1/3$. Use the Law of Total Probability:

$$P(A) = P(A \cap B) + P(A \cap B^C)$$

$$= P(B)P(A \mid B) + P(B^C)P(A \mid B^C)$$

$$= \frac{1}{3}\left(\frac{1}{6}\right) + \frac{2}{3}\left(\frac{3}{4}\right) = \frac{10}{18} = \frac{5}{9}$$

4.73   Use Bayes' Rule:

$$P(S_i \mid A) = \frac{P(S_i)P(A \mid S_i)}{P(S_1)P(A \mid S_1) + P(S_2)P(A \mid S_2) + P(S_3)P(A \mid S_3)}$$

For $i = 1$, $P(S_1 \mid A) = \dfrac{0.2(0.2)}{0.2(0.2) + 0.5(0.1) + 0.3(0.3)} = \dfrac{0.04}{0.18} = 0.2222$

For $i = 2$, $P(S_2 \mid A) = \dfrac{0.05}{0.18} = 0.2778$ and for $i = 3$, $P(S_3 \mid A) = \dfrac{0.09}{0.18} = 0.5000$

4.75   Define the following events: V: crime is violent

R: crime is reported

It is given that $P(V) = 0.2$, $P(V^C) = 0.8$, $P(R \mid V) = 0.9$, $P(R \mid V^C) = 0.7$.

a   The overall reporting rate for crimes is

$$P(R) = P(V)P(R \mid V) + P(V^C)P(R \mid V^C) = 0.2(0.9) + 0.8(0.7) = 0.74$$

b   Use Bayes' Rule: $P(V \mid R) = \dfrac{P(V)P(R \mid V)}{P(R)} = \dfrac{0.2(0.9)}{0.74} = 0.24$

and $P(V^C \mid R) = \dfrac{P(V^C)P(R \mid V^C)}{P(R)} = \dfrac{0.8(0.7)}{0.74} = 0.76$

c   Notice that the proportion of non-violent crimes (0.8) is much larger than the proportion of violent crimes (0.2). Therefore, when a crime is reported, it is more likely to be a non-violent crime.

4.77   Define the following events: A: passenger uses airport A

B: passenger uses airport B

C: passenger uses airport C

D: a weapon is detected

Suppose that a passenger is carrying a weapon. It is given that

$P(D \mid A) = 0.9$ $P(A) = 0.5$

$P(D \mid B) = 0.5$ $P(B) = 0.3$

$P(D \mid C) = 0.4$ $P(C) = 0.2$

The probability of interest is

$$P(A \mid D) = \frac{P(A)P(D \mid A)}{P(A)P(D \mid A) + P(B)P(D \mid B) + P(C)P(D \mid C)} = \frac{0.5(0.9)}{0.5(0.9) + 0.3(0.5) + 0.2(0.4)} = 0.6618$$

Similarly, $P(C \mid D) = \dfrac{0.2(0.4)}{0.5(0.9) + 0.3(0.5) + 0.2(0.4)} = \dfrac{0.08}{0.68} = 0.1176$

4.79   Define the events: A: athlete has been disqualified previously
                                     B: athlete is disqualified for the next six weeks
It is given that $P(B\mid A^{C}) = 0.15$, $P(B\mid A) = 0.50$, and $P(A) = 0.30$. The event of interest is event B, which can be written as the union of two mutually exclusive events:
$$B = (A \cap B) \cup (A^{C} \cap B)$$
Then, using the Law of Total Probability,
$$P(B) = P(A \cap B) + P(A^{C} \cap B) = P(B\mid A)P(A) + P(B\mid A^{C})P(A^{C}) = 0.5(0.3) + 0.15(0.7) = 0.255$$

4.81   Define the following events, under the assumptions that an incorrect return has been filed.
            G_1: individual guilty of cheating
            G_2: individual not guilty (filed incorrectly due to lack of knowledge)
            D: individual denies knowledge of error
It is given that $P(G_1) = 0.05$, $P(G_2) = 0.02$, $P(D\mid G_1) = 0.80$. Note that $P(D\mid G_2) = 1$ since if the individual has incorrectly filed due to lack of knowledge, that person will, with probability 1, deny knowledge of the error. Using Bayes' Rule,
$$P(G_1 \mid D) = \frac{P(G_1)P(D\mid G_1)}{P(G_1)P(D\mid G_1) + P(G_2)P(D\mid G_2)} = \frac{0.05(0.80)}{0.05(0.80) + 0.02(1)} = 0.6667$$

4.83   **a**   The number of points scored is a discrete random variable taking the countably infinite number of values, 0, 1, 2, …
           b   Shelf life is a continuous random variable, since it can take on any positive real value.
           c   Height is a continuous random variable, taking on any positive real value.
           d   Length is a continuous random variable, taking on any positive real value.
           e   Number of near collisions is a discrete random variable, taking the values 0, 1, 2, …

4.85   **a**   Since one of the requirements of a probability distribution is that $\sum_{x} p(x) = 1$, we need
$$p(4) = 1 - (0.1 + 0.3 + 0.4 + 0.1 + 0.05) = 1 - 0.95 = 0.05$$
           b   The probability histogram is shown in the figure below.

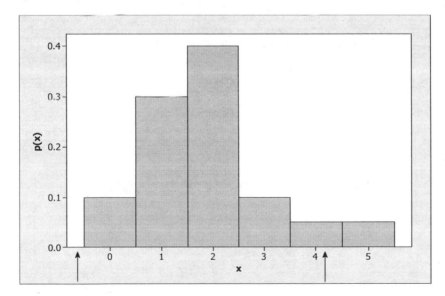

c For the random variable X given here, $\mu = E(x) = \sum xp(x) = 0(0.1) + 1(0.3) + \cdots + 5(0.05) = 1.85$.
The variance of X is defined as

$$\sigma^2 = E\left[(X-\mu)^2\right] = \sum(x-\mu)^2 p(x) = (0-1.85)^2(0.1) + (1-1.85)^2(0.3) + \cdots + (5-1.85)^2(0.05) = 1.4275$$

and $\sigma = \sqrt{1.4275} = 1.19$

d The interval of interest is $\mu \pm 2\sigma = 1.85 \pm 2.38$ or -0.53 to 4.23. This interval is shown on the probability histogram above. Then $P(-0.53 \le X \le 4.23) = P(0 \le X \le 4) = 0.95$.

e Since the probability that x falls in the interval $\mu \pm 2\sigma$ is 0.95 from part **d**, we would expect <u>most</u> of the observations to fall in this interval.

4.87 **a** Since each of the six possible values, $x = 1, 2, 3, 4, 5, 6$, is equally likely with $p(x) = 1/6$ for all values of x, the graph of the probability distribution has a flat shape, called the *discrete uniform probability distribution*, shown in the figure below.

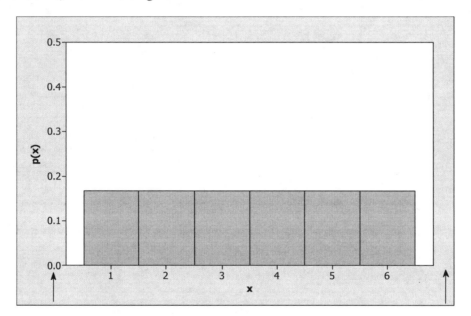

b The average value of x is $\mu = E(X) = \sum xp(x) = 1\left(\dfrac{1}{6}\right) + 2\left(\dfrac{1}{6}\right) + \cdots + 6\left(\dfrac{1}{6}\right) = 3.5$.

c The variance of X is defined as

$$\sigma^2 = E\left[(X-\mu)^2\right] = \sum(x-\mu)^2 p(x) = (1-3.5)^2\left(\dfrac{1}{6}\right) + (2-3.5)^2\left(\dfrac{1}{6}\right) + \cdots + (6-3.5)^2\left(\dfrac{1}{6}\right) = 2.9167$$

and $\sigma = \sqrt{2.9167} = 1.71$

d The interval of interest is $\mu \pm 2\sigma = 3.5 \pm 3.42$ or $.08$ to 6.92. This interval is shown on the probability histogram above. Then $P(0.08 \le X \le 6.92) = P(1 \le X \le 6) = 1$.

4.89 **a** Define   D: person prefers David Letterman
              J: person prefers Jay Leno
There are eight simple events in the experiment:

       DDD   DDJ
       DJJ   DJD
       JDJ   JDD
       JJD   JJJ

and the probabilities for X = number who prefer Jay Leno = 0, 1, 2, 3 are shown below.

$$P(X = 0) = P(DDD) = (0.48)^3 = 0.1106$$

$$P(X = 1) = P(DDJ) + P(DJD) + P(JDD) = 3(0.52)(0.48)^2 = 0.3594$$

$$P(X = 2) = P(DJJ) + P(JJD) + P(JDJ) = 3(0.52)^2(0.48) = 0.3894$$

$$P(X = 3) = P(JJJ) = (0.52)^3 = 0.1406$$

b The probability histogram is shown below.

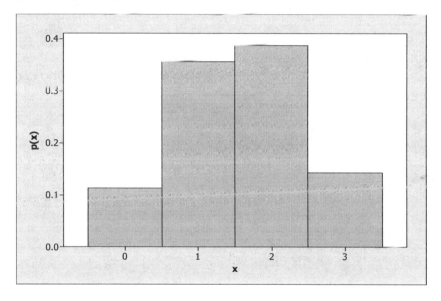

c $P(X = 1) = 0.3594$

d The average value of X is

$$\mu = E(X) = \sum xp(x) = 0(0.1106) + 1(0.3594) + 2(0.3894) + 3(0.1406) = 1.56$$

The variance of X is

$$\sigma^2 = E\left[(X - \mu)^2\right] = \sum (x - \mu)^2 p(x)$$

$$= (0 - 1.56)^2(0.1106) + (1 - 1.56)^2(0.3594) + (2 - 1.56)^2(0.3894) + (3 - 1.56)^2(0.1406)$$

$$= 0.7488$$

and $\sigma = \sqrt{0.7488} = 0.865$

4.91   If a \$5 bet is placed on the number 18, the gambler will either win \$175 $(35 \times \$5)$ with probability 1/38 or lose \$5 with probability 37/38. Hence, the probability distribution for X, the gambler's gain is

x	$p(x)$
−5	37/38
175	1/38

The expected gain is $\mu = E(X) = \sum xp(x) = -5(37/38) + 175(1/38) = \$ -0.26$.

The expected gain is in fact negative, a loss of $0.26.

4.93 Similar to Exercise 4.92. The random variable X can take on the values 0, 1, or 2. The associated probabilities can be found by summing probabilities of the simple events for the respective numerical events or by using the laws of probability

$P(x = 0) = P(\text{nondefective on first selection})P(\text{nondefective on second} \mid \text{nondefective on first})$

$$\times P(\text{nondefective on third} \mid \text{nondefective on first and second}) = \frac{4}{6}\left(\frac{3}{5}\right)\left(\frac{2}{4}\right) = \frac{1}{5}$$

$$P(x = 1) = P(DNN) + P(NDN) + P(NND) = \frac{2}{6}\left(\frac{4}{5}\right)\left(\frac{3}{4}\right) + \frac{4}{6}\left(\frac{2}{5}\right)\left(\frac{3}{4}\right) + \frac{4}{6}\left(\frac{3}{5}\right)\left(\frac{2}{4}\right) = \frac{3}{5}$$

$$P(x = 2) = P(DDN) + P(DND) + P(NDD) = \frac{2}{6}\left(\frac{1}{5}\right)\left(\frac{4}{4}\right) + \frac{2}{6}\left(\frac{4}{5}\right)\left(\frac{1}{4}\right) + \frac{4}{6}\left(\frac{2}{5}\right)\left(\frac{1}{4}\right) = \frac{1}{5}$$

The probability distribution for X and the probability histogram follow.

x	0	1	2
$p(x)$	1/5	3/5	1/5

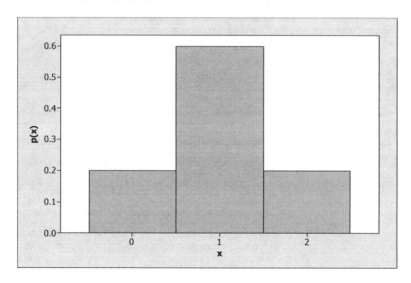

4.95 Consider the event $x = 3$. This will occur only if either A or B wins three sets in a row; that is, if the event AAA or BBB occurs. Then

$$P(x = 3) = P(AAA) + P(BBB) = [P(A)]^3 + [P(B)]^3 = (0.6)^3 + (0.4)^3 = 0.28$$

Consider the event $x = 4$. This will occur if three A-wins are spread over four sets (with the last A-win in the fourth set) or if three B-wins are similarly spread over four sets. The associated simple events are

ABAA	BABB	AABA
BAAA	ABBB	BBAB

and the probability that $x = 4$ is

$$p(4) = 3(0.6)^3(0.4) + 3(0.6)(0.4)^3 = 0.3744$$

The event $x = 5$ will occur if four A-wins are spread over five sets (with the last A-win in the fifth set) or similarly for B. The associated simple events are

ABBAA	AABBA	BBAAA	BAABA	ABABA	BABAA
ABBAB	AABBB	BBAAB	BAABB	ABABB	BABAB

and the probability that $x = 5$ is

$$p(5) = 6(0.6)^3(0.4)^2 + 6(0.6)^2(0.4)^3 = 0.3456$$

Notice that $p(3) + p(4) + p(5) = 0.28 + 0.3744 + 0.3456 = 1.00$.

4.97   **a** $E(X) = 2(0.12) + 3(0.80) + 4(0.06) + 5(0.02) = 2.98$

   b $E(X) = 3(0.14) + 4(0.80) + 5(0.04) + 6(0.02) = 3.94$

   c $E(X) = 4(0.04) + 5(0.80) + 6(0.12) + 7(0.04) = 5.16$

4.99   **a** $\mu = E(X) = \sum xp(x) = 3(.03) + 4(.05) + \cdots + 13(.01) = 7.9$

   b $\sigma^2 = \sum(x - \mu)^2 p(x) = (3 - 7.9)^2(0.03) + (4 - 7.9)^2(0.05) + \cdots + (13 - 7.9)^2(0.01) = 4.73$ and

   $\sigma = \sqrt{4.73} = 2.1749$

   c   Calculate $\mu \pm 2\sigma = 7.9 \pm 4.350$ or 3.55 to 12.25. Then, referring to the probability distribution of X,

   $P(3.55 < X < 12.25) = P(4 \le X \le 12) = 1 - p(3) - p(13) = 1 - 0.04 = 0.96$.

4.101   The company will either gain ($15.50 – 14.80$) if the package is delivered on time, or will lose $14.80 if the package is not delivered on time. We assume that, if the package is not delivered within 24 hours, the company does not collect the $15.50 delivery fee. Then the probability distribution for x, the company's gain is

x	$p(x)$
0.70	0.98
–14.80	0.02

and

$\mu = E(X) = 0.70(0.98) - 14.80(0.02) = 0.39$

The expected gain per package is $0.39.

4.103   Since there are four possible shapes for each of the three slots, there are a total of $N = (4)(4)(4) = 64$ possible configurations for the three slots. Of these, only $n_A = 4$ (CCC, LLL, SSS, or BBB) will result in a win. Hence, the probability of winning is $P(\text{win}) = n_A / N = 4/64 = 1/16$.

4.105   **a**   This experiment consists of two patients, each swallowing one of four tablets (two cold and two aspirin). There are four tablets to choose from: call them C_1, C_2, A_1, and A_2. The resulting simple events are then all possible ordered pairs that can be formed from the four choices.

(C_1C_2)	(C_2C_1)	(A_1C_1)	(A_2C_1)
(C_1A_1)	(C_2A_1)	(A_1C_2)	(A_2C_2)
(C_1A_2)	(C_2A_2)	(A_1A_2)	(A_2A_1)

Notice that it is important to consider the order in which the tablets are chosen, since it makes a difference, for example, which patient (A or B) swallows the cold tablet.

   b $A = \{(C_1C_2), (C_1A_1), (C_1A_2), (C_2A_1), (C_2C_1), (C_2A_2)\}$

   c $B = \{(C_1A_1), (C_1A_2), (C_2A_1), (C_2A_2), (A_1C_1), (A_1C_2), (A_2C_1), (A_2C_2)\}$

   d $C = \{(A_1A_2), (A_2A_1)\}$

4.107 Four customers enter a store that sells two styles of digital video recorders (DVRs). Each customer seeks to purchase one of the two styles. Let the number "1" represent a customer seeking to purchase style 1 and the number "2" represent a customer seeking to purchase style 2. The sample space consists of the following 16 four-tuplets.

$$
\begin{array}{cccc}
1111 & 2111 & 1221 & 2212 \\
1112 & 1122 & 2121 & 2122 \\
1121 & 1212 & 2211 & 1222 \\
1211 & 2112 & 2221 & 2222 \\
\end{array}
$$

The event A, "all four customers seek to purchase the same style of DVR," consists of the two simple events 1111 and 2222. Since the two styles are assumed to be in equal demand, we assume that each of the 16 simple events is equally likely, and we assign the probability 1/16 to each. Hence, $P(A) = 2/16 = 1/8$.

4.109 Define the random variable x to be daily sales; x can take the values 0, $50,000$, or $100,000$, depending on the number of customers the salesperson contacts. The associated probabilities are shown below:

$P(x = 0) = P(\text{contact one, fail to sell}) + P(\text{contact two, fail to sell})$

$= P(\text{contact one}) P(\text{fail to sell}) + P(\text{contact two}) P(\text{fail with first}) P(\text{fail with second})$

$= (1/3)(9/10) + (2/3)(9/10)(9/10)$

$= 9/30 + 162/300 = 252/300$

Similarly, $P(x = 50,000) = P(\text{contact one, sell}) + P(\text{contact two, sell to one})$

$= P(\text{contact one, sell}) + P(\text{contact two, sell to first only}) + P(\text{contact two, sell to second only})$

$= (1/3)(1/10) + (2/3)(1/10)(9/10) + (2/3)(9/10)(1/10) = 46/300$

Finally, $P(x = 100,000) = P(\text{contact two, fail to sell to both})$

$= (2/3)(1/10)(1/10) = 2/300$

Then $E(X) = 0(252/300) + 50,000(46/300) + 100,000(2/300) = 8333.33$. Thus, the expected value of daily sales is $8333.33.

4.111 In this exercise, x may take the values 0, 1, 2, or 3, and the probabilities associated with x are evaluated as in Exercise 4.110.

a $P(X = 0) = (0.2)^3 = 0.008$

$P(X = 1) = 3(0.8)(0.2)^2 = 0.096$

$P(X = 2) = 3(0.8)^2 (0.2) = 0.384$

$P(X = 3) = (0.8)^3 = 0.512$

The reader may verify that the probabilities sum to one and that $0 \le p(x) \le 1$ for $x = 0, 1, 2$, and 3. The requirements for a probability distribution have been satisfied.

b   The alarm will function if $x = 1, 2$, or 3.

Hence, $P(\text{alarm functions}) = p(1) + p(2) + p(3) = 0.096 + 0.384 + 0.512 = 0.992$.

c $\mu = E(X) = \sum xp(x) = 0(0.008) + 1(0.096) + 2(0.384) + 3(0.512) = 2.4$

$\sigma^2 = \sum (x - \mu)^2 p(x) = (0 - 2.4)^2 (0.008) + (1 - 2.4)^2 (0.096)$

$\qquad\qquad\qquad + (2 - 2.4)^2 (0.384) + (3 - 2.4)^2 (0.512) = 0.48$

4.113 The completed table is shown below, and each of the possible pairings are equally likely with probability 1/16.

ss yy	Ss yY	ssYy	ss YY
sS yy	sS yY	sS Yy	sS YY
Ss yy	Ss yY	Ss Yy	Ss YY
SS yy	SS yY	SS Yy	SS YY

    a Smooth yellow peas result from all pairing having at least one S and at least one Y. Hence, $P(\text{smooth yellow}) = 9/16$.

    b Smooth green peas result when the pairing has at least one S and the pair yy. Hence, $P(\text{smooth green}) = 3/16$.

    c Wrinkled yellow peas result when the pairing has at least one Y and the pair ss. Hence, $P(\text{wrinkled yellow}) = 3/16$.

    d Wrinkled green peas result only when the pairing is ss yy. Hence, $P(\text{wrinkled green}) = 1/16$.

    e Define: A: offspring has smooth yellow peas
                B: offspring has one s allele
                C: offspring has one s allele and one y allele

Then $P(A) = 9/16$; $P(A \cap B) = 6/16$; $P(A \cap C) = 4/16$. Using the definition of conditional

probability, $P(B \mid A) = \dfrac{P(A \cap B)}{P(A)} = \dfrac{6/16}{9/16} = \dfrac{2}{3}$ and $P(C \mid A) = \dfrac{P(A \cap C)}{P(A)} = \dfrac{4/16}{9/16} = \dfrac{4}{9}$.

4.115   **a** **Experiment:** Four union members, two from a minority group, are assigned to four one-person jobs, two of which are the most desirable and two of which are the least desirable.

    b **Sample space:** Let us assume that jobs 1 and 2 are the most desirable ones. Define M_1 and M_2 to be the minority workers and W_1 and W_2 to be the other two workers. A typical simple event is $(M_1 M_2 W_1 W_2)$, which implies that minority workers 1 and 2 are assigned jobs 1 and 2, while the other workers are assigned jobs 3 and 4. There are 24 simple events.

E_1: $(M_1 M_2 W_1 W_2)$ E_7: $(M_2 M_1 W_1 W_2)$ E_{13}: $(W_1 M_1 M_2 W_2)$ E_{19}: $(W_2 M_1 M_2 W_1)$
E_2: $(M_1 W_1 M_2 W_2)$ E_8: $(M_2 M_1 W_2 W_1)$ E_{14}: $(W_1 M_1 W_2 M_2)$ E_{20}: $(W_2 M_1 W_1 M_2)$
E_3: $(M_1 W_1 W_2 M_2)$ E_9: $(M_2 W_1 M_1 W_2)$ E_{15}: $(W_1 M_2 M_1 W_2)$ E_{21}: $(W_2 M_2 M_1 W_1)$
E_4: $(M_1 W_2 W_1 M_2)$ E_{10}: $(M_2 W_1 W_2 M_1)$ E_{16}: $(W_1 M_2 W_2 M_1)$ E_{22}: $(W_2 M_2 W_1 M_1)$
E_5: $(M_1 W_2 M_2 W_1)$ E_{11}: $(M_2 W_2 W_1 M_1)$ E_{17}: $(W_1 W_2 M_1 M_2)$ E_{23}: $(W_2 W_1 M_1 M_2)$
E_6: $(M_1 M_2 W_2 W_1)$ E_{12}: $(M_2 W_2 M_1 W_1)$ E_{18}: $(W_1 W_2 M_2 M_1)$ E_{24}: $(W_2 W_1 M_2 M_1)$

    c As jobs 3 and 4 are the least desirable (they correspond to positions 3 and 4 of one ordered foursome), the probability that the two members from the minority group are assigned to these jobs is

$$P(E_{17}) + P(E_{18}) + P(E_{23}) + P(E_{24}) = 4/24 = 1/6$$

4.117 Define the following events: B: man takes the bus
                                      S: man takes the subway
                                      L: the man is late

It is given that $P(B) = 0.3$, $P(S) = 0.7$, $P(L \mid B) = 0.3$, $P(L \mid S) = 0.2$. Using Bayes' Rule,

$$P(B \mid L) = \frac{P(L \mid B)P(B)}{P(L \mid B)P(B) + P(L \mid S)P(S)} = \frac{(0.3)(0.3)}{(0.3)(0.3) + (0.2)(0.7)} = \frac{0.09}{0.23} = 0.3913$$

4.119   **a**   If the fourth van tested is the last van with brake problems, then in the first three tests, we must find one van with brake problems and two without. That is, in choosing three from the six vans, we must find one faulty and two that are not faulty. Think of choosing three balls—one white and two red—from a total of six, and the probability can be calculated as

$$P\left(\text{one faulty and two not}\right) = \frac{C_1^2 C_2^4}{C_3^6} = \frac{2(6)}{20} = \frac{3}{5}$$

Once this is accomplished, the van with brake problems must be chosen on the fourth test. Using the *mn* Rule, the probability that the fourth van tested is the last with faulty brakes is $\frac{3}{5}\left(\frac{1}{3}\right) = \frac{1}{5}$.

b   In order that no more than four vans must be tested, you must find one or both of the faulty vans in the first four tests. Proceed as in part **a**, this time choosing four from the six vans, and

$$P\left(\text{one or two faulty vans}\right) = \frac{C_0^2 C_4^4 + C_1^2 C_3^4}{C_4^6} = \frac{1+8}{15} = \frac{9}{15}$$

c   If it is known that the first faulty van is found in the first two tests, there are four vans left from which to select those tested third and fourth. Of these four, only one is faulty. Hence,

$$P\left(\text{one faulty and one not} \mid \text{one faulty in first two tests}\right) = \frac{C_1^1 C_1^3 + C_1^2 C_3^4}{C_2^4} = \frac{3}{6} = \frac{1}{2}$$

4.121   Similar to Exercise 4.120.

a   The probability of being a 6/49 winner with a single ticket purchase $= \frac{1}{C_6^{49}} = \frac{1}{13,983,816}$

b   Multiple tickets purchase with the same set of numbers does not increase the probability of winning 6/49.

$$P(\text{probability of being a 6/49 winner with two tickets with the same numbers}) = \frac{1}{C_6^{49}} = \frac{1}{13,983,816}$$

c $P(\text{probability of being a 6/49 winner with two tickets with different numbers}) = \frac{2}{C_6^{49}} = \frac{2}{13,983,816}$

d   If you know the winning numbers, selecting the same numbers twice will increase the share of the jackpot if there are other winners as well. However, if one is only guessing, selecting the same number twice does not increase the odds of winning.

e   Since the second ticket numbers must be among the 43 that are not on the first ticket,

$$P(\text{none repeated}) = \frac{C_6^{43}}{C_6^{49}} = 0.436$$

4.123   Define   A: union strike fund is adequate to support a strike
                C: union–management team makes a contract settlement within two weeks

It is given that $P(C) = 0.5$, $P(A) = 0.6$, $P(A \cap C) = 0.3$. Then

$$P(C \mid A) = \frac{P(A \cap C)}{P(A)} = \frac{0.3}{0.6} = 0.5$$

Since $P(C) = 0.5$ and $P(C \mid A) = 0.5$, it appears that the settlement of the contract is independent of the ability of the union strike fund to support the strike.

4.125 Let Y represent the value of the premium that the insurance company charges and let X be the insurance company's gain. There are four possible values for x. If no accident occurs or if an accident results in no damage to the car, the insurance company gains y dollars. If an accident occurs and the car is damaged, the company will gain either $y - 22,000$ dollars, $y - 0.6(22,000)$ dollars, or $y - 0.2(22,000)$ dollars, depending upon whether the damage to the car is total, 60% of market value, or 20% of market value, respectively. The following probabilities are known:

$P(\text{accident occurs}) = 0.15$ $P(\text{total loss} \mid \text{accident occurs}) = 0.08$

$P(60\% \text{ loss} \mid \text{accident occurs}) = 0.12$ $P(20\% \text{ loss} \mid \text{accident occurs}) = 0.80$

Hence,

$P(X = y - 20,000) = P(\text{accident})P(\text{total loss} \mid \text{accident}) = 0.15(0.08) = 0.012$

Similarly,

$P(X = y - 13,200) = 0.15(0.12) = 0.018$ and $P(X = y - 4,400) = 0.15(0.80) = 0.12$

The gain X and its associated probability distribution are shown below. Note that $p(y)$ is found by subtraction.

x	$p(x)$
$y - 22,000$	0.012
$y - 13,200$	0.018
$y - 4400$	0.12
y	0.85

Letting the expected gain equal zero, the value of the premium is obtained.

$E(X) = \sum xp(x) = 0.012(y - 22,000) + 0.018(y - 13,200) + 0.12(y - 4,400) + 0.85y$

$E(X) = y - (264 + 237.6 + 528) = y - 1,029.6$

$y = \$1,029.6$

4.127 This exercise provides an example of a lot acceptance sampling plan. Seven items are drawn from a large lot of bearings and we wish to calculate the probability of accepting the lot; that is, the probability of observing no defectives in the sample of seven. In order to obtain $P(\text{acceptance})$, it is necessary to assume that the lot is large enough so that the probability of getting a defective is not noticeably affected by repeated draws. For example, consider a lot which contains 10,000 items, 5,000 of which are defective. The probability of getting a defective on the first draw is 5,000/10,000 or 1/2. Assume that a defective has been drawn. Then the probability of getting a defective on the second draw is 4,999/9,999, which is not noticeably different from 1/2. Define the following events:

    D: draw a defective

    G: draw a nondefective, where $G - D^C$ and $P(G) = 1 - P(D)$

    A: the lot is accepted

In each case, the desired probability is $P(A) = P(GGGGGGG) = [P(G)]^7$.

If all the items in the lot are nondefective, then $P(D) = 0$, $P(G) = 1$ and the probability of acceptance is $P(A) = 1$. If 1/10 are defective, then $P(D) = 0.1$, $P(G) = 0.9$, and $P(A) = (0.9)^7 = 0.4783$. If 1/2 are defective, then $P(D) = 0.5$, $P(G) = 0.5$, and $P(A) = (0.5)^7 = 0.00781$.

4.129 In this exercise, we assume that the presence or absence of disease in any pair of four pairs of identical twins represent independent events. If there is no difference in the effect of the drugs, the probability that one drug causes a greater drop in blood pressure than the other is 0.5. Then

$P(\text{reading for drug A exceeds reading for drug B for all 4 pairs}) = (0.5)^4 = 0.0625$

If we do observe the above event, we can reach one of two conclusions:

- The two drugs are equally effective and we have observed a rare event
- Drug B is more effective than drug A

Since the probability of the above event is very small, we would draw the second conclusion.

4.131   The objective is to determine how many times a coin must be tossed in order that the following inequality will be true: $P(\text{observe at least one head}) \geq 0.9$.

Using the complement of this event, we have: $1 - P(\text{observe no heads}) \geq 0.9$ or $P(\text{observe no heads}) \leq 0.1$

Since the probability of observing a tail on a given toss is 0.5, $P(\text{observe no heads in } n \text{ tosses}) = (0.5)^n$. Evaluating this probability for increasing values of n, we obtain the following table.

n	P(observe no heads)
1	0.5
2	0.25
3	0.125
4	0.0625

Note that the inequality will be satisfied if and only if n is greater than or equal to 4. Thus, the coin must be tossed four times.

4.133 **a**   Define the events   R: subject chooses red
N: subject does not choose red

Then $P(R) = \dfrac{1}{3}$ and $P(N) = \dfrac{2}{3}$. There are 8 simple events in the experiment:

NNN $(x = 0)$ RRN $(x = 2)$

RNN $(x = 1)$ RNR $(x = 2)$

NRN $(x = 1)$ NRR $(x = 2)$

NNR $(x = 1)$ RRR $(x = 3)$

Then

$$P(X = 0) = P(NNN) = P(N)P(N)P(N) = \left(\frac{2}{3}\right)^3 = \frac{8}{27}$$

$$P(X = 1) = 3P(N)P(N)P(R) = 3\left(\frac{2}{3}\right)^2\left(\frac{1}{3}\right) = \frac{12}{27}$$

$$P(X = 2) = 3P(N)P(R)P(R) = 3\left(\frac{2}{3}\right)\left(\frac{1}{3}\right)^2 = \frac{6}{27}$$

$$P(X = 3) = P(RRR) = P(R)P(R)P(R) = \left(\frac{1}{3}\right)^3 = \frac{1}{27}$$

The probability distribution for X is shown in the table.

x	0	1	2	3
$p(x)$	8/27	12/27	6/27	1/27

b   The probability histogram is shown below.

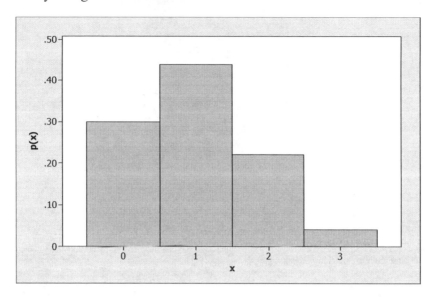

4.135   **a** $P(T \cap P) = \dfrac{27}{70} = 0.386$

b $P(T^c \cap N) = 0$

c $P(T \cap N) = \dfrac{4}{70} = 0.057$

d $P(P \mid T) = \dfrac{P(T \cap P)}{P(T)} = \dfrac{27/70}{31/70} = \dfrac{27}{31} = 0.871$

e $P(\text{false negative}) = P(N \mid T) = \dfrac{P(T \cap N)}{P(T)} = \dfrac{4/70}{31/70} = \dfrac{4}{31} = 0.129$

4.137   **a**   There are six volunteers, from whom we must choose two people for the committee. The number of choices is then $C_2^6 = \dfrac{6(5)}{2(1)} = 15.$

If the number of women chosen from the two women is x, and the number of men chosen from the four men must be $2 - x$. Then

$$P(X = 0) = \frac{C_0^2 C_2^4}{15} = \frac{6}{15}$$

$$P(X = 1) = \frac{C_1^2 C_1^4}{15} = \frac{8}{15}$$

$$P(X = 2) = \frac{C_2^2 C_0^4}{15} = \frac{1}{15}$$

and the probability distribution for X is shown in the table.

x	0	1	2
$p(x)$	6/15	8/15	1/15

b $P(X = 2) = \dfrac{1}{15}$

$\sigma^2 = \sum (x - \mu)^2\, p(x) = (0 - \dfrac{2}{3})^2 \left(\dfrac{6}{15} \right) + (1 - \dfrac{2}{3})^2 \left(\dfrac{8}{15} \right) + (2 - \dfrac{2}{3})^2 \left(\dfrac{1}{15} \right) = \dfrac{48}{135} = \dfrac{16}{45}$

c $P(X = 2) = \dfrac{1}{15}$

4.139   The probabilities can be found by summing the necessary cells of the probability table given in the question and dividing by 200, the total number of individuals.

a $P(Y) = \dfrac{96}{200} = 0.48$

b $P(M \cap AE) = \dfrac{20}{200} = 0.10$

c $P(M \mid S) = \dfrac{P(M \cap S)}{P(S)} = \dfrac{16/200}{61/200} = \dfrac{16}{61} = 0.262$

Case Study: Probability and Decision Making in the Congo

Let p be the probability that a single person successfully completes the jump, and assume that the event that any one person successfully completes the jump is independent of the outcome of the other 11 individual jumps. Define the events:

$\qquad$ J: all members of the team successfully complete the jump
$\qquad$ A_1: Ross successfully completes the jump
$\qquad$ A_2: Elliot successfully completes the jump
$\qquad$ A_3: Munro successfully completes the jump
$\qquad$ $\vdots$
$\qquad$ A_{12}: Porter 8 successfully completes the jump

Then J is the intersection of the events A_1, A_2, ..., A_{12} and

$$P(J) = P(A_1 \cap A_2 \cap A_3 ... \cap A_{12}) = P(A_1)P(A_2)\cdots P(A_{12}) = p(p)(p)\cdots p = p^{12}$$

Substituting $P(J) = 0.7980$ into this expression and solving for p, we find $p - 0.9814$. Thus, Houston is basing its probability of a successful team jump on a probability equal to 0.9814 that a single individual will successfully land in the soft volcanic scree.

Project 4-A: Child Safety Seat Survey, Part 2 (continued from Project 3-A)

a   The probability table is as follows:

Age Group	Rear-Facing Infant Seat	Forward-facing Infant Seat	Booster Seat	Seat Belt Only	Total
Infant	0.07535	0.02165	0.00042	0.00000	0.09742
Toddler	0.02040	0.20108	0.04871	0.00125	0.27144
School	0.00000	0.04080	0.18734	0.13530	0.36345
Older	0.00000	0.00000	0.00666	0.26103	0.26769
Total	0.09575	0.26353	0.24313	0.39759	1.00000

b   The probability that a random child is in a rear-facing infant seat is the total probability for that column, 0.09575.

c   The probability that a random child is an infant is the total probability in the first row, 0.09742.

d   Of the 652 toddlers, 117 use the booster seat, and so $117/652 = 0.17945$ is the probability that a random child is in a booster seat, given that they are a toddler.

e   Of the 230 children who are in a rear-facing infant seat, 181 of them are infants, and so $181/230 = 0.78696$ is the probability the child is an infant given that they are in a rear-facing infant seat.

f   The probability a random child is a toddler is 0.27144. The probability a random child is in a forward-facing infant seat is 0.26353. If we add up these two probabilities, we obtain the correct answer, provided that we subtract their joint probability once (otherwise, we would be double-counting that specific joint probability). Thus, the answer is $0.27144 + 0.26353 - 0.20108 = 0.33389$.

g   Of the 652 children who are toddlers, 483 are in a forward-facing infant seat, and so $483/652 = 0.74080$ is the probability that the child is in a forward-facing infant seat given the child is a toddler.

h   No, the types of restraint the child uses and age are not mutually exclusive events. Both events can simultaneously occur with non-zero probability.

i   No, the types of restraint the child uses and age are not independent events. The type of restraint used clearly changes with age.

j   Given that 633 children were using a forward-facing infant seat and 483 of these were toddlers, the answer is $483/633 = 0.76303$.

Project 4-B: False Results in Medical Testing

a   The probability the test comes backs positive is equal to the probability that it is positive and the person truly has it $0.02(0.9) = 0.018$, plus the probability the test comes back positive but the person truly does not have the disease $0.98(0.11) = 0.1078$; the sum of these is 0.1258.

b   No, this is not surprising, given that 11% of those who do not have the disease showed a false-positive result. We did not expect the number to be higher. An alternative way might be to set up the whole probability table.

c   This conditional probability equals P(truly has the disease and the test was positive)/P(test was positive) or $0.018/0.1258 = 0.143084$.

d   This conditional probability equals P(truly has the disease and the test was negative)/P(test was negative) or $0.02(0.10)/[0.02(.10) + 0.98(0.89)] = 0.002288$.

e   A "false positive" indicates that the person doesn't have the disease, but the test says the person does. By contrast, a "false negative" indicates that the person does truly have the disease, but the test says the person does not.

Project 4-C: Selecting Condiments

a   Let M denote mustard and N non-mustard. Then,

For $P(X = 0)$, all three condiments must be non-mustard: $NNN = (7/10)(6/9)(5/8) = 0.291667$.

For $P(X = 1)$, $MNN + NMN + NNM = (3/10)(7/9)(6/8) + (7/10)(3/9)(6/8) + (7/10)(6/9)(3/8) = 0.525$.

For $P(X = 2)$, $MMN + MNM + NMM = (3/10)(2/9)(7/8) + (3/10)(7/9)(2/8) + (7/10)(3/9)(2/8) = 0.175$.

For $P(X = 3)$, $MMM = (3/10)(2/9)(1/8) = 0.008333$.

In summary, $P(X = 0) = 0.291667$; $P(X = 1) = 0.525$; $P(X = 2) = 0.175$; $P(X = 3) = 0.008333$.

b $\mu = \text{Mean}(X) = 0(0.291667) + 1(0.525) + 2(0.175) + 3(0.008333) = 0.9$;

$\sigma^2 = \text{Var}(X) = \Sigma(x - \mu)^2 p(x) = (0 - 0.9)^2(0.291667) + (1 - 0.9)^2(0.525) + (2 - 0.9)^2(0.175) + (3 - 0.9)^2(0.008333) = 0.49$.

c   The answer is $p(0) + p(1) = 0.291667 + 0.525 = 0.816667$.

d   The answer is $1 - P(\text{no mustard was selected}) = 1 - 0.291667 = 0.708333$.

e $P(x \text{ is within 1 standard deviation of the mean}) = P(0.9 - 0.7 < x < 0.9 + 0.7) = P(0.2 < x < 1.6) = P(x = 1)$
= 0.525.

f   **i**   The probability distribution is the same as in part **a**, since there are the same number of ketchup and mustard. When $(x = 0)$, the total winnings, y, is $-\$15(3) = -\$45$; When $(x = 1)$, $y = \$25 - \$15 - \$15$ $= -\$5$; When $(x = 2)$, $y = \$25+\$25 - \$15 = \$35$; and when $(x = 3)$, $y = \$25(3) = \$75$.
Thus, in summary, $P(Y = -\$45) = 0.291667$; $P(Y = -\$5) = 0.525$; $P(Y = \$35) = 0.175$; $P(Y = \$75)$ $= 0.008333$.

      ii   Clearly, all of the probabilities are positive, and they all sum to 1.

      iii   The expected value of y is $-45(0.291667) - 5(0.525) + 35(0.175) + 75(0.008333) = -\$9.00$ (i.e., the expected loss is $9).

Chapter 5: Several Useful Discrete Distributions

5.1   **a** $P(X \le 3) = p(0) + p(1) + p(2) + p(3) =$

$C_0^8 0.7^0 0.3^8 + C_1^8 0.7^1 0.3^7 + C_2^8 0.7^2 0.3^6 + C_3^8 0.7^3 0.3^5 =$

$0.00006561 + 0.0001225 + 0.010002 + 0.046675 = 0.057968$

    b $P(X > 3) = 1 - P(X < 3) = 1 - p(0) - p(1) - p(2) =$

$C_0^8 0.7^0 0.3^8 - C_1^8 0.7^1 0.3^7 - C_2^8 0.7^2 0.3^6 =$

$1 - (0.00007 + 0.00012 + 0.01000) = 0.98981$

    c $P(X < 3) = p(0) + p(1) + p(2) =$

$C_0^8 0.7^0 0.3^8 + C_1^8 0.7^1 0.3^7 + C_2^8 0.7^2 0.3^6 =$

$0.00006561 + 0.0001225 + 0.010002 = 0.011292$

    d $P(X = 3) = p(3) = C_3^8 0.7^3 0.3^5 = 0.04668$

    e $P(3 < X \le 5) = p(3) + p(4) + p(5) =$

$C_3^8 0.7^3 0.3^5 + C_4^8 0.7^4 0.3^4 + C_5^8 0.7^5 0.3^3 =$

$0.04668 + 0.13614 + 0.25412 = 0.43693$

5.3   The random variable X is not a binomial random variable since the balls are selected without replacement. For this reason, the probability p of choosing a red ball changes from trial to trial.

5.5   **a** $C_2^8 (0.3)^2 (0.7)^6 = \dfrac{8(7)}{2(1)}(0.09)(0.117649) = 0.2965$

    b $C_0^4 (0.05)^0 (0.95)^4 = (0.95)^4 - 0.8145$

    c $C_3^{10} (0.5)^3 (0.5)^7 = \dfrac{10(9)(8)}{3(2)(1)}(0.5)^{10} = 0.1172$

    d $C_1^7 (0.2)^1 (0.8)^6 = 7(0.2)(0.8)^6 = 0.3670$

5.7   **a**   For $n = 7$ and $p = 0.3$, $P(X = 4) = C_4^7 (0.3)^4 (0.7)^3 = 0.097$

    b   These probabilities can be found individually using the binomial formula, or alternatively using the cumulative binomial tables in Appendix I

$P(X \le 1) = p(0) + p(1)$

$= C_0^7 (0.3)^0 (0.7)^7 + C_1^7 (0.3)^1 (0.7)^6$

$= (0.7)^7 + 7(0.3)(0.7)^6 = 0.08235 + 0.24706 = 0.329$

or directly from the binomial tables in the row marked $a = 1$.

    c   Refer to part **b**: $P(X > 1) = 1 - P(X \le 1) = 1 - 0.329 = 0.671$

    d $\mu = np = 7(0.3) = 2.1$

    e $\sigma = \sqrt{npq} = \sqrt{7(0.3)(0.7)} = \sqrt{1.47} = 1.212$

5.9   Notice that when $p = 0.8$, $p(x) = C_x^6 (0.8)^x (0.2)^{6-x}$. In Exercise 5.8, with

$p = 0.2$, $p(x) = C_x^6 (0.2)^x (0.8)^{6-x}$. The probability that $X = k$ when $p = 0.8$ — $C_k^6 (0.8)^k (0.2)^{n-k}$ — is the

same as the probability that $X = n - k$ when $p = 0.2$ — $C_{n-k}^6 (0.2)^{n-k} (0.8)^k$. This follows because

$$C_k^n = \frac{n!}{k!(n-k)!} = C_{n-k}^n$$

Therefore, the probabilities $p(x)$ for a binomial random variable X when $n = 6$ and $p = 0.8$ will be the mirror images of those found in Exercise 5.8 and the probability histogram is shown below.

x	0	1	2	3	4	5	6
$p(x)$	0.000	0.002	0.015	0.082	0.246	0.393	0.262

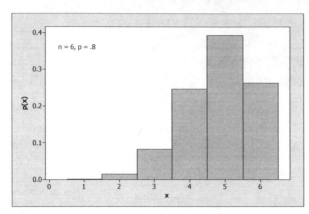

5.11

a For $n = 10$ and $p = 0.4$, $P(X = 4) = C_4^{10}(0.4)^4(0.6)^6 = 0.251$.

b To calculate $P(X \geq 4) = p(4) + p(5) + \cdots + p(10)$ it is easiest to write

$$P(X \geq 4) = 1 - P(X < 4) = 1 - P(X \leq 3)$$

These probabilities can be found individually using the binomial formula, or alternatively using the cumulative binomial tables in Appendix I.

$$P(X = 0) = C_0^{10}(0.4)^0(0.6)^{10} = 0.006 \qquad P(X = 1) = C_1^{10}(0.4)^1(0.6)^9 = 0.040$$

$$P(X = 2) = C_2^{10}(0.4)^2(0.6)^8 = 0.121 \qquad P(X = 3) = C_3^{10}(0.4)^3(0.6)^7 = 0.215$$

The sum of these probabilities gives $P(X \leq 3) = 0.382$ and $P(x \geq 4) = 1 - 0.382 = 0.618$.

c Use the results of parts **a** and **b**.

$$P(X > 4) = 1 - P(X \leq 4) = 1 - (0.382 + 0.251) = 0.367$$

d From part **c**, $P(X \leq 4) = P(X \leq 3) + P(X = 4) = 0.382 + 0.251 = 0.633$.

e $\mu = np = 10(0.4) = 4$

f $\sigma = \sqrt{npq} = \sqrt{10(0.4)(0.6)} = \sqrt{2.4} = 1.549$

5.13

a $P(X \geq 4) = 1 - P(X \leq 3) = 1 - 0.099 = 0.901$

b $P(X = 2) = P(X \leq 2) - P(X \leq 1) = 0.017 - 0.002 = 0.015$

c $P(X < 2) = P(X \leq 1) = 0.002$

d $P(X > 1) = 1 - P(X \leq 1) = 1 - 0.002 = 0.998$

5.15

a $P(X < 12) = P(X \leq 11) = 0.748$

b $P(X \leq 6) = 0.610$

c $P(X > 4) = 1 - P(X \leq 4) = 1 - 0.633 = .0367$

d $P(X \geq 6) = 1 - P(X \leq 5) = 1 - 0.034 = 0.966$

e $P(3 < X < 7) = P(X \leq 6) - P(X \leq 3) = 0.828 - 0.172 = 0.656$

5.17 **a** $\mu = 100(0.01) = 1;\ \sigma = \sqrt{100(0.01)(0.99)} = 0.99$

b $\mu = 100(0.9) = 90;\ \sigma = \sqrt{100(0.9)(0.1)} = 3$

c $\mu = 100(0.3) = 30;\ \sigma = \sqrt{100(0.3)(0.7)} = 4.58$

d $\mu = 100(0.7) = 70;\ \sigma = \sqrt{100(0.7)(0.3)} = 4.58$

e $\mu = 100(0.5) = 50;\ \sigma = \sqrt{100(0.5)(0.5)} = 5$

5.19 **a** $p(0) = C_0^{20}(0.1)^0 (0.9)^{20} = 0.1215767$

$p(1) = C_1^{20}(0.1)^1 (0.9)^{19} = 0.2701703$

$p(2) = C_2^{20}(0.1)^2 (0.9)^{18} = 0.2851798$

$p(3) = C_3^{20}(0.1)^3 (0.9)^{17} = 0.1901199$

$p(4) = C_4^{20}(0.1)^4 (0.9)^{16} = 0.0897788$

so that $P(X \le 4) = p(0) + p(1) + p(2) + p(3) + p(4) = 0.9568255$

b Using Table 1, Appendix 1, $P(X \le 4)$ is read directly as 0.957.

c Adding the entries for $x = 0,1,2,3,4$, we have $P(X \le 4) = 0.956826$.

d $\mu = np - 20(0.1) = 2$ and $\sigma = \sqrt{npq} = \sqrt{1.8} = 1.3416$

e For $k = 1$, $\mu \pm \sigma = 2 \pm 1.342$ or 0.658 to 3.342 so that

$P(0.658 \le X \le 3.342) = P(1 \le X \le 3) = 0.2702 + 0.2852 + 0.1901 = 0.7455$

For $k = 2$, $\mu \pm 2\sigma = 2 \pm 2.683$ or -0.683 to 4.683 so that

$P(-0.683 \le X \le 4.683) = P(0 \le X \le 4) = 0.9569$

For $k = 3$, $\mu + 3\sigma = 2 \pm 4.025$ or -2.025 to 6.025 so that

$P(-2.025 \le X \le 6.025) = P(0 \le X \le 6) = 0.9977$

f The results are consistent with Tchebysheff's Theorem and the Empirical Rule.

5.21 Although there are trials (telephone calls) that result in either a person who will answer (S) or a person who will not (F), the number of trials, *n*, is not fixed in advance. Instead of recording *x*, the number of *successes* in *n* trials, you record *x*, the number of *trials* until the first success. This is *not* a binomial experiment.

5.23 Define *X* to be the number of alarm systems that are triggered. Then $p = P(\text{alarm is triggered}) = 0.99$ and $n = 9$. Since there is a table available in Appendix I for $n = 9$ and $p = 0.99$, it should be used rather than the binomial formula to calculate the necessary probabilities.

a $P(\text{alarm is triggered}) = P(X \ge 1) = 1 - P(X = 0) = 1 - 0.000 = 1.000$

b $P(\text{more than seven}) = P(X > 7) = 1 - P(X \le 7) = 1 - 0.003 = 0.997$

c $P(\text{eight or fewer}) = P(X \le 8) = 0.086$

5.25 Define *X* to be the number of cars that are black. Then $p = P(\text{black}) = 0.1$ and $n = 25$. Use Table 1 in Appendix I.

a $P(X \ge 5) = 1 - P(X \le 4) = 1 - 0.902 = 0.098$

b $P(X \le 6) = 0.991$

c $P(X > 4) = 1 - P(X \le 4) = 1 - 0.902 = 0.098$

d $P(X = 4) = P(X \le 4) - P(X \le 3) = 0.902 - 0.764 = 0.138$

e $P(3 \le X \le 5) = P(X \le 5) - P(X \le 2) = 0.967 - 0.537 = 0.430$

f $P(\text{more than 20 } not \text{ black}) = P(\text{less than 5 black}) = P(X \le 4) = 0.902$

5.27 Define a success to be a NHL player who was born outside the United States. Assuming that the trials are independent and that p is constant from trial to trial, this problem satisfies the requirements for the binomial experiment with $n=12$ and $p = 0.8$. You can use either the binomial formula or Table 1, Appendix I. We will use the table for calculations, similar to Exercise 5.1.

a $P(X \ge 5) = 1 - P(X < 5) = 1 - P(X \le 4) = 1 - 0.001 = 0.999$

b $P(X = 7) = P(X \le 7) - P(X \le 6) = 0.073 - 0.019 = 0.054$

c $P(X < 6) = P(X \le 5) = 0.004$

5.29 The mean number of bills that would have to be forgiven is given by $\mu = np = 2000(0.3) = 600$; the variance of x is $\sigma^2 = npq = 2000(0.3)(0.7) = 420$ and $\sigma = \sqrt{420} = 20.4939$. It is necessary to approximate $P(X > 700)$. From Tchebysheff's Theorem we know that at least $\left(1 - 1/k^2\right)$ of the measurements lie within $k\sigma$ of the mean. The value $x = 700$ is 100 units away from the mean $\mu = 600$. This distance is equivalent to $100/\sigma = 4.88$ standard deviations from the mean. For a point $k = 4.88$ standard deviations from the mean, Tchebysheff's Theorem concludes that at least $\left[1 - 1/(4.88)^2\right] = 0.96$ of the measurements lie within 4.88σ of the mean (i.e., 600 ± 100). Therefore, at most $1 - 0.96 = 0.04$ of the measurements are less than 500 or greater than 700. Since the distribution is fairly mound-shaped and symmetric ($p = 0.3$ and n large), we can say that at most 0.04 but more likely 0.02 of the measurements are greater than 700.

5.31 Define X to be the number of times the mouse chooses the red door. Then, if the mouse actually has no preference for colour, $p = P(\text{red door}) = 0.5$ and $n = 10$. Since $\mu = np = 5$ and $\sigma = \sqrt{npq} = 1.58$, you would expect that, if there is no colour preference, the mouse should choose the red door

$$\mu \pm 2\sigma \Rightarrow 5 \pm 3.16 \Rightarrow 1.84 \text{ to } 8.16$$

or between 2 and 8 times. If the mouse chooses the red door more than 8 or less than 2 times, the unusual results might suggest a colour preference.

5.33 Define X to be the number of Canadians who look for services close to the highway. Then, $n = 25$ and $p = 0.4$.

a $\mu = np = 25(0.4) = 10$ and $\sigma = \sqrt{npq} = \sqrt{25(0.4)(0.6)} = 2.449$

b $\mu \pm 2\sigma \Rightarrow 10 \pm 4.898 \Rightarrow 5.102$ to 14.898. Since X can take only integer values from 0 to 25, this interval consists of the values of X in the range $6 \le X \le 14$.

c Using Table 1 in Appendix I, $P(6 \le X \le 14) = P(X \le 14) - P(X \le 5) = 0.966 - 0.029 = 0.937$. This value agrees with Tchebysheff's Theorem (at least 3/4 of the measurements in this interval) and also with the Empirical Rule (approximately 95% of the measurements in this interval).

5.35 Define X to be the number of Canadians who consume fewer vegetable servings on a typical winter day than on a typical summer day. Then, $n = 15$ and $p = 0.5$. Using the binomial tables in Appendix I,

a $P(X = 8) = P(X \le 8) - P(X \le 7) = 0.696 - 0.500 = 0.196$

b $P(X \le 4) = 0.059$

c $P(X > 10) = 1 - P(X \le 10) = 1 - 0.941 = 0.059$

5.37 Use the Poisson formula with $\mu = 3$.

 a $\quad P(x = 0) = \dfrac{3^0 e^{-3}}{0!} = 0.0498$

 b $\quad P(x = 1) = \dfrac{3^1 e^{-3}}{1!} = 0.1494$

 c $\quad P(X > 1) = 1 - P(X \le 1) = 1 - p(0) - p(1) = 1 - 0.0498 - 0.1494 = 0.8008$

5.39 Using $p(x) = \dfrac{\mu^x e^{-\mu}}{x!} = \dfrac{2^x e^{-2}}{x!}$,

 a $\quad P(X = 0) = \dfrac{2^0 e^{-2}}{0!} = 0.135335$

 b $\quad P(X = 1) = \dfrac{2^1 e^{-2}}{1!} = 0.27067$

 c $\quad P(X > 1) = 1 - P(X \le 1) = 1 - 0.135335 - 0.27067 = 0.593994$

 d $\quad P(X = 5) = \dfrac{2^5 e^{-2}}{5!} = 0.036089$

5.41 a $\quad$ Using Table 1, Appendix I, $P(X \le 2) = 0.677$

 b $\quad$ With $\mu = np = 20(0.1) = 2$, the approximation is $p(x) \approx \dfrac{2^x e^{-2}}{x!}$. Then

$$P(X \le 2) \approx \frac{2^0 e^{-0}}{0!} + \frac{2^1 e^{-1}}{1!} + \frac{2^2 e^{-2}}{2!}$$
$$= 0.135335 + 0.27067 + 0.27067 = 0.677$$

 c $\quad$ The approximation is quite accurate.

5.43 Let X be the number of misses during a given month. Then X has a Poisson distribution with $\mu = 5$.

 a $\quad p(0) = e^{-5} = 0.0067$

 b $\quad p(5) = \dfrac{5^5 e^{-5}}{5!} = 0.1755$

 c $\quad P(X \ge 5) = 1 - P(X \le 4) = 1 - 0.440 = 0.560$ from Table 2, Appendix I.

5.45 Let X be the number of fatalities for the current year, with $\mu = 2.5$.

 a $\quad P(X = 2) = P(X \le 2) - P(X \le 1) = 0.544 - 0.287 = 0.257$

 b $\quad P(X \ge 2) = 1 - P(X \le 1) = 1 - 0.287 = 0.713$

 c $\quad P(X \le 1) = 0.287$

 d $\quad P(X \ge 1) = 1 - P(X \le 0) = 1 - 0.082 = 0.918$

5.47 The random variable X, number of bacteria, has a Poisson distribution with $\mu = 2$. The probability of interest is

$$P(X \text{ exceeds maximum count}) = P(X > 5)$$

Using the fact that $\mu = 2$ and $\sigma = \sqrt{2} = 1.414$, most of the observations should fall within $\mu \pm 2\sigma$ or 0 to 4. Hence, it is unlikely that X will exceed 5. In fact, the exact Poisson probability is

$$P(X > 5) = 1 - P(X \le 5) = 1 - 0.983 = 0.017$$

5.49 **a** $\dfrac{C_1^2 C_1^2}{C_2^5} = \dfrac{3(2)}{10} = 0.6$

b $\dfrac{C_2^4 C_1^3}{C_3^7} = \dfrac{6(3)}{35} = 0.5143$

c $\dfrac{C_4^5 C_0^3}{C_4^8} = \dfrac{5(1)}{70} = 0.0714$

5.51 The formula for $p(x)$ is $p(x) = \dfrac{C_x^6 C_{5-x}^4}{C_5^{10}}$ for $x = 1, 2, 3, 4, 5$.

a Since there are only 4 "failures" and we are selecting 5 items, we must select at least one "success." Hence, $P(X = 0) = 0$.

b $P(X \geq 2) = 1 - P(X \leq 1) = 1 - p(1) = 1 - \dfrac{C_1^6 C_4^4}{C_5^{10}} = 1 - \dfrac{6}{252} = 0.9762$

c $P(X = 2) = \dfrac{C_2^6 C_3^4}{C_5^{10}} = \dfrac{15(4)}{252} = 0.2381$

5.53 The formula for $p(x)$ is $p(x) = \dfrac{C_x^5 C_{3-x}^3}{C_3^8}$ for x = number of blue candies = $0, 1, 2, 3$.

a $P(X = 2) = \dfrac{C_2^5 C_1^3}{C_3^8} = \dfrac{10(3)}{56} = 0.5357$

b $P(X = 0) = \dfrac{C_0^5 C_3^3}{C_3^8} = \dfrac{1}{56} = 0.0179$

c $P(X = 3) = \dfrac{C_3^5 C_0^3}{C_3^8} = \dfrac{10}{56} = 0.1786$

5.55 **a** The random variable X has a hypergeometric distribution with $N = 5, M = 2$, and $n = 2$. Then,

$$p(x) = \dfrac{C_x^2 C_{2-x}^3}{C_2^5} \text{ for } x = 0, 1, 2$$

b Using the formulas given in this section of the text,

$$\mu = n\left(\dfrac{M}{N}\right) = 2\left(\dfrac{2}{5}\right) = \dfrac{4}{5} = 0.8$$

$$\sigma^2 = n\left(\dfrac{M}{N}\right)\left(\dfrac{N-M}{N}\right)\left(\dfrac{N-n}{N-1}\right) = 2\left(\dfrac{2}{5}\right)\left(\dfrac{3}{5}\right)\left(\dfrac{3}{4}\right) = \dfrac{9}{25} = 0.36$$

$$\sigma = \sqrt{0.36} = 0.6$$

c The probability distribution and histogram for X are shown below.

X	0	1	2
$p(x)$	3/10	6/10	1/10

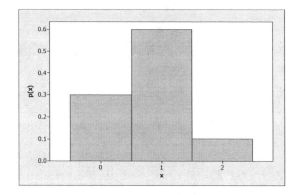

5.57 The random variable X has a hypergeometric distribution with $N = 10$, $M = 5$, and $n = 4$. Then,

$$p(x) = \frac{C_x^5 C_{4-x}^5}{C_4^{10}} \text{ for } x = 0, 1, 2, 3, 4$$

a $P(X = 4) = \frac{C_4^5 C_0^5}{C_4^{10}} = \frac{5}{210} = \frac{1}{42}$

b $P(X \le 3) = 1 - P(X = 4) = 1 - \frac{1}{42} = \frac{41}{42}$

c $P(2 \le X < 3) = p(2) + p(3) = \frac{C_2^5 C_2^5 + C_3^5 C_1^5}{C_4^{10}} = \frac{10(10) + 10(5)}{210} = \frac{150}{210} = \frac{5}{7}$

5.59 The Poisson random variable can be used as an approximation when n is large and p is small so that $np < 7$. The Poisson random variable can also be used to model the number of events occurring in a specific period of time or space.

5.61 The random variable X is defined to be the number of heads observed when a coin is flipped three times. Then $p = P(\text{success}) = P(\text{head}) = 1/2$, $q = 1 - p = 1/2$ and $n = 3$. The binomial formula yields the following results.

a $P(X = 0) = p(0) = C_0^3 (1/2)^0 (1/2)^3 = 1/8$ $\qquad$ $P(X = 1) = p(1) = C_1^3 (1/2)^1 (1/2)^2 = 3/8$

$P(X = 2) = p(2) = C_2^3 (1/2)^2 (1/2)^1 = 3/8$ $\qquad$ $P(X = 3) = p(3) = C_3^3 (1/2)^3 (1/2)^0 = 1/8$

b The associated probability histogram is shown below.

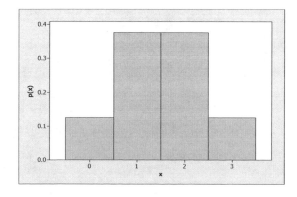

    c $\mu = np = 3(1/2) = 1.5$ and $\sigma = \sqrt{npq} = \sqrt{3(1/2)(1/2)} = 0.866$

    d   The desired intervals are

$$\mu \pm \sigma = 1.5 \pm 0.866 \quad \text{or} \quad 0.634 \text{ to } 2.366$$

$$\mu \pm 2\sigma = 8 \pm 1.732 \quad \text{or} \quad -0.232 \text{ to } 3.232$$

The values of x that fall in this first interval are $x = 1$ and $x = 2$, and the fraction of measurement in this interval will be $3/8 + 3/8 = 3/4$. The second interval encloses all four values of x and thus the fraction of measurements within 2 standard deviations of the mean will be 1, or 100%. These results are consistent with both Tchebysheff's Theorem and the Empirical Rule.

5.63   It is given that $n = 20$, $p = 0.5$, and $X =$ number of patients surviving 10 years.

    a $P(X \geq 1) = 1 - P(X = 0) = 1 - 0.000 = 1$

    b $P(X \geq 10) = 1 - P(X \leq 9) = 1 - 0.412 = 0.588$

    c $P(X \geq 15) = 1 - P(X \leq 14) = 1 - 0.979 = 0.021$

5.65   **a**   Define X to be the integer between 0 and 9 chosen by a person. If the digits are equally likely to be chosen, then $p(x) = \dfrac{1}{10}$ for $x = 0, 1, 2, \ldots, 9$.

    b $P(4, 5, \text{ or } 6 \text{ is chosen}) = p(4) + p(5) + p(6) = \dfrac{3}{10}$

    c $P(\text{not } 4, 5, \text{ or } 6) = 1 - \dfrac{3}{10} = \dfrac{7}{10}$

5.67   Let X be the number of Canadians in the sample of $n = 15$ who are in favour of income splitting for couples. Then X has a binomial distribution with $p = 0.77 \approx 0.80$

    a $p(x) = C_x^{15}(.8)^x (.2)^{15-x}$ for $x = 0, 1, 2, \ldots, 15$.

    b   From Table 1, $P(X \leq 8) = 0.018$.

    c $P(X > 8) = 1 - P(X \leq 8) = 1 - 0.018 = 0.982$.

    d   From Table 1 in Appendix I, look down the column for $p = 0.8$ to find the largest cumulative probability which is still less than or equal to 0.10. This probability is 0.061 with $P(X \leq 9) = 0.061$. Therefore, the largest value of c is $c = 9$.

5.69   Let X be the number of reality TV fans in a sample of $n = 20$ who say their favourite reality show involves escaping from remote locations. Then X has a binomial distribution with $p = 0.5$.

    a $P(X = 16) = P(X \leq 16) - P(X \leq 15) = 0.999 - 0.994 = 0.005$

    b $P(15 \leq X \leq 18) = P(X \leq 18) - P(X \leq 14) = 1 - 0.979 = 0.021$

    c $P(X \leq 5) = 0.021$. This would be an unlikely occurrence, since it occurs less than 1 time in 20.

5.71   Define X to be the number of students favouring the issue, with $n = 25$ and $p = P(\text{student favours the issue})$ assumed to be 0.8. Using the binomial tables in Appendix I,

$$P(X \leq 15) = 0.017$$

Thus, the probability of observing $x = 15$ or the more extreme values, $x = 0, 1, 2, \ldots, 14$ is quite small under the assumption that $p = 0.8$. We probably should conclude that p is actually smaller than 0.8.

5.73 **a** $p = P(\text{rain according to the forecaster}) = 0.3$

b With $n = 25$ and $p = 0.3$, $\mu = np = 25(0.3) = 7.5$ and $\sigma = \sqrt{npq} = \sqrt{5.25} = 2.29129$

c The observed value, $x = 10$, lies $z = \dfrac{10 - 7.5}{2.29} = 1.09$ standard deviations above the mean.

d The observed event is not unlikely under the assumption that $p = 0.3$. We have no reason to doubt the forecaster.

5.75 The random variable X, the number of neighbours per square metre, has a Poisson distribution with $\mu = 4$. Use the Poisson formula or Table 2 in Appendix I.

a $P(X = 0) = 0.018$

b $P(X \le 3) = 0.433$

c $P(X \ge 5) = 1 - P(X \le 4) = 1 - 0.629 = 0.371$

d With $\mu = 4$ and $\sigma = \sqrt{\mu} = 2$, approximately 95% of the values of x should lie in the interval
$\mu \pm 2\sigma \Rightarrow 4 \pm 4 \Rightarrow 0 \text{ to } 8$

In fact, using Table 2, we can calculate the probability of observing between 0 and 8 neighbours per square metre to be $P(X \le 8) = 0.979$, which is close to our approximation.

5.77 **a** The random variable x, the number of chickens with blue feathers, has a binomial distribution with $n = 20$ and $p = P(\text{blue feathers}) = P(Bb) + P(bB) = 0.5$.

b $\mu = np = 20(0.5) = 10$.

c From Table 1, Appendix I, $P(X < 5) = P(X \le 4) = 0.006$.

d From Table 1, $P(10 \le X \le 12) = P(X < 12) - P(X \le 9) = 0.868 - 0.412 = 0.456$.

5.79 **a** Since cases of insulin-dependent diabetes is not likely to be contagious, these cases of the disorder occur independently at a rate of 5 per 100,000 per year. This random variable can be approximated by the Poisson random variable with $\mu = 5$.

b Use Table 2, Appendix I, to find $P(X \le 3) = 0.265$.

c $P(3 \le X \le 7) = P(X \le 7) - P(X \le 2) = 0.867 - 0.125 = 0.742$.

d The probability of observing 10 or more cases per 100,000 in a year is
$P(X \ge 10) = 1 - P(X \le 9) = 1 - 0.968 = 0.032$

This is an occurrence that we would not expect to see very often, if in fact $\mu = 5$.

5.81 The random variable x, the number of adults who prefer milk chocolate to dark chocolate, has a binomial distribution with $n = 5$, $p = 0.47$. Use the binomial formula.

a $P(X = 5) = p(5) = C_5^5 0.47^5 0.53^0 = 0.022935$

b $P(X = 3) = p(3) = C_3^5 0.47^3 0.53^2 = 0.291639$

c $P(X \ge 1) = 1 - P(X = 0) = 1 - C_0^5 0.47^0 0.53^5 = 1 - 0.04182 = 0.95818$

5.83   The random variable X, the number of British Columbians who support to prohibit the sale of cigarettes and tobacco products in pharmacies, has a binomial distribution with $n = 5$ and $p = 0.66$.

    a   Since $p = 0.66$ is not in Table 1, you must use the binomial formula to find
$$P(X = 5) = C_5^5 (0.66)^5 (0.34)^0 = 0.1252$$

    b   The probability that exactly three of the families select a restaurant because of its great food is
$$P(X = 3) = C_3^5 (0.66)^3 (0.34)^2 = 0.3323$$

    c $P(X \geq 1) = 1 - P(X = 0) = 1 - C_0^5 (0.66)^0 (0.34)^5 = 1 - 0.0045 = 0.9955$

5.85   The random variable X, the number of Canadians who oppose toward U.S. drilling in Arctic, has a binomial distribution with $n = 12$ and $p = 0.9$. Use Table 1 in Appendix I to find the necessary probabilities.

    a $P(X > 6) = 1 - P(X \leq 6) = 1 - 0.001 = 0.999$

    b $P(X \leq 4) = 0$

    c $P(X = 10) = P(X \leq 10) - P(X \leq 9) = 0.341 - 0.111 = 0.230$

5.87   The random variable X, the number of questionnaires that are filled out and returned, has a binomial distribution with $n = 20$ and $p = 0.7$. Use Table 1 in Appendix I to find the necessary probabilities.

    a $P(X = 10) = P(X \leq 10) - P(X \leq 9) = 0.048 - 0.017 = 0.031$

    b $P(X \geq 12) = 1 - P(X \leq 11) = 1 - 0.113 = 0.887$

    c $P(X \leq 10) = 0.048$

5.89   The random variable X, the number of treated birds who are still infected with the parasite, has a binomial distribution with $n = 25$. If the diet supplement is ineffective, then the proportion of infected birds should still be $p = 0.3$, even after two weeks of treatment.

    a   Using Table 1 with $n = 25$ and $p = 0.3$, we find $P(X \leq 3) = 0.033$.

    b   If the treatment is effective, reducing the value of p to $p = 0.1$, then $P(X \leq 3) = 0.764$.

5.91   The random variable X, the number of salesmen who will be involved in a serious accident during the coming year, has a binomial distribution with $n = 100$ and $p = 0.01$. To use the Poisson approximation, calculate
$\mu = np = 100(0.01) = 1$. The probability that $x = 2$ is approximated as $P(X = 2) = \dfrac{1^2 e^{-1}}{2!} = 0.183940$

5.93   The random variable X, the number of applicants who will actually enroll in the first year class, has a binomial distribution with $n = 1360$ and $p = 0.9$. Calculate $\mu = np = 1360(0.9) = 1224$ and
$\sigma = \sqrt{npq} = \sqrt{1360(0.9)(0.1)} = 11.06$. Then approximately 95% of the values of x should lie in the interval
$$\mu \pm 2\sigma \Rightarrow 1224 \pm 2(11.06) \Rightarrow 1201.87 \text{ to } 1246.12 \text{ or between 1202 and 1246}$$

5.95   The random variable X has a hypergeometric distribution with $N = 8$, $M = 2$, and $n = 4$. Then,
$$P(X = 0) = \frac{C_0^2 C_4^6}{C_4^8} = \frac{15}{70} = 0.214 \text{ and } P(X = 2) = \frac{C_2^2 C_2^6}{C_4^8} = \frac{15}{70} = 0.214$$

5.97   Define X to be the number of successful operations. Then $p = P(\text{success}) = 0.8$ and $n = 5$.

     a $P(X = 5) = C_5^5 (0.8)^5 (0.2)^0 = (0.8)^5 = 0.3277$

     b $P(X = 4) = C_4^5 (0.8)^4 (0.2)^1 = 5(0.8)^4 (0.2) = 0.4096$

     c $P(X < 2) = p(0) + p(1) = C_0^5 (0.8)^0 (0.2)^5 + C_1^5 (0.8)^1 (0.2)^4 = 0.00032 + 0.0064 = 0.0067$

5.99   Define X to be the number of failures observed among the four engines. Then $p = P(\text{engine fails}) = 0.01$ and $q = 1 - p = 0.99$, with $n = 4$.

     a $P(\text{no failures}) = P(X = 0) = C_0^4 (0.01)^0 (0.99)^4 = 0.9606$

     b $P(\text{no more than one failure}) = P(X \leq 1) = p(0) + p(1)$

$$= C_0^4 (0.01)^0 (0.99)^4 + C_1^4 (0.01)^1 (0.99)^3 = 0.9606 + 0.0388 = 0.9994$$

5.101   Define X to be the number of senior undergrad students in the group who say they will pursue a graduate program after graduation. Then X has a binomial distribution with $n = 50$ and $p = 0.2$.

     a $\mu = np = 50(0.2) = 10$ and $\sigma = \sqrt{npq} = \sqrt{50(0.2)(0.8)} = 2.828$

     b $P(X \geq 15) = 0.0607$. This is an unlikely event.

     c   The z score $z = \dfrac{x - \mu}{\sigma} = \dfrac{15 - 10}{2.828} = 1.77$ indicates that $x = 15$ lies at 1.77 standard deviations above the mean. This confirms the answer in part **b**.

Case Study: How Safe Is Plastic Surgery? Myth versus Fact!

Do breast implants increase the suicide rate?

1   Let X be the number of suicide cases for breast-implant recipients, and let μ be the average number of suicide cases for Ontario and Quebec. Then, the reasonable estimate of μ is given by
$$58 = 0.75\mu + \mu \text{ or } \mu = 58/1.75 = 33.14$$
Yes, 75% is the correct percentage.

2   Since X has a Poisson distribution with $\mu = 33.14$, the standard deviation of X is $\sigma = \sqrt{\mu} = \sqrt{33.14} = 5.76$.

3   The z-score for the observed value of x is $z = \dfrac{x - \mu}{\sigma} = \dfrac{58 - 33.14}{5.76} = 4.32$.

This is a very large number. It is very likely that the breast implants do increase the suicide rate.

Do breast implants reduce cancer risk?

1   Let X be the number of cancer deaths for breast-implant recipients, and let μ be the average number of cancer deaths among the general female population in Ontario and Quebec. Note that $(303 - 229)/303 = 24.42$; the given percentage of 24.5 is correct.

2   The reasonable estimate of μ is 303.

3   Since X has a Poisson distribution with $\mu = 303$, the standard deviation of X is $\sigma = \sqrt{\mu} = \sqrt{303} = 17.41$.

4   The z-score for the observed value of x is $z = \dfrac{x - \mu}{\sigma} = \dfrac{58 - 303}{17.41} = -14.07$.

This is a very small number. It is very likely that the breast implants do reduce cancer risk.

Project 5: Relations among Useful Discrete Probability Distributions

a **i** The probability distribution can be written as: $p(x) = \dfrac{C_x^7 C_{5-x}^{13}}{C_5^{20}}$, for $x = 0, 1, 2, 3, 4, 5$.

ii The mean of X is $\mu = n\left(\dfrac{M}{N}\right) = 5\left(\dfrac{7}{20}\right) = 1.75$, and the variance of X is

$$\sigma^2 = n\left(\dfrac{M}{N}\right)\left(\dfrac{N-M}{N}\right)\left(\dfrac{N-n}{N-1}\right) \cdot = 5\left(\dfrac{7}{20}\right)\left(\dfrac{20-7}{20}\right)\left(\dfrac{20-5}{20-1}\right) = 0.898026 .$$

iii For two standard deviations from the mean, the interval is $1.75 \pm 2(0.898026)^{.5} = (-0.14529, 3.64529)$. This would encompass $x = 0, 1, 2, 3$. Now, $p(0) + p(1) + p(2) + p(3) = 0.969298$. This result agrees with Tchebysheff's Theorem given in the text that at least a 3/4 proportion of the data lie within two standard deviations of the mean. For three standard deviations from the mean, the interval is $0.75 \pm 3(0.898026)^{.5} = (-1.09293, 4.59293)$. This would encompass $x = 0, 1, 2, 3, 4$. Now, $p(0) + p(1) + p(2) + p(3) + p(4) = 0.998646$. This result agrees with Tchebysheff's Theorem given in the text that at least an 8/9 proportion of the data lie within three standard deviations of the mean.

iv The answer is $1 - p(0) - 0.916989$.

b **i** Using the hypergeometric distribution, $p(2) = \dfrac{C_2^{80} C_{5-2}^{100}}{C_5^{180}} = 0.343200$.

ii Using the binomial distribution $p(2) = C_2^5 \left(\dfrac{80}{180}\right)^2 \left(1 - \dfrac{80}{180}\right)^{5-2} = 0.338702$; the approximation is decent, as the number selected (5) is small compared to the total sample size (180). The textbook states that if $\left(\dfrac{n}{N}\right)$ is less than or equal to 0.1, the hypergeometric distribution is well approximated by the binomial. Clearly, $\left(\dfrac{5}{180}\right)$ satisfies this criteria.

iii Hypergeometric distribution: The mean of X is $\mu = n\left(\dfrac{N}{M}\right) = 5\left(\dfrac{80}{180}\right) = 2.222222$, and the variance of X is $\sigma^2 = n\left(\dfrac{M}{N}\right)\left(\dfrac{N-M}{N}\right)\left(\dfrac{N-n}{N-1}\right) = 5\left(\dfrac{80}{180}\right)\left(\dfrac{180-80}{180}\right)\left(\dfrac{180-5}{180-1}\right) = 1.206980$.

Binomial distribution: The mean of X is $\mu = np = 5\left(\dfrac{80}{180}\right) = 2.222222$, and the variance of X is

$$\sigma^2 = npq = 5\left(\dfrac{80}{180}\right)\left(1 - \dfrac{80}{180}\right) = 1.234568.$$

In summary, the mean for the two distributions are identical. The variances are only slightly different.

c **i** In this case, $\mu = 28{,}572(0.00007) = 2.00004$ for the Poisson distribution, and thus the probability that no children will have cancer is $p(0) = \dfrac{2.00004^0 e^{-2.00004}}{0!} = 0.135330$.

ii The probability that at most two will have cancer is
$$P(X \le 2) = p(0) + p(1) + p(2)$$
$$= \dfrac{2.00004^0 e^{-2.00004}}{0!} + \dfrac{2.00004^1 e^{-2.00004}}{1!} + \dfrac{2.00004^2 e^{-2.00004}}{2!} = 0.676666$$

iii The probability that at least 7 will not have cancer is equal to the probability that up to 3 do develop cancer: that is, $p(0) + p(1) + p(2) + p(3)$. In a sample of 10 children, $\mu = np = (10)(0.00007) = 0.0007$. Thus, using the Poisson distribution to approximate each of the four binomial probabilities, we obtain:

$$p(0) + p(1) + p(2) + p(3) = \frac{0.007^0 e^{-0.007}}{0!} + \frac{0.007^1 e^{-0.007}}{1!} + \frac{0.007^2 e^{-0.007}}{2!} + \frac{0.007^3 e^{-0.007}}{3!} + =$$

$0.999300245 + 0.000699510 + 0.000000245 + 0.0000000001 = 0.9999999999999$

which is a virtual certainty.

Chapter 6: The Normal Probability Distribution

6.1 **a** $P(z < 2) = A(2) = 0.9772$

      b $P(z > 1.16) = 1 - P(z \le 1.16) = 1 - A(1.16) = 1 - 0.8770 = 0.1230$

      c $P(-2.33 < z < 2.33) = A(2.33) - A(-2.33) = 0.0.9901 - 0.0099 = 0.7802$

      d $P(z < 1.88) = A(1.88) = 0.9699$

6.3 **a**   It is necessary to find the area to the left of $z = 1.6$. That is, $A = A(1.6) = 0.9452$.

      b   The area to the left of $z = 1.83$ is $A = A(1.83) = 0.9664$.

      c $A = A(0.90) = 0.8159$

      d $A = A(4.58) \approx 1$. Notice that the values in Table 3, Appendix I, approach 1 as the value of z increases. When the value of z is larger than $z = 3.49$ (the largest value in the table), we can assume that the area to its left is approximately 1.

6.5 **a** $P(-1.43 < z < 0.68) = A(0.68) - A(-1.43) = 0.7517 - 0.0764 = 0.6753$

      b $P(0.58 < z < 1.74) = A(1.74) - A(0.58) = 0.9591 \quad 0.7190 - 0.2401$

      c $P(-1.55 < z < -0.44) = A(-0.44) - A(-1.55) = 0.3300 \quad 0.0606 - 0.2694$

      d $P(z > 1.34) = 1 - A(1.34) = 1 - 0.9099 = 0.0901$

      e   Since the value of $z = -4.32$ is not recorded in Table 3, Appendix I, you can assume that the area to the left of $z = -4.32$ is very close to 0. Then $P(z < -4.32) \approx 0$.

6.7 Now we are asked to find the z-value corresponding to a particular area.

      a   We need to find a z_0 such that $P(z > z_0) = 0.025$. This is equivalent to finding an indexed area of $1 - 0.025 = 0.975$. Search the interior of Table 3, Appendix I, until you find the four-digit number 0.9750. The corresponding z-value is 1.96; that is, $A(1.96) = 0.9750$. Therefore, $z_0 = 1.96$ is the desired z-value (see the figure below).

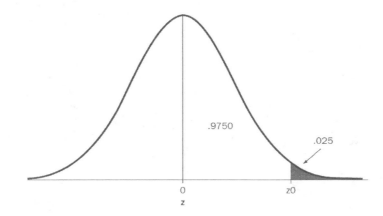

    b   We need to find a z_0 such that $P(z < z_0) = 0.9251$ (see below). Using Table 3, we find a value such that the indexed area is 0.9251. The corresponding z-value is $z_0 = 1.44$.

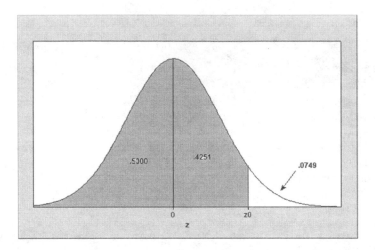

6.9   **a**   Similar to Exercise 6.7b. The value of z_0 must be positive and $A(z_0) = 0.9505$. Hence, $z_0 = 1.65$.

       b   It is given that the area to the left of z_0 is 0.0505, shown as A_1 in the figure below. The desired value is not tabulated in Table 3, Appendix I, but falls between two tabulated values, 0.0505 and 0.0495. Hence, using linear interpolation (as done in Exercise 6.6b), z_0 will lie halfway between –1.64 and –1.65, or $z_0 = -1.645$.

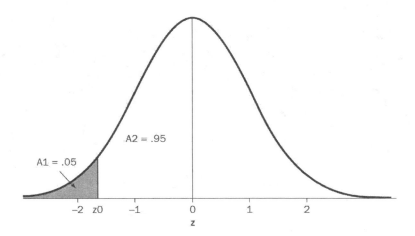

6.11   The *p*th percentile of the standard normal distribution is a value of *z*, which has area *p*/100 to its left. Since all four percentiles in this exercise are greater than the 50th percentile, the value of *z* will all lie to the right of $z = 0$, as shown for the 90th percentile in the figure on the next page.

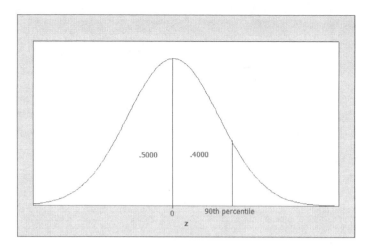

a   From the figure, the area to the left of the 90th percentile is 0.9000. From Table 3, Appendix I, the appropriate value of z is closest to $z = 1.28$ with area 0.8997. Hence, the 90th percentile is approximately $z = 1.28$.

b   As in part **a**, the area to the left of the 95th percentile is 0.9500. From Table 3, the appropriate value of z is found using linear interpolation (see Exercise 6.9b) as $z = 1.645$. Hence the 95th percentile is $z = 1.645$.

c   The area to the left of the 98th percentile is 0.9800. From Table 3, the appropriate value of z is closest to $z = 2.05$ with area 0.9798. Hence, the 98th percentile is approximately $z = 2.05$.

d   The area to the left of the 99th percentile is 0.9900. From Table 3, the appropriate value of z is closest to $z = 2.33$ with area 0.9901. Hence, the 99th percentile is approximately $z = 2.33$.

6.13   Similar to Exercise 6.12,

a   Calculate $z_1 = \dfrac{1.00 - 1.20}{0.15} = -1.33$ and $z_2 = \dfrac{1.10 - 1.20}{0.15} = -0.67$. Then

$$P(1.00 < X < 1.10) = P(-1.33 < z < -0.67) = 0.2514 - 0.0918 = 0.1596$$

b   Calculate $z = \dfrac{x - \mu}{\sigma} = \dfrac{1.38 - 1.20}{0.15} = 1.2$. Then

$$P(X > 1.38) = P(z > 1.2) = 1 - 0.8849 = 0.1151$$

c   Calculate $z_1 = \dfrac{1.35 - 1.20}{0.15} = 1$ and $z_2 = \dfrac{1.50 - 1.20}{0.15} = 2$. Then

$$P(1.35 < X < 1.50) = P(1 < z < 2) = 0.9772 - 0.8413 = 0.1359$$

6.15   The 99th percentile of the standard normal distribution was found in Exercise 6.11d to be $z = 2.33$. Since the relationship between the general normal random variable X and the standard normal z is $z = \dfrac{x - \mu}{\sigma}$, the corresponding percentile for this general normal random variable is found by solving for $x = \mu + z\sigma$:

$$2.33 = \frac{x - 35}{10}$$
$$x - 35 = 23.3 \quad \text{or} \quad x = 58.3$$

6.17 The random variable X is normal with unknown μ and σ. However, it is given that

$$P(X>4)=P\left(z>\frac{4-\mu}{\sigma}\right)=0.9772 \text{ and } P(X>5)=P\left(z>\frac{5-\mu}{\sigma}\right)=0.9332. \text{ These probabilities are}$$

shown in the figure below.

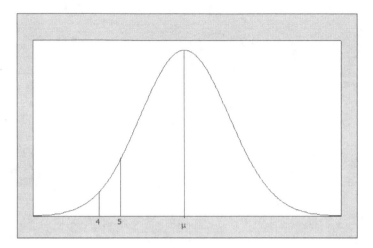

The value $\dfrac{4-\mu}{\sigma}$ is negative, with $A\left(\dfrac{4-\mu}{\sigma}\right)=1-0.9772=0.0228$ or $\dfrac{4-\mu}{\sigma}=-2$ (i)

The value $\dfrac{5-\mu}{\sigma}$ is also negative, with $A\left(\dfrac{5-\mu}{\sigma}\right)=1-0.9332=0.0668$ or $\dfrac{5-\mu}{\sigma}=-1.5$ (ii)

Equations (i) and (ii) provide two equations in two unknowns which can be solved simultaneously for μ

and σ. From (i), $\sigma=\dfrac{\mu-4}{2}$, which when substituted into (ii) yields

$$5-\mu=-1.5\left(\frac{\mu-4}{2}\right)$$
$$10-2\mu=-1.5\mu+6$$
$$\mu=8$$

and from (i), $\sigma=\dfrac{8-4}{2}=2.$

6.19 The random variable X, the height of a Canadian male, has a normal distribution with $\mu=177$ and $\sigma=8$.

a $P(X>185)=P\left(z>\dfrac{185-177}{8}\right)=P(z>1.00)=1-0.8413=0.1587$

b $P(170<X<185)=P\left(\dfrac{170-177}{8}<z<\dfrac{185-177}{8}\right)=P(-0.875<z<1.00)=0.8413-0.1908=0.6505$

c $z=\dfrac{188-177}{8}=1.375$

This would not be considered an unusually large value, since it is less than two standard deviations from the mean.

6.21 The random variable X, cerebral blood flow, has a normal distribution with $\mu = 74$ and $\sigma = 16$.

a $P(60 < X < 80) = P\left(\dfrac{60-74}{16} < z < \dfrac{80-74}{16}\right) = P(-0.88 < z < 0.38) = 0.6480 - 0.1894 = 0.4586$

b $P(X > 100) = P\left(z > \dfrac{100-74}{16}\right) = P(z > 1.62) = 1 - 0.9474 = 0.0526$

c $P(X < 40) = P\left(z < \dfrac{40-74}{16}\right) = P(z < -2.12) = 0.0170$

6.23 The random variable X, total weight of 8 people, has a mean of $\mu = 550$ and a variance $\sigma^2 = 445$. It is necessary to find $P(X > 590)$ and $P(X > 680)$ if the distribution of x is approximately normal. The z-value corresponding to $x_1 = 590$ is $z_1 = \dfrac{x_1 - \mu}{\sigma} = \dfrac{590 - 550}{\sqrt{445}} = \dfrac{40}{21.095} = 1.90$. Hence,

$$P(X > 590) = P(z > 1.90) = 1 - A(1.90) = 1 - 0.9713 = 0.0287$$

Similarly, the z-value corresponding to $x_2 = 680$ is $z_2 = \dfrac{x_2 - \mu}{\sigma} = \dfrac{680 - 550}{\sqrt{445}} = 6.16$

and $P(X > 680) = P(z > 6.16) = 1 - A(6.16) \approx 1 - 1 \approx 0$.

6.25 It is given that X, the unsupported stem diameter of a sunflower plant, is normally distributed with $\mu = 35$ and $\sigma = 3$.

a $P(X > 40) = P\left(z > \dfrac{40-35}{3}\right) = P(z > 1.67) = 1 - 0.9525 = 0.0475$

b From part **a**, the probability that one plant has stem diameter of more than 40 mm is 0.0475. Since the two plants are independent, the probability that two plants both have diameters of more than 40 mm is $(0.0475)(0.0475) = 0.00226$

c Since 95% of all measurements for a normal random variable lie within 1.96 standard deviations of the mean, the necessary interval is
$$\mu \pm 1.96\sigma \implies 35 \pm 1.96(3) \implies 35 \pm 5.88$$
or in the interval 29.12 to 40.88.

d The 90th percentile of the standard normal distribution was found in Exercise 6.11a to be $z = 1.28$. Since the relationship between the general normal random variable X and the standard normal z is $z = \dfrac{x - \mu}{\sigma}$, the corresponding percentile for this general normal random variable is found by solving for $x = \mu + z\sigma$.
$$x = 35 + 1.28(3) \quad \text{or} \quad x = 38.84$$

6.27 **a** It is given that the prime interest rate forecasts, x, are approximately normal with mean $\mu = 4.5$ and standard deviation $\sigma = 0.1$. It is necessary to determine the probability that X exceeds 4.75. Calculate $z = \dfrac{x - \mu}{\sigma} = \dfrac{4.75 - 4.5}{0.1} = 2.5$. Then $P(X > 4.75) = P(z > 2.5) = 1 - 0.9938 = 0.0062$.

b Calculate $z = \dfrac{x - \mu}{\sigma} = \dfrac{4.375 - 4.5}{0.1} = -1.25$. Then $P(X < 4.375) = P(z < -1.25) = 0.1056$.

6.29 It is given that the counts of the number of bacteria are normally distributed with $\mu = 85$ and $\sigma = 9$. The z-value corresponding to $x = 100$ is $z = \dfrac{x - \mu}{\sigma} = \dfrac{100 - 85}{9} = 1.67$ and
$$P(X > 100) = P(z > 1.67) = 1 - 0.9525 = 0.0475$$

6.31 Let w be the number of words specified in the contract. Then X, the number of words in the manuscript, is normally distributed with $\mu = w + 20,000$ and $\sigma = 10,000$. The publisher would like to specify w so that

$$P(X < 100,000) = 0.95$$

As in Exercise 6.30, calculate

$$z = \frac{100,0000 - (w + 20,000)}{10,000} = \frac{80,000 - w}{10,000}$$

Then $P(X < 100,000) = P\left(z < \dfrac{80,000 - w}{10,000}\right) = 0.95$. It is necessary that $z_0 = (80,000 - w)/10,000$ be such that

$$P(z < z_0) = 0.95 \;\Rightarrow\; A(z_0) = 0.9500 \;\text{ or }\; z_0 = 1.645$$

Hence,

$$\frac{80,000 - w}{10,000} = 1.645 \;\text{ or }\; w = 63,550$$

6.33 The amount of money spent at shopping centres on Sundays is normally distributed with $\mu = 85$ and $\sigma = 10$.

a The z-value corresponding to $x = 90$ is $z = \dfrac{x - \mu}{\sigma} = \dfrac{90 - 85}{10} = 0.5$. Then

$$P(X > 90) = P(z > 0.5) = 1 - 0.6915 = 0.3085$$

b The z-value corresponding to $x = 100$ is $z = \dfrac{x - \mu}{\sigma} = \dfrac{100 - 85}{10} = 1.5$. Then

$$P(90 < X < 100) = P(0.5 < z < 1.5) = 0.9332 - 0.6915 = 0.2417$$

c First, find $P(X > 100) = P(z > 1.5) = 1 - 0.9332 = 0.0668$ for a single shopper. For two shoppers, use the Multiplication Rule.

$$P(\text{both shoppers spend more than \$100}) = P(\text{1st spends more than \$100}) \times P(\text{2nd spends more than \$100})$$
$$= (0.0668)(0.0668) = 0.0045$$

6.35 **a** Since $np = 15$ and $nq = 10$ are both greater than 5, normal approximation to binomial is appropriate.

b $\mu = np = 25(0.6) = 15$ and $\sigma = \sqrt{npq} = \sqrt{25(0.6)(0.4)} = 2.4495$

c To find the probability of more than 9 successes, we need to include the values $x = 10, 11, \ldots, 25$. To include the entire block of probability for the first value of $x = 10$, we need to start at 9.5. Then the probability of more than 9 successes is approximated as $P(X > 9) = P(X \geq 10) = P(X > 9.5)$. Now, we will find z by using the value of x obtained after the continuity correction applied; i.e.,

$z = \dfrac{x - \mu}{\sigma} = \dfrac{9.5 - 15}{2.4495} = -2.25$. Thus, $P(X > 9.5) = P(z > -2.25) = 1 - 0.0122 = 0.9878$.

6.37 **a** The normal approximation will be appropriate if both np and nq are greater than 5. For this binomial experiment, $np = 25(0.3) = 7.5$ and $nq = 25(0.7) = 17.5$ and the normal approximation is appropriate.

b For the binomial random variable, $\mu = np = 7.5$ and $\sigma = \sqrt{npq} = \sqrt{25(0.3)(0.7)} = 2.291$.

c The probability of interest is the area under the binomial probability histogram corresponding to the rectangles $x = 6, 7, 8$, and 9 in the figure given on the next page.

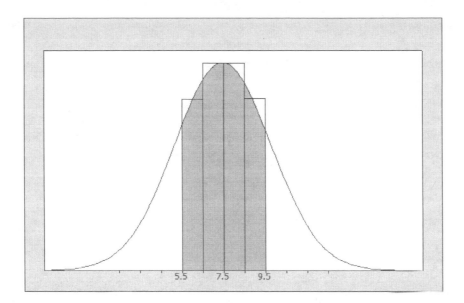

To approximate this area, use the "correction for continuity" and find the area under a normal curve with mean $\mu = 7.5$ and $\sigma = 2.291$ between $x_1 = 5.5$ and $x_2 = 9.5$. The z-values corresponding to the two values of x are

$$z_1 = \frac{5.5 - 7.5}{2.291} = -0.87 \quad \text{and} \quad z_2 = \frac{9.5 - 7.5}{2.291} = 0.87$$

The approximating probability is $P(5.5 < X < 9.5) = P(-0.87 < z < 0.87) = 0.8078 - 0.1922 = 0.6156$.

d From Table 1, Appendix I,

$$P(6 \leq X < 9) = P(X \leq 9) - P(X < 5) = 0.811 - 0.193 = 0.618$$

which is not too far from the approximate probability calculated in part **c**.

6.39 Similar to Exercise 6.38.

a The approximating probability will be $P(X > 22.5)$, where X has a normal distribution with

$\mu = 100(0.2) = 20$ and $\sigma = \sqrt{100(0.2)(0.8)} = 4$. Then

$$P(X > 22.5) = P\left(z > \frac{22.5 - 20}{4}\right) = P(z > 0.62) = 1 - 0.7324 = 0.2676$$

b The approximating probability is now $P(X > 21.5)$ since the entire rectangle corresponding to $x = 22$ must be included.

$$P(X > 21.5) = P\left(z > \frac{21.5 - 20}{4}\right) = P(z > 0.38) = 1 - 0.6480 = 0.3520$$

c To include the entire rectangles for $x = 21$ and $x = 24$, the approximating probability is

$$P(20.5 < X < 24.5) = P(.12 < z < 1.12) = 0.8686 - 0.5478 = 0.3208$$

d To include the entire rectangle for $x = 25$, the approximating probability is

$$P(X < 25.5) = P(z < 1.38) = 0.9162$$

6.41 Using the binomial tables for $n = 20$ and $p = 0.3$, you can verify that

a $P(X = 5) = P(X \leq 5) - P(X \leq 4) = 0.416 - 0.238 = 0.178$

b $P(X \geq 7) = 1 - P(X \leq 6) = 1 - 0.608 = 0.392$

6.43 Similar to previous exercises.

a With $n = 20$ and $p = 0.4$, $P(X \geq 10) = 1 - P(X \leq 9) = 1 - 0.755 = 0.245$.

b To use the normal approximation, find the mean and standard deviation of this binomial random variable: $\mu = np = 20(0.4) = 8$ and $\sigma = \sqrt{npq} = \sqrt{20(0.4)(0.6)} = \sqrt{4.2} = 2.191$

Using the continuity correction, it is necessary to find the area to the right of 9.5. The z-value corresponding to $x = 9.5$ is

$$z = \frac{9.5 - 8}{2.191} = 0.68 \text{ and } P(X \geq 10) \approx P(z > 0.68) = 1 - 0.7517 = 0.2483$$

Note that the normal approximation is very close to the exact binomial probability.

6.45 **a** The approximating probability will be $P(X > 20.5)$ where X has a normal distribution with

$\mu = 50(0.731) = 36.55$ and $\sigma = \sqrt{50(0.731)(0.269)} = 3.136$. Then

$$P(X > 20.5) = P\left(z > \frac{20.5 - 36.55}{3.136}\right) = P(z > -5.12) \approx 1 - 0 = 1.00$$

b The approximating probability is

$$P(X < 14.5) = P\left(z < \frac{14.5 - 36.55}{3.136}\right) = P(z < -7.03) = 0$$

c If fewer than 28 students *do not* support same sex marriage, then $50 - 28 = 22$ or more do support same sex marriage. The approximating probability is

$$P(X > 21.5) = P\left(z > \frac{21.5 - 36.55}{3.136}\right) = P(z > -4.80) \approx 1 - 0 = 1$$

d As long as your class can be assumed to be a representative sample of all Canadians, the probabilities in parts **a–c** will be accurate.

6.47 Define X to be the number of guests claiming a reservation at the motel. Then

$p = P(\text{guest claim reservation}) = 1 - 0.1 = 0.9$ and $n = 215$. The motel has only 200 rooms. Hence, if

$x > 200$, a guest will not receive a room. The probability of interest is then $P(X \leq 200)$. Using the normal

approximation, calculate

$$\mu = np = 215(0.9) = 193.5 \text{ and } \sigma = \sqrt{215(0.9)(0.1)} = \sqrt{19.35} = 4.399$$

The probability $P(X \leq 200)$ is approximated by the area under the appropriate normal curve to the left of

200.5. The z-value corresponding to $x = 200.5$ is $z = \dfrac{200.5 - 193.5}{\sqrt{19.35}} = 1.59$ and

$$P(X \leq 200) \approx P(z < 1.59) = 0.9441$$

6.49 Define X to be the number of Peruvian adults who support death penalty. Then the random variable X has a binomial distribution with $n = 503$ and $p = 0.81$. Calculate

$$\mu = np = 503(0.81) = 407.43 \text{ and } \sigma = \sqrt{503(0.81)(0.19)} = \sqrt{77.4117} = 8.8$$

a Using the normal approximation with correction for continuity, we find

$$P(X = 420) = P(419.5 < X < 420.5) = P\left(\frac{419.5 - 407.43}{8.8} < z < \frac{420.5 - 407.43}{8.8}\right)$$
$$= P(1.37 < z < 1.49) = 0.9319 - 0.9147 = 0.0172$$

b The approximating probability is

$$P(X < 419.5) = P\left(z < \frac{419.5 - 407.43}{8.8}\right) = P(z < 1.37) = 0.9147$$

c   The approximating probability is

$$P(X > 420.5) = P\left(z > \frac{420.5 - 407.43}{8.8}\right) = P(z > 1.49) = 1 - 0.9319 = 0.0681$$

d   You can only assume that Peruvian adults in Lima are representative sample of all adults in the capital city, but not of all adults in the entire nation.

6.51   Define X to be the number of consumers who preferred a Pepsi product. Then the random variable X has a binomial distribution with $n = 500$ and $p = 0.25$, if Pepsi's market share is indeed 25%. Calculate

$$\mu = np = 500(0.25) = 125 \text{ and } \sigma = \sqrt{500(0.25)(0.75)} = \sqrt{93.75} = 9.6825$$

a   Using the normal approximation with correction for continuity, we find the area between 149.5 and 150.5:

$$P(149.5 < X < 150.5) = P\left(\frac{149.5 - 125}{9.6825} < z < \frac{150.5 - 125}{9.6825}\right) = P(2.53 < z < 2.63)$$

$$= 0.9957 - 0.9943 = 0.0014$$

b   Find the area between 119.5 and 150.5:

$$P(119.5 < X < 150.5) = P\left(\frac{119.5 - 125}{9.6825} < z < \frac{150.5 - 125}{9.6825}\right) - P(-0.57 < z < 2.63)$$

$$= 0.9957 - 0.2843 = 0.7114$$

c   Find the area to the left of 149.5

$$P(X < 149.5) = P\left(z < \frac{149.5 - 125}{9.6825}\right) = P(z < 2.53) = 0.9943$$

d   The value $x = 232$ lies $z = \dfrac{232 - 125}{9.6825} = 11.05$ above the mean, if Pepsi's market share is indeed 25%.

This is such an unusual occurrence that we would conclude that Pepsi's market share is higher than claimed.

6.53   Refer to Exercise 6.52, and let X be the number of Canadians who feel they will have to cut back on spending. Then X has a binomial distribution with $n = 100$ and $p = 0.37$.

a   The average value of x is $\mu = np = 100(0.37) = 37$.

b   The standard deviation of x is $\sigma = \sqrt{npq} = \sqrt{100(0.37)(0.63)} = 4.828$.

c   The z-score for $x = 50$ is $z = \dfrac{x - \mu}{\sigma} = \dfrac{50 - 37}{4.828} = 2.69$, which lies between two and three standard deviations away from the mean. This is considered a somewhat unusual occurrence.

6.55   To find the area under the standard normal curve between two values, z_1 and z_2, calculate the difference in their cumulative areas, $A = A(z_2) - A(z_1)$.

a $P(-2 < z < 2) = A(2.0) - A(-2) = 0.9772 - 0.0228 = 0.9554$

b $P(-2.3 < z < -1.5) = A(-2.3) - A(-1.5) = 0.0668 - 0.0107 = 0.0561$

6.57   Now we are asked to find the z-value corresponding to a particular area.

a   We need to find a z_0 such that $P(z > z_0) = 0.9750$. This is equivalent to finding an area of $1 - 0.9750 = 0.025$ in the left tail. Search the interior of Table 3, Appendix I, until you find the four-digit number 0.025. The corresponding z-value is -1.96; that is, $A(-1.96) = 0.025$. Therefore, $z_0 = -1.96$.

b   We need to find a z_0 such that $P(z > z_0) = 0.3594$. This is equivalent to finding an area of $1 - 0.3594 = 0.6406$ to the left of z_0. Search the interior of Table 3 until you find the four-digit number 0.6406. The corresponding z-value is 0.36; that is, $A(0.6406) = 0.36$. Therefore, $z_0 = 0.36$.

6.59 Random variable x is normally distributed with $\mu = 5$ and $\sigma = 2$.

    a The z-value corresponding to $x = 1.2$ is $z = \dfrac{x - \mu}{\sigma} = \dfrac{1.2 - 5}{2} = -1.9$ and corresponding to $x = 10$ is

        $z = \dfrac{x - \mu}{\sigma} = \dfrac{10 - 5}{2} = 2.5$. Then $P(1.2 < X < 10) = P(-1.9 < z < 2.5) = 0.9938 - 0.0287 = 0.9651$.

    b The z-value corresponding to $x = 7.5$ is $z = \dfrac{x - \mu}{\sigma} = \dfrac{7.5 - 5}{2} = 1.25$. Then

        $P(X > 7.5) = P(z > 1.25) = 1 - P(z \le 1.25) = 1 - 0.8944 = 0.1056$.

    c The z-value corresponding to $x = 0$ is $z = \dfrac{x - \mu}{\sigma} = \dfrac{0 - 5}{2} = -2.5$. Then

        $P(X \le 0) = P(z \le -2.5) = 0.0062$.

6.61 **a** We need to find area to the left of $z = 1.2$. That is, $A = A(1.2) = 0.8849$.

    b We need to find area to the left of $z = -0.99$. That is, $A = A(-0.99) = 0.1611$.

    c We need to find area to the left of $z = 1.46$. That is, $A = A(1.46) = 0.9279$.

    d We need to find area to the left of $z = -0.42$. That is, $A = A(-0.42) = 3,372$.

6.63 **a** $P(z > -0.75) = 1 - A(-0.75) = 1 - 0.2266 = 0.7734$

    b $P(z < 1.35) = A(1.35) = 0.9115$

6.65 $P(-1.48 < z < 1.48) = 0.9306 - 0.0694 = 0.8612$.

6.67 Let the random variable X be the life span of drill bits. X has a normal distribution with $\mu = 75$ and $\sigma = 12$.

    a $P(X < 60) = P\left(z < \dfrac{60 - 75}{12}\right) = P(z < -1.25) = 0.1056$

    b $P(X \ge 60) = P\left(z < \dfrac{60 - 75}{12}\right) = P(z \ge -1.25) = 1 - 0.1056 = 0.8944$

    c $P(X > 90) = P\left(z < \dfrac{90 - 75}{12}\right) = P(z > 1.25) = 1 - 0.8944 = 0.1056$

6.69 For this exercise, it is given that the population of bolt diameters is normally distributed with $\mu = 0.498$ and $\sigma = 0.002$. The fraction of acceptable bolts will be those that lie in the interval from 0.496 to 0.504. All others are unacceptable. The desired fraction of acceptable bolts is calculated, and the fraction of unacceptable bolts (shaded in the figure on the next page) is obtained by subtracting from the total probability, which is 1.

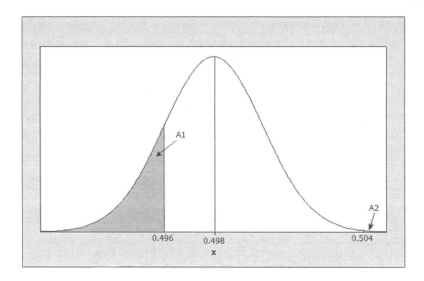

The fraction of acceptable bolts is then

$$P(0.496 \leq X \leq 0.504) = P\left(\frac{0.496 - 0.498}{0.002} \leq z \leq \frac{0.504 - 0.498}{0.002}\right)$$

$$= P(-1 \leq z < 3) = 0.9987 - 0.1587 = 0.8400$$

and the fraction of unacceptable bolts is $1 - 0.84 = 0.16$.

6.71   The random variable X is approximately normally distributed with $\mu = 1230$ and $\sigma = 120$.

a   The z-value corresponding to $x = 1400$ is $z = \dfrac{x - \mu}{\sigma} = \dfrac{1400 - 1230}{120} = 1.42$ and

$$P(X > 1400) = P(z > 1.42) = 1 - 0.9222 = 0.0778.$$

b   The z-value corresponding to $x = 1000$ is $z = \dfrac{x - \mu}{\sigma} = \dfrac{1000 - 1230}{120} = -1.92$ and

$$P(\text{restaurant does not break even}) = P(X < 1000) = P(z < -1.92) = 0.0274.$$

6.73   It is given that x is normally distributed with $\mu = 10$ and $\sigma = 2.7$. The probability of interest is

$$P(X > 15) = P\left(z > \frac{15 - 10}{2.7}\right) = P(z > 1.85) = 1 - 0.9678 = 0.0322$$

6.75   It is given that $\mu = 1.4$ and $\sigma = 0.7$. If we assume that X, the service time for one vehicle, is normally distributed, the probability of interest is

$$P(X > 1.6) = P\left(z > \frac{1.6 - 1.4}{0.7}\right) = P(z > 0.29) = 1 - 0.6141 = 0.3859$$

6.77   **a**   No. The errors in forecasting would tend to be skewed, with more underestimates than overestimates.

b   Let X be the number of estimates that are in error by more than 15%. Then X has a binomial distribution with $n = 100$ and $p = P(\text{estimate is in error by more than } 15\%) = 0.5$. Using the normal approximation to the binomial distribution,

$$P(X > 60) \approx P\left(z > \frac{60.5 - 100(0.5)}{\sqrt{100(0.5)(0.5)}}\right) = P(z > 2.1) = 1 - 0.9821 = 0.0179$$

6.79 The 3000 light bulbs utilized by the manufacturing plant comprise the entire population (that is, this is not a sample from the population) whose length of life is normally distributed with mean $\mu = 500$ and standard deviation $\sigma = 50$. The objective is to find a particular value, x_0, so that

$$P(X \leq x_0) = 0.01$$

That is, only 1% of the bulbs will burn out before they are replaced at time x_0. Then

$$P(X \leq x_0) = P(z \leq z_0) = 0.01 \quad \text{where} \quad z_0 = \frac{x_0 - 500}{50}$$

From Table 3, Appendix I, the value of z corresponding to an area (in the left tail of the distribution) of 0.01 is $z_0 = -2.33$. Solving for x_0 corresponding to $z_0 = -2.33$,

$$-2.33 = \frac{x_0 - 500}{50} \quad \Rightarrow \quad -116.5 = x_0 - 500 \quad \Rightarrow \quad x_0 = 383.5$$

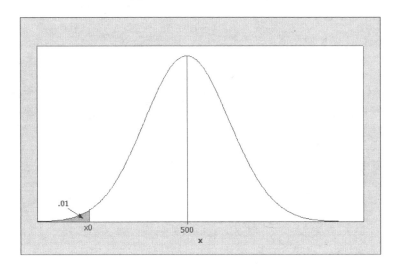

6.81 The random variable of interest is X, the number of persons not showing up for a given flight. This is a binomial random variable with $n = 160$ and $p = P(\text{person does not show up}) = 0.05$. If there is to be a seat available for every person planning to fly, then there must be at least five persons who do not show up. Hence, the probability of interest is $P(X \geq 5)$. Calculate

$$\mu = np = 160(0.05) = 8 \quad \text{and} \quad \sigma = \sqrt{npq} = \sqrt{160(0.05)(0.95)} = \sqrt{7.6} = 2.7$$

Referring to the figure on the next page, a correction for continuity is made to include the entire area under the rectangle associated with the value $x = 5$, and the approximation becomes $P(X \geq 4.5)$. The z-value corresponding to $x = 4.5$ is $z = \frac{x - \mu}{\sigma} = \frac{4.5 - 8}{\sqrt{7.6}} = -1.27$, so that

$$P(X \geq 4.5) = P(z \geq -1.27) = 1 - 0.1020 = 0.8980.$$

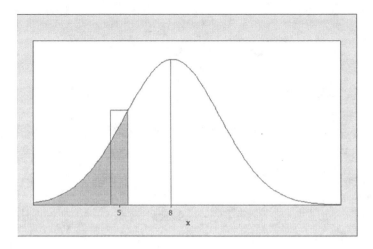

6.83 **a** Let X be the number of plants with red petals. Then X has a binomial distribution with $n = 100$ and $p = 0.75$.

b Since $np = 100(0.75) = 75$ and $nq = 100(0.25)$ are both greater than 5, the normal approximation is appropriate.

c Calculate $\mu = np = 100(0.75) = 75$ and $\sigma = \sqrt{npq} = \sqrt{100(0.75)(0.25)} = \sqrt{18.75} = 4.33$. A correction for continuity is made to include the entire area under the rectangles corresponding to $x = 70$ and $x = 80$. Hence, the approximation will be

$$P(69.5 < X < 80.5) = P\left(\frac{69.5 - 75}{4.33} < z < \frac{80.5 - 75}{4.33}\right) = P(-1.27 < z < 1.27) = 0.8980 - 0.1020 = 0.7960$$

d The probability that 53 or fewer plants have red flower is approximated as

$$P(X < 53.5) = P\left(z < \frac{53.5 - 75}{4.33}\right) = P(z < -4.97) \approx 0$$

This would be considered an unusual event.

e If the value $p = 0.75$ is correct, the only explanation for the unusual occurrence in part **d** is that the $n = 100$ seeds do not represent a random sample from the population of peony plants. Perhaps the sample became contaminated in some way; some other uncontrolled variable is affecting the flower colour.

6.85 For the binomial random variable X, the mean and standard deviation are calculated under the assumption that there is no difference between the effect of TV and reading on calorie intake, and hence that $p = 0.5$. Then

$$\mu = np = 30(0.5) = 15 \quad \text{and} \quad \sigma = \sqrt{npq} = \sqrt{30(0.5)(0.5)} = 2.7386$$

If there is no difference between TV and reading, the z-score for the observed value of x, $x = 19$, is

$$z = \frac{x - \mu}{\sigma} = \frac{19 - 15}{2.7386} = 1.461$$

That is, the observed value lies 1.461 standard deviations above the mean. This is not an unlikely occurrence. Hence, we would have no reason to believe that there is a difference between calorie intake for TV watchers versus readers.

6.87 The random variable Y, the percentage of tax returns audited, has a normal distribution with $\mu = 1.55$ and $\sigma = 0.45$.

    a $P(Y > 2) = P\left(z > \dfrac{2 - 1.55}{0.45}\right) = P(z > 1) = 1 - 0.8413 = 0.1587$

    b   Define X to be the number of provinces in which more than 2% of its returns were audited. Then X has a binomial distribution with

$$\mu = np = 50(0.1587) = 7.935 \quad \text{and} \quad \sigma = \sqrt{npq} = \sqrt{50(0.1587)(0.8413)} = 2.583$$

       The expected value of X is $E(X) = \mu = 7.935$.

    c $P(X \geq 15) = P\left(z > \dfrac{14.5 - 7.935}{2.583}\right) = P(z > 2.54) = 1 - 0.9945 = 0.0055$ is quite small; hence, we

       conclude that "as many as 15 of the 50 provinces will have more than 2% of their income tax returns audited" as quite unlikely.

6.89 The scores are approximately normal with mean $\mu = 75$ and standard deviation $\sigma = 12$. We need to find a value of x, say $x = c$, such that $P(X > c) = 0.15$. The z-value corresponding to $x = c$ is

$$z = \frac{x - \mu}{\sigma} = \frac{c - 75}{12}$$

From Table 3, the z-value corresponding to an area of 0.15 in the right tail of the normal distribution is a value that has area 0.8500 to its left. The closest value given in the table is $z = 1.04$. Then

$$\frac{c - 75}{12} = 1.04 \Rightarrow c = 75 + 1.04(12) = 87.48$$

The proper score to designate "extroverts" would be any score higher than 87.48.

6.91 It is given that X, the percent of retail price at which the collection sells, is normally distributed with $\mu = 45$ and $\sigma = 4.5$.

    a   If the collection is worth \$30,000 and is selling for more than \$15,000, then x is more than

       50 (percent). Calculate $z = \dfrac{x - \mu}{\sigma} = \dfrac{50 - 45}{4.5} = 1.11$

       Then $P(X > 50) = P(z > 1.11) = 1 - 0.8665 = 0.1335$.

    b $P(X < 50) = P(z < 1.11) = 0.8665$ from part **a**.

    c   The value \$12,000 is 40 percent of the collection's worth. Calculate $z = \dfrac{x - \mu}{\sigma} = \dfrac{40 - 45}{4.5} = -1.11$

       Then $P(X < 40) = P(z < -1.11) = 0.1335$.

6.93 Define X to be the salaries of assistant professors. It is given that X is normally distributed with $\mu = 74,000$ and $\sigma = 6000$.

    a $P(X < 65,000) = P\left(z < \dfrac{65,000 - 74,000}{6000}\right) = P(z < -1.50) = 0.0668$

    b $P(65,000 < X < 70,000) = P\left(\dfrac{65,000 - 74,000}{6000} < z < \dfrac{70,000 - 74,000}{6000}\right)$

$$= P(-1.50 < z < -0.67) = 0.2514 - 0.0668 = 0.1846$$

Case Study: "Are You Going to Curve the Grades?"

In order to implement the traditional interpretation of "curving the grades," the proportions shown in the table need to be applied to the normal curve, as shown in the figure below.

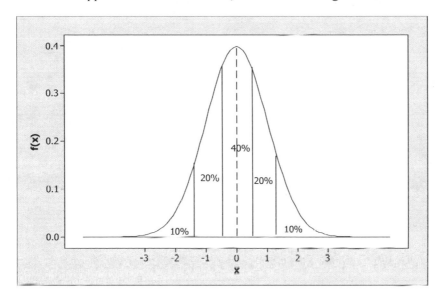

1   The C grades constitute the middle 40%; that is, 20% on either side of the mean. The lower boundary has an area of 0.3 to its left. From Table 3, Appendix I, we need to find a value of z such that $A(z) = 0.3$. The closest value in the table is 0.3015 with $z = -0.52$. The upper boundary is then $z = 0.52$.

2   The cut-off for the lowest D and highest B grades constitute the lower and upper boundaries of the middle 80%; that is, 40% on either side of the mean. The lower boundary has an area of 0.1 to its left, so we need to find a value of z such that $A(z) = 0.1$. The closet value in the Table 3 is 0.1003 with $z = -1.28$. The upper boundary is then $z = 1.28$.

3   If the grades of this larger class have a mean of 79.972 and a standard deviation of 12.271, the appropriate cut-offs are ±0.5 standard deviations and ±1.5 standard deviations from the mean. Calculate

$$79.972 + 0.5(12.271) \Rightarrow 79.972 \pm 6.1355 \Rightarrow 73.8365 \text{ and } 86.1075$$
$$79.972 \pm 1.5(12.271) \Rightarrow 79.972 \pm 18.4065 \Rightarrow 61.5655 \text{ and } 98.3785$$

The cut-off points are shown in the table below.

Letter Grade	A	B	C	D	F
Score	98.38 and above	86.11 to 98.38	73.84 to 86.11	61.57 to 73.84	Below 61.57

4   In the "curving" scheme, the student with a score of 92 would receive a B rather than an A on an absolute standard scale. This student would definitely not benefit by "curving the grades." Curving grades will only serve its designed purpose when the data is approximately mound-shaped, in order to achieve the desired percentages. Since this data is clearly skewed to the left, the "curving" procedure does not have the desired effect for most students. Only a few students (those who score between 70–73 and those who score 60–61) will benefit when the grades are "curved."

Project 6-A: The Spectrum of Prematurity

a **i** The probability of having a birth with mild prematurity is $P(33 \leq X < 37)$, since mild prematurity extends to 36 *completed weeks*. Now,

$$P(33 \leq X < 37) = P\left(\frac{33-40}{2} < z < \frac{37-40}{2}\right) = P(-3.5 < z < -1.5) = P(z < -1.5) - P(z < -3.5)$$

$$= 0.0668 - 0.0002 = 0.0666$$

ii The probability of having a birth with extreme prematurity is

$$P(X < 28) = P\left(z < \frac{28-40}{2}\right) = P(z < -6) \approx 0$$

iii For the lower quartile, $z = -0.675$, and for the upper quartile, $z = 0.675$. Since $z = \frac{x-\mu}{\sigma}$, $x = \mu + z\sigma$.

Thus, the lower quartile is $z = 40 + (-0.675)(2) = 38.65$ and the upper quartile is $z = 40 + 0.675(2) = 41.35$.

iv Yes, this would be very unusual. After only 24 weeks of gestation before birth, we would consider this to be *extreme prematurity*, which, as shown in part **ii** above, is extremely unlikely.

v For the 20th percentile, $z = -0.84$. Since $z = \frac{x-\mu}{\sigma}$, $x = \mu + z\sigma$. Thus, $x = 40 + (-0.84)(2) = 38.32$.

vi 83.4% corresponds to $z = 0.97$. Since $z = \frac{x-\mu}{\sigma}$, $x = \mu + z\sigma$. Thus, 83.4% of the gestational time occurs before $x = 40 + 0.97(2) = 41.94$.

b **i** The probability of having a birth with moderate prematurity is $P(999.5 \text{ g} \leq X < 1500 \text{ g})$. Note that it is ambiguous from the question whether or not 1500 g exactly is mild or moderate prematurity. For this problem, $\mu = 3400$ g and $\sigma = 800$ g. Notice that it is necessary to use the same units (grams or kilograms) consistently. Therefore,

$$P(999.5 \text{ g} \leq X < 1500 \text{ g}) = P\left(\frac{999.5-3400}{800} < z < \frac{1500-3400}{800}\right) = P(-3 < z < -2.375)$$

$$= P(z < -2.375) - P(z < -3) = 0.0088 - 0.0013 = 0.0075$$

ii The probability of having birth with extreme prematurity is

$$P(X < 1000) = P\left(z < \frac{999.5-3400}{800}\right) = P(z < -3) = 0.0013$$

iii The probability of having a baby weighing at least 6 kg (6000 g) is

$$P(X > 5999.5) = P\left(z > \frac{5999.5-3400}{800}\right) = P(z > 3.249) = 0.0006$$

Since this probability is so low, having a baby weighing this much is highly unlikely.

iv To be in the top 5% corresponds to the 95th percentile, where $z = 1.645$. Since $z = \frac{x-\mu}{\sigma}$, $x = \mu + z\sigma$.

Thus, the value of x we need is $x = 3.4 \text{ kg} + 1.645(0.8 \text{ kg}) = 4.716 \text{ kg}$.

v 87.70% above is the same as 12.3% below, corresponding to $z = -1.16$. Since $x = \mu + z\sigma$, $x = 3.4 - 1.16(.8) = 2.472$ kg. Thus, 87.70% of the birth weights will be above 2.472 kg.

vi The information will result in two equations with two unknowns. The probability that x exceeds 4 kg with probability 0.975 implies that $z = -1.96$ at $x = 4$. The probability that x exceeds 5 kg with probability 0.95 implies that $z = -1.645$ at $x = 5$. Since $x = \mu + z\sigma$, we get two equations: $4 = \mu - 1.96\sigma$, $5 = \mu - 1.645\sigma$. Subtracting the first equation from the second yields: $1 = 0.315\sigma$, or $\sigma = 3.1746$ kg. Then, $\mu = 10.2222$ kg. Such a high average weight on this planet is not comparable to the average weight of humans. Their babies are almost three times as heavy, on average.

Project 6-B: Premature Babies in Canada

a The normal approximation to the binomial would not be appropriate in this instance. The rule of thumb illustrated in the text states that the normal approximation will be adequate if both np and nq are greater than 5. In our case, $np = 25(0.086) = 2.15$, which is clearly less than 5.

b Since Alberta has an SGA rate of 8.7%, we would expect $0.087(200) = 17.4$ SGA births in a random sample of 200.

c The SGA rate for Ontario is 8.9%. Since $np = 200(0.089) = 17.8 > 5$, and $nq = 200(0.911) > 5$, we may use the normal approximation to the binomial, with $\mu = np = 17.8$ and

$\sigma = \sqrt{npq} = \sqrt{200(0.089)(0.911)} = 4.026885$. And so,

$$P(X \geq 60) \approx P(X > 59.5) = P\left(z > \frac{x-\mu}{\sigma}\right) = P\left(z > \frac{59.5-17.8}{4.026885}\right) = P(z > 10.355) \approx 0$$

d The SGA rate for Canada was 8.3%. Since $np = 500(0.083) = 41.5 > 5$, and $nq = 500(0.917) > 5$, we may use the normal approximation to the binomial, with $\mu = np = 41.5$ and

$\sigma = \sqrt{npq} = \sqrt{500(0.083)(0.917)} = 6.168914$. Thus, the probability that at most 50 of these 500 will be declared SGA is

$$P(X \leq 50) \approx P(X < 50.5) = \left(z < \frac{50.5-41.5}{6.168914}\right) = P(z < 1.459) \approx 0.9279$$

Furthermore, the probability that more than 10% of the births will be SGA is equivalent to more than $500(10\%) = 50$ births being SGA. But this is just the complement of the probability of having at most 50 SGA births. Thus, the probability that more than 10% of the births will be SGA is simply $1 - 0.9279 = 0.0721$.

e The probability that at least 1 birth out of 25 is SGA is $1-P$(none are SGA). The exact binomial probability that none are SGA is $p(0) = C_0^{25}(0.083)^0(0.917)^{25} = 0.114613$. Thus, the exact probability that at least 1 birth is SGA is $1 - 0.114613 = 0.885387$. For the approximate probability, we note that $\mu = np = 25(0.083) = 2.075$. Thus, we don't expect our approximation to be that good. Proceeding, we also note that $\sigma = \sqrt{npq} = \sqrt{25(0.083)(0.917)} = 1.379411$. Thus, the approximate probability that at least 1 of

these 25 will be SGA is $P(X > 0.5) = \left(z > \frac{0.5-2.075}{1.379411}\right) = P(z > -1.142) \approx 0.8729$. The approximate probability is not as bad as anticipated, with a discrepancy of only $0.8854-0.8729 = 0.0125$ or 1.25%.

Chapter 7: Sampling Distributions

7.1   You can select a simple random sample of size $n = 20$ using Table 10 in Appendix I. First, choose a starting point and consider the first three digits in each number. Since the experimental units have already been numbered from 000 to 999, the first 20 can be used. The three digits OR the (three digits – 500) will identify the proper experimental unit. For example, if the three digits are 742, you should select the experimental unit numbered $742 - 500 = 242$. The probability that any three-digit number is selected is $2/1000 = 1/500$. One possible selection for the sample size $n = 20$ is

242	134	173	128	399
056	412	188	255	388
469	244	332	439	101
399	156	028	238	231

7.3   Each student will obtain a different sample, using Table 10 in Appendix I.

7.5   If all of the town citizenry is likely to pass this corner, a sample obtained by selecting every tenth person is probably a fairly random sample.

7.7   The migration within such a long period of four years may be the most critical issue hindering the coverage of the entire population effectively. People with no permanent address and those sharing with someone else may not have a formal record with MPAC. This will result in inadequate coverage of the eligible population.

7.9   Use a randomization scheme similar to that used in Exercise 7.1. Number each of the 100 individuals from 00 to 99. To choose the 50 individuals who will receive the experimental treatment, select 50 two-digit random numbers from Table 10, Appendix I. Each two-digit number will identify the proper experimental unit. The other 50 individuals will be placed in the control group.

7.11 **a**   Since the question is particularly sensitive to people of different ethnic origins, the answers may not always be truthful, depending on the ethnicity of the interviewer and the person being interviewed.

      b   Notice that the percentage in favour of affirmative action increases as the ethnic origin of the interviewer changes from Caucasian to Asian to African-American. The people being interviewed may be changing their response to match what they perceive to be the response that the interviewer wants to hear.

7.13 **a**   Since each subject must be randomly assigned to enter a tai chi or a wellness education class with equal probability, assign the digits 0–4 to the tai chi treatment, and the digits 5–9 to the wellness treatment. As each subject enters the study, choose a random digit using Table 10, Appendix I, and assign the appropriate treatment.

      b   The randomization scheme in part **a** does not generate an equal number of subjects in each group.

7.15 **a**   The first question is more unbiased.

      b   Notice that the percentage for the health care category drops dramatically when the phrase "that is, one about which you are most concerned" is added to the question.

7.17   Regardless of the shape of the population from which we are sampling, the sampling distribution of the sample mean will have a mean μ equal to the mean of the population from which we are sampling, and a standard deviation equal to $\sigma/\sqrt{n}$.

    a $\mu = 10$; $\sigma/\sqrt{n} = 3/\sqrt{36} = 0.5$

    b $\mu = 5$; $\sigma/\sqrt{n} = 2/\sqrt{100} = 0.2$

    c $\mu = 120$; $\sigma/\sqrt{n} = 1/\sqrt{8} = 0.3536$

7.19 **a** The sketch of the normal distribution with mean $\mu = 5$ and standard deviation $\sigma/\sqrt{n} = 0.2$ is left to the students. The interval 5 ± 0.4 or 4.6 to 5.4 should be located on the $\bar{x}$ axis.

      b The probability of interest $P\left(-0.15 < (\bar{x} - \mu) < 0.15\right)$ and is shown below.

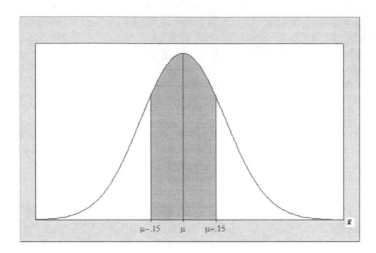

      c $P\left(-0.15 < (\bar{x} - \mu) < 0.15\right) = P\left(\dfrac{-0.15}{0.2} < \dfrac{(\bar{x} - \mu)}{\sigma/\sqrt{n}} < \dfrac{0.15}{0.2}\right)$

$$= P(-0.75 < z < 0.75)$$
$$= 0.7734 - 0.2266$$
$$= 0.5468$$

7.21 **a** For the data given in the text, the mean and standard deviation are calculated as

$$\bar{x} = \frac{\sum x_i}{n} = \frac{224.3}{50} = 4.486$$

and the standard deviation of the sample is

$$s = \sqrt{s^2} = \sqrt{\frac{\sum x_i^2 - \dfrac{\left(\sum x_i\right)^2}{n}}{n-1}} = \sqrt{\frac{1025.23 - \dfrac{(224.3)^2}{50}}{49}} = \sqrt{\frac{0.244}{9}} = 0.623.$$

      b The values calculated in part a are close to the theoretical values of the mean and standard deviation for the sampling distribution of $\bar{x}$, given in the text as

$$\mu_{\bar{x}} = \mu = 4.4 \quad \text{and} \quad \sigma_{\bar{x}} = \frac{\sigma}{\sqrt{n}} = \frac{2.15}{\sqrt{10}} = 0.680.$$

7.23 For a population with $\sigma = 1$, the standard error of the mean is $\sigma/\sqrt{n} = 1/\sqrt{n}$.

The values of $\sigma/\sqrt{n}$ for various values of n are tabulated below and plotted on the next page. Notice that the standard error *decreases* as the sample size *increases*.

n	1	2	4	9	16	25	100
$SE(\bar{x}) = \sigma/\sqrt{n}$	1.00	0.707	0.500	0.333	0.250	0.200	0.100

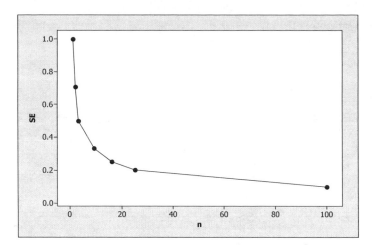

7.25 For a population with $\sigma = 5$, the standard error of the mean is $\sigma/\sqrt{n} = 5/\sqrt{n}$.

The values of $\sigma/\sqrt{n}$ for various values of n are tabulated and plotted below. Notice that the standard error *decreases* as the sample size *increases*.

n	1	2	4	9	16	25	100
$SE(\bar{x}) = \sigma/\sqrt{n}$	5.000	3.536	2.500	1.667	1.250	1.000	0.500

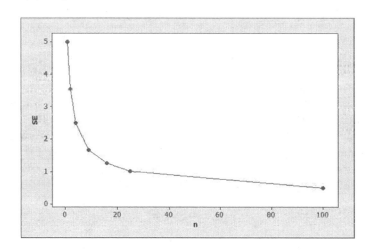

7.27 Calculate $z = \dfrac{\bar{x} - \mu}{\sigma/\sqrt{n}} = \dfrac{55 - 53}{21/\sqrt{49}} = 0.67$, so that $P(\bar{x} > 55) = P(z > 0.67) = 1 - 0.7486 = 0.2514$.

7.29 When $\bar{x} = 105$, $z = \dfrac{\bar{x} - \mu}{\sigma/\sqrt{n}} = \dfrac{105 - 100}{20/\sqrt{40}} = 1.58$. Similarly, when $\bar{x} = 110$, $z = \dfrac{\bar{x} - \mu}{\sigma/\sqrt{n}} = \dfrac{110 - 100}{20/\sqrt{40}} = 3.16$.

Thus, $P(105 < \bar{x} < 110) = P(1.58 < z < 3.16) = 0.9992 - 0.9429 = 0.0563$.

7.31 **a** Age of equipment, technician error, technician fatigue, equipment failure, difference in chemical purity, contamination from outside sources, and so on.

      b The variability in the average measurement is measured by the standard error, $\sigma/\sqrt{n}$. In order to decrease this variability you should increase the sample size n.

7.33   The number of bacteria in one cubic metre of water can be thought of as the sum of 1,000,000 random variables, each of which is the number of bacteria in a particular cubic centimetre of water. Hence, the Central Limit Theorem insures the approximate normality of the sum.

7.35   **a**   The population from which we are randomly sampling $n = 35$ measurements is not necessarily normally distributed. However, the sampling distribution of $\bar{x}$ does have an approximate normal distribution, with mean μ and standard deviation $\sigma/\sqrt{n}$. The probability of interest is

$$P\left(|\bar{x} - \mu| < 1\right) = P\left(-1 < (\bar{x} - \mu) < 1\right)$$

Since $z = \dfrac{\bar{x} - \mu}{\sigma/\sqrt{n}}$ has a standard normal distribution, we need only find $\sigma/\sqrt{n}$ to approximate the above probability.

Though σ is unknown, it can be approximated by $s = 12$ and $\sigma/\sqrt{n} \approx 12/\sqrt{35} = 2.028$. Then

$$P\left(|\bar{x} - \mu| < 1\right) = P\left(-1/2.028 < z < 1/2.028\right)$$
$$= P\left(-0.49 < z < 0.49\right) = 0.6879 - 0.3121 = 0.3758$$

   b   No. There are many possible values for x, the actual percent tax savings, as given by the probability distribution for x.

7.37   **a**   The random variable $T = \sum x_i$, where x_i is normally distributed with mean $\mu = 630$ and standard deviation $\sigma = 40$ for $i = 1, 2, 3$. The Central Limit Theorem states that T is normally distributed with mean $n\mu = 3(630) = 1890$ and standard deviation $\sigma\sqrt{n} = 40\sqrt{3} = 69.282$.

   b   Calculate $z = \dfrac{T - 1890}{69.282} = \dfrac{2000 - 1890}{69.282} = 1.59$.

Then $P(T > 2000) = P(z > 1.59) = 1 - 0.9441 = 0.0559$.

7.39   **a**   Since the original population is normally distributed, the sample mean $\bar{x}$ is also normally distributed (for any sample size) with mean $\mu = 37$ and standard deviation $\sigma/\sqrt{n} = 0.2/\sqrt{130} = 0.0175$.

The z-value corresponding to $\bar{x} = 36.81$ is $z = \dfrac{\bar{x} - \mu}{\sigma/\sqrt{n}} = \dfrac{36.81 - 37}{0.0175} = -10.86$ and

$$P(\bar{x} < 36.81) = P(z < -10.86) \approx 0$$

   b   Since the probability is extremely small, the average temperature of 36.81°C is very unlikely.

7.41   **a** $p = 0.3$; $SE(\hat{p}) = \sqrt{\dfrac{pq}{n}} = \sqrt{\dfrac{0.3(0.7)}{100}} = 0.0458$

   b $p = 0.1$; $SE(\hat{p}) = \sqrt{\dfrac{pq}{n}} = \sqrt{\dfrac{0.1(0.9)}{400}} = 0.015$

   c $p = 0.6$; $SE(\hat{p}) = \sqrt{\dfrac{pq}{n}} = \sqrt{\dfrac{0.6(0.4)}{250}} = 0.0310$

7.43   **a**   The sampling distribution will be approximately normal with mean $p = 0.3$ and $SE = 0.0458$. The interval that lies within 0.08 of the population proportion is $(0.3 - 0.08, 0.3 + 0.08)$ or $(0.22, 0.38)$.

   b   The probability of interest is $P\left(|\hat{p} - p| \le 0.08\right) = P\left(-0.08 \le (\hat{p} - p) \le 0.08\right)$

Since $\hat{p}$ is approximately normal, with standard deviation $SE(\hat{p}) = 0.0458$ from Exercise 7.41,

$$P\left(-0.08 \le (\hat{p} - p) \le 0.08\right) = P\left[\dfrac{-0.08}{0.0458} \le z \le \dfrac{0.08}{0.0458}\right]$$
$$= P\left(-1.75 \le z \le 1.75\right) = 0.9599 - 0.0401 = 0.9198$$

7.45 **a** $P(\hat{p} \leq 0.43) = P\left(z \leq \dfrac{0.43 - 0.4}{\sqrt{0.4(0.6)/75}}\right) = P(z \leq 0.53) = 0.7019$

   b $P(0.35 < \hat{p} < 0.43) = P\left(\dfrac{0.35 - 0.4}{\sqrt{0.4(0.6)/75}} < z < \dfrac{0.43 - 0.4}{\sqrt{0.4(0.6)/75}}\right) \Rightarrow$

   $P(0.35 < \hat{p} < 0.43) = P(-0.88 < z < 0.53) = 0.7019 - 0.1894 = 0.5125$

7.47 The values $SE = \sqrt{pq/n}$ for $n = 100$ and various values of p are tabulated and graphed below. Notice that SE is maximum for $p = 0.5$ and becomes very small for p near 0 and 1.

p	0.01	0.10	0.30	0.50	0.70	0.90	0.99
$SE(\hat{p})$	0.0099	0.03	0.0458	0.05	0.0458	0.03	0.0099

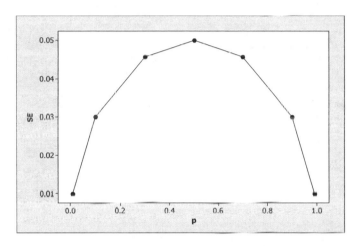

7.49 **a** For $n = 80$ and $p - 0.25$, $np = 20$ and $nq = 60$ are both greater than 5. Therefore, the normal approximation and sampling distribution of $\hat{p}$ will be appropriately normal.

   b The mean of the sampling distribution of $\hat{p}$ is $p = 0.25$ and $SE = \sqrt{\dfrac{pq}{n}} = \sqrt{\dfrac{0.25(0.75)}{80}} = 0.04841$.

   c $P(0.18 < \hat{p} < 0.44) = P\left(\dfrac{0.18 - 0.25}{0.0481} < z < \dfrac{0.44 - 0.25}{0.0481}\right) \Rightarrow$

   $P(0.18 < \hat{p} < 0.44) = P(-1.45 < z < 3.92) \approx 1 - 0.0735 = 0.9265$

7.51 **a** The random variable $\hat{p}$, the sample proportion of adults who would like either a DVD player or GPS system for their next road trip, has binomial distribution with $n = 1000$ and $p = 0.56$. Since $np = 560$ and $nq = 440$ are both greater than 5, we can use normal distribution to approximate this binomial distribution with mean $np = 460$ and $SE = \sqrt{\dfrac{pq}{n}} = \sqrt{\dfrac{0.56(0.44)}{1000}} = 0.0157$.

   b $P(\hat{p} > 0.6) = P\left(z > \dfrac{0.6 - 0.56}{0.0157}\right) = P(z > 2.55) = 1 - 0.9946 = 0.0054$

   c $P(0.5 < \hat{p} < 0.6) = P\left(\dfrac{0.5 - 0.56}{0.0157} < z < \dfrac{0.6 - 0.56}{0.0157}\right) = P(-3.82 < z < 2.55) \approx 0.9946 - 0 = 0.9946$

d   The value $\hat{p} = 0.7$ lies $z = \dfrac{\hat{p} - p}{\sqrt{\dfrac{pq}{n}}} = \dfrac{0.7 - 0.56}{0.0157} = 8.92$ standard deviations above the mean. This is an

unlikely occurrence, assuming that $p = 0.56$. Perhaps, the sampling was not random, or the 56% is not correct.

7.53   **a**   The random variable $\hat{p}$, the sample proportion of students who used the Internet as a major resource in the past year, has a binomial distribution with $n = 1000$ and $p = 0.66$. Since $np = 660$ and $nq = 340$ are both greater than 5, this binomial distribution can be approximated by a normal

distribution with mean $p = 0.66$ and $SE = \sqrt{\dfrac{0.66(0.34)}{1000}} = 0.0150$.

      b $P(\hat{p} > 0.68) = P\left(z > \dfrac{0.68 - 0.66}{0.0150}\right) = P(z > 1.33) = 1 - 0.9082 = 0.0918$

      c $P(0.64 < \hat{p} < 0.68) = P(-1.33 < z < 1.33) = 0.9082 - 0.0918 = 0.8164$

      d   The value $\hat{p} = 0.70$ lies $z = \dfrac{\hat{p} - p}{\sqrt{\dfrac{pq}{n}}} = \dfrac{0.70 - 0.66}{0.0150} = -2.67$ standard deviations from the mean. This is a

somewhat unlikely occurrence, assuming that $p = 0.66$, and would tend to contradict the reported figure.

7.55   The random variable $\hat{p}$, the sample proportion of overweight children in a random sample of $n = 100$, has a binomial distribution with $n = 100$ and $p = 0.25$. Since $np = 25$ and $nq = 75$ are both greater than 5, this binomial distribution can be approximated by a normal distribution with mean $p = 0.25$ and

$SE = \sqrt{\dfrac{0.25(0.75)}{100}} = 0.0433$

      a $P(\hat{p} > 0.25) = P\left(z > \dfrac{0.25 - 0.25}{0.0433}\right) = P(z > 0) = 0.5$

      b $P(\hat{p} < 0.12) = P\left(z < \dfrac{0.12 - 0.25}{0.0433}\right) = P(z < -3.00) \approx 0.0013$

      c $P(\hat{p} > 0.30) = P\left(z > \dfrac{0.30 - 0.25}{0.0433}\right) = P(z > 1.15) \approx 1 - .8749 = 0.1251$. Since the z-score is less than

2, it is not unlikely to find 30% of the children to be overweight.

7.57   **a**   The upper and lower control limits are

$$UCL = \bar{\bar{x}} + 3\dfrac{s}{\sqrt{n}} = 20.74 + 3\dfrac{0.87}{\sqrt{10}} = 20.74 + 0.83 = 21.57$$

$$LCL = \bar{\bar{x}} - 3\dfrac{s}{\sqrt{n}} = 20.74 - 3\dfrac{0.87}{\sqrt{10}} = 20.74 - 0.83 = 19.91$$

      b   Control charts are used to monitor the process variable, detecting shifts that might indicate control problems.

      c   The control chart is constructed by plotting two horizontal lines: one, the upper control limit; and the other, the lower control limit. Values of $\bar{x}$ are plotted, and should remain within the control limits. If not, the process should be checked.

7.59   The $\bar{x}$ chart is used to monitor the average value of a sample of quantitative data, while the p chart is used to monitor qualitative data by counting the number of defective items and tracking the percentage defective.

7.61   **a**   The upper and lower control limits for a p chart are

$$UCL = \overline{p} + 3\sqrt{\frac{\overline{p}(1-\overline{p})}{n}} = 0.041 + 3\sqrt{\frac{0.041(0.959)}{200}} = 0.041 + 0.042 = 0.083$$

$$LCL = \overline{p} - 3\sqrt{\frac{\overline{p}(1-\overline{p})}{n}} = 0.041 - 3\sqrt{\frac{0.041(0.959)}{200}} = 0.041 - 0.042 = -0.001$$

or LCL = 0 (since p cannot be negative).

       b   The control chart is constructed by plotting two horizontal lines: one, the upper control limit; and the other, the lower control limit. Values of $\hat{p}$ are plotted, and should remain within the control limits. If not, the process should be checked.

7.63   The upper and lower control limits for a p chart are

$$UCL = \overline{p} + 3\sqrt{\frac{\overline{p}(1-\overline{p})}{n}} = 0.021 + 3\sqrt{\frac{0.021(0.979)}{400}} = 0.021 + 0.022 = 0.043$$

$$LCL = \overline{p} - 3\sqrt{\frac{\overline{p}(1-\overline{p})}{n}} = 0.021 - 3\sqrt{\frac{0.021(0.979)}{400}} = 0.021 - 0.022 = -0.001$$

or LCL = 0 (since p cannot be negative). The manager can use the control chart to detect changes in the production process which might produce an unusually large number of defectives.

7.65   The upper and lower control limits are

$$UCL = \overline{\overline{x}} + 3\frac{s}{\sqrt{n}} = 7.24 + 3\frac{.07}{\sqrt{3}} = 7.24 + .12 = 7.36$$

$$LCL = \overline{\overline{x}} - 3\frac{s}{\sqrt{n}} = 7.24 - 3\frac{.07}{\sqrt{3}} = 7.24 - .12 = 7.12$$

7.67   The upper and lower control limits are

$$UCL = \overline{\overline{x}} + 3\frac{s}{\sqrt{n}} = 900 + 3\frac{6}{\sqrt{5}} = 900 + 8.05 = 908.05$$

$$LCL = \overline{\overline{x}} - 3\frac{s}{\sqrt{n}} = 900 - 3\frac{6}{\sqrt{5}} = 900 - 8.05 = 891.95$$

The control chart is constructed by plotting two horizontal lines: one, the upper control limit; and the other, the lower control limit. Values of $\overline{x}$ are plotted, and should remain within the control limits. If not, the process should be checked.

7.69   **a** $C_2^4 = \dfrac{4!}{2!2!} = 6$ samples are possible.

       b–c   The six samples along with the sample means for each are shown below.

Sample	Observations	$\overline{x}$
1	6, 1	3.5
2	6, 3	4.5
3	6, 2	4.0
4	1, 3	2.0
5	1, 2	1.5
6	3, 2	2.5

d Since each of the six distinct values of $\bar{x}$ are equally likely (due to random sampling), the sampling distribution of $\bar{x}$ is given as $p(\bar{x}) = \dfrac{1}{6}$ for $\bar{x} = 1.5, 2, 2.5, 3.5, 4, 4.5$. The graph of the sampling distribution is shown below.

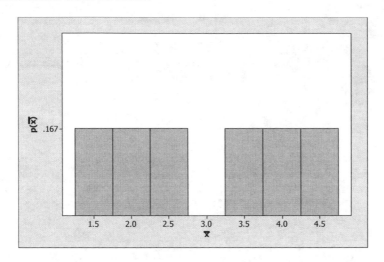

e The population mean is $\mu = (6 + 1 + 3 + 2)/4 = 3$. Notice that none of the samples of size $n = 2$ produce a value of $\bar{x}$ exactly equal to the population mean.

7.71 **a** The sampling distribution of $\bar{x}$ will (regardless of the original sampled distribution) will have a mean $\mu = 1$ and standard deviation (or *standard error*) $\sigma/\sqrt{n} = 0.36/\sqrt{5} = 0.161$.

b Calculate $z = \dfrac{\bar{x} - \mu}{\sigma/\sqrt{n}} = \dfrac{1.3 - 1}{0.36/\sqrt{5}} = 1.86$, so that $P(\bar{x} > 1.3) = P(z > 1.86) = 1 - 0.9686 = 0.0314$.

c $P(\bar{x} < 0.5) = P\left(z < \dfrac{0.5 - 1}{0.161}\right) = P(z < -3.11) = 0.0009$

d $P(|\bar{x} - \mu| > 0.4) = P\left(|z| > \dfrac{0.4}{0.161}\right) = P(|z| > 2.48) = P(z > 2.48) + P(z < -2.48) = 0.0132$

7.73 **a** The distribution of lead content readings for individual water specimens is probably skewed to the right, with a few specimens containing a very large amount of lead. This conclusion is confirmed by looking at the mean and standard deviation, 0.033 and 0.10, respectively. The large standard deviation does not allow the measurements to spread over the range $\mu \pm 2\sigma$ without ranging into negative levels (which are impossible).

b Since the sample of 23 daily lead levels is drawn from a population of means based on $n = 40$ observations, the sample is being drawn from an approximately normal population, according to the Central Limit Theorem.

c For the sample means in part **b**, the sampling distribution has mean $\mu = 0.033$ and standard deviation $\sigma/\sqrt{n} = 0.10/\sqrt{40} = 0.0158$.

7.75 It is given that $n = 3$, $\mu = 410$, and $\sigma = 45$. Then

$$P(\text{sample mean satisfies ANSI}) = P(\bar{x} < 386)$$

$$= P\left(\dfrac{\bar{x} - \mu}{\sigma/\sqrt{n}} < \dfrac{386 - 410}{45/\sqrt{3}}\right) = P(z < -0.92)$$

$$= 0.1788$$

7.77 **a** Since the data already existed before the researcher decided to study it, this is an observational study.
  b Since the subject of the study is a sensitive one, there will be problems of non-response and/or inaccurate responses to the questions.

7.79 **a** This is an observational study, since the data existed before the researcher decided to observe or describe it.
  b The researcher should be concerned about non-response and untruthful responses, due to the sensitive nature of the question.

7.81 **a** For this binomial random variable with $n = 500$ and $p = 0.85$, the mean and standard deviation of $\hat{p}$ are

$$p = 0.85 \text{ and } SE = \sqrt{\frac{0.85(0.15)}{500}} = 0.01597$$

  b Since $np = 500(0.85) = 425$ and $nq = 75$ are both greater than 5, the normal approximation is appropriate.

  c $P(\hat{p} > 0.82) = P\left(z > \frac{0.82 - 0.85}{0.01597}\right) = P(z > -1.88) = 1 - 0.0301 = 0.9699$

  d $P(0.83 < \hat{p} < 0.88) = P\left(\frac{0.83 - 0.85}{0.01597} < z < \frac{0.88 - 0.85}{0.01597}\right)$
$$= P(-1.25 < z < 1.88) = 0.9699 - 0.1056 = 0.8643$$

  e For a normal (or approximately normal) random variable, the interval $\mu \pm 2.58\sigma$ will contain 99% of the measurements. For this binomial random variable $\hat{p}$, this interval is
  $$p \pm 2.58 \quad SE \Rightarrow 0.85 \pm 2.58(0.01597)$$
  $$0.85 \pm 0.04 \quad \text{or} \quad 0.81 \text{ to } 0.89$$

7.83 Define x_i to be the weight of a particular man or woman using the elevator. It is given that x_i is approximately normally distributed with $\mu = 65$ and $\sigma = 16$. Then, according to the Central Limit Theorem, the sum or total weight, Σx_i, will be normally distributed with mean $n\mu = 65n$ and standard deviation $\sqrt{n}\sigma = 16\sqrt{n}$. It is necessary to find a value of n such that
$$P(\Sigma x_i > 900) = 0.01$$

The z-value corresponding to $\Sigma x_i = 900$ is
$$z = \frac{\Sigma x_i - n\mu}{\sigma\sqrt{n}} = \frac{900 - 65n}{16\sqrt{n}}$$

so that we need
$$P\left(z > \frac{900 - 65n}{16\sqrt{n}}\right) = 0.01$$

From Table 3, we conclude that $\frac{900 - 65n}{16\sqrt{n}} = 2.33$. Manipulating the above equation, we obtain a quadratic equation in n.
$$(900 - 65n) = 37.28\sqrt{n}$$
$$810,000 - 118,389.7984n + 4,225n^2 = 0$$

Using the quadratic formula, the necessary value of n is found.
$$n = \frac{-b \pm \sqrt{b^2 - 4ac}}{2a} = \frac{118,389.7984 \pm 18087.13259}{8,450}$$

Choosing the smaller root of the equation,

$$n = \frac{100,302.6658}{8,450} = 11.87$$

Hence, $n = 12$ will provide a sample size with $P\left(\sum x_i > 900\right) \approx 0.01$. In fact, for $n = 11$,

$$P\left(\sum x_i > 900\right) = P(z > 3.49) = 1 - 0.9998 = 0.0002$$

while for $n = 12$,

$$P\left(\sum x_i > 900\right) = P(z > 2.17) = 1 - 0.9850 = 0.0150$$

7.85   **a**   The total production is the sum of 10 observations on the random variable x described in Exercise 7.84. Hence, its mean is $10(131.2) = 1312$ and its standard deviation is $3.677\sqrt{10} = 11.628$.

   b $P(\text{production} < 1280) = P\left(z < \dfrac{1280 - 1312}{11.628}\right) = P(z < -2.75) = 0.0030$

7.87   The probability that a shipment of 100 bulbs will have no more than 4% defective is $P(\hat{p} \le 0.04)$. Since $\hat{p}$ is approximately normal with mean $p \approx 0.032$ and $SE \approx \sqrt{\dfrac{\overline{p}(1 - \overline{p})}{n}} = \sqrt{\dfrac{0.032(0.968)}{100}} = 0.0176$,

$$P(\hat{p} \le 0.04) = P\left(z \le \frac{0.04 - 0.032}{0.0176}\right) = P(z \le 0.45) = 0.6736$$

7.89   **a**   If the process is in control, $\sigma = 35.5$. Calculate $\overline{\overline{x}} = \dfrac{654.9 + 603.8 + \cdots + 603.8}{30} = \dfrac{17532.9}{30} = 584.43$.

   With $n = 5$, the upper and lower control limits are

$$\overline{\overline{x}} \pm 3\frac{s}{\sqrt{n}} = 584.43 \pm 3\frac{35.5}{\sqrt{5}} = 584.43 \pm 47.6282$$

   or $LCL = 536.8018$ and $UCL = 632.0582$

   b   The centreline is $\overline{\overline{x}} = 584.43$ and the graph is omitted. Only two samples exceed the UCL; the process is probably in control.

7.91   Answers will vary. One solution is to number the containers from 01 to 20. Refer to Table 10 in Appendix I, and select 20 two-digit numbers, choosing a random starting point. If the two-digit number is greater than 20, subtract 20 from the number consecutively, until you have a number between 01 and 20. Continue until 10 numbers have been chosen. These 10 containers will be stored at one temperature; the other 10 will be stored at the second temperature.

7.93   Similar to Exercise 7.92. Since the package weights are normal with mean 454 and standard deviation 17, the total weight for a box of 24 packages will also have a normal distribution with mean $n\mu = 24(454) = 10896$ and standard deviation $\sigma\sqrt{n} = 17\sqrt{24} = 83.2827$. Let T be the total weight for the box. Then

$$P(T > 11113) = P\left(z > \frac{11113 - 10896}{83.2827}\right)$$
$$= P(z > 2.61) = 1 - 0.9955 = 0.0045$$

Case Study: Sampling the Roulette at Monte Carlo

1   Each bet results in a gain of (– \$5) if he loses and \$175 if he wins. Thus, the probability distribution of the gain x on a single \$5 bet is

X	$p(x)$
–5	37/38
175	1/38

2   Then

$$E(X) = \sum xp(x) = (-5)(37/38) + 175(1/38) = -0.2632$$

$$\sigma_x^2 = \sum x^2 p(x) - \mu^2 = (-5)^2(37/38) + (175)^2(1/38) - (-0.2632)^2 = 830.1939$$

3   The gain for the evening is the sum $S = \sum x_i$ of the gains or losses for the 200 bets of \$5 each. When the sample size is large, the Central Limit Theorem assures that this sum will be approximately normal with mean

$$\mu_S = n\mu = 200(-0.2632) = -\$52.64$$

and variance

$$\sigma_S^2 = n\sigma_x^2 = 200(830.1939) = 166,038.78$$

$$\sigma_S = \sqrt{166,038.78} = 407.48$$

The total winnings will vary from –\$1000 (if the gambler loses all 200 bets) to \$35,000 (if the gambler wins all 200 bets), a range of \$36,000. However, most of the winnings (95%) will fall in the interval

$$\mu_S \pm 2\sigma_S = -52.64 \pm 2(407.43)$$

or –\$867.50 to \$762.22. The large gains are highly improbable.

4   The loss of \$1000 on any one night will occur only if there are no wins in 200 bets of \$5. The probability of this event is $\left(\dfrac{37}{38}\right)^{200} = 0.005$. Define y to be the number of evenings on which a loss of \$1000 occurs.

Then y has a binomial distribution with $p = 0.005$ and $n = 365$. Using the Poisson approximation to the binomial with $\mu = np = 1.825$, the probability of interest is approximately

$$p(7) \approx \frac{(1.825)^7 e^{-1.825}}{7!} = 0.002$$

which is highly improbable.

5   The largest evening's winnings, \$1160, is not surprising. It lies $z = \dfrac{1160 - (-52.64)}{407.43} = 2.98$ standard deviations above the mean, so that $P(\text{winnings} \geq 1160) = P(z \geq 2.98) = 1 - 0.9986 = 0.0014$ for any one evening. The probability of observing winnings of \$1160 or greater on one evening out of 365 is then approximated using the Poisson approximation with $\mu = 365(0.0014) = 0.511$ or

$$p(1) \approx \frac{(0.511)^1 e^{-.511}}{1!} = 0.3065$$

Project 7-A: Canada's Average IQ Just Jumped a Bunch— Stephen Hawking's Coming to Canada!

a   We first need to assume that the population is normal, with a mean of 140 and standard deviation of 5. Then, the probability a random professor has an IQ below 130 can be found as follows:

Calculate $z = \dfrac{x - \mu}{\sigma} = \dfrac{130 - 140}{5} = -2$, so that $P(z < 130) = 0.0228$.

b   **i**   Since we cannot assume that the population is normal, we must invoke the Central Limit Theorem. The CLT tells us, when n is large ($n > 30$), that sampling distribution of $\bar{x}$ is approximately normal.

ii   The sampling distribution is normal with a mean of 140 and a standard deviation of $\dfrac{\sigma}{\sqrt{n}} = \dfrac{5}{\sqrt{81}} = 0.\overline{5}$.

iii   We calculate $z = \dfrac{x - \mu}{\sigma / \sqrt{n}} = \dfrac{130 - 140}{0.\overline{5}} = -18$, so that $p(\bar{x} < 130) = P(z < -18) \approx 0$. The sampling

distribution of $\bar{x}$ is much less variable than the single observation in part **a** above, which accounts for the fact that it is much less likely to get an average IQ less than 130 with a large sample than with a single observation.

iv   No. Since our sample size is already relatively large, Stephen Hawking's score of 187 will not have much of an effect on the average IQ score.

v   No. Even if we consider the probability of a professor's IQ score being below 130.5, we still obtain a z-score well under -3.5. This means that the probability that the average IQ score of selected Canadian professors is less than or equal to 130 would still remain essentially zero.

vi   No, there is no way of calculating the exact probability that the sample average IQ is 135, due to the fact that the normal distribution is a continuous distribution.

vii   Given that we have a relatively large sample (81), a sample mean of 130 would make the claim that $\mu = 140$ suspect. A formal hypothesis test should be conducted to test this. However, it is very possible that μ is actually less than 140.

viii   If we want to calculate the probability that the sample mean differs by more than 2 from the population mean, we must calculate two things: $P = (\bar{x} > 142)$ and $P = (\bar{x} < 138)$. First, calculate

$z = \dfrac{x - \mu}{\sigma / \sqrt{n}} = \dfrac{142 - 140}{0.\overline{5}} = 3.6$, so that $P = (\bar{x} > 142) \approx 0$, and $z = \dfrac{\bar{x} - \mu}{\sigma / \sqrt{n}} = \dfrac{138 - 140}{0.\overline{5}} = -3.6$, so that

$P = (z < 138) \approx 0$. Hence, the probability of the sample mean differing from the population mean by more than 2 is $P = (138 > \bar{x} > 142) = P(\bar{x} < 142) + P(\bar{x} > 142) \approx 0$

ix   Since the normal distribution is a symmetric distribution, we can consider only finding an X such that $P(X < \bar{x}) = P(z < \bar{z}) = 0.025$. The other half must be symmetric. Looking at Table 3, Appendix I, the value of z corresponding the probability $P(\bar{z} < z) = 0.025$ is $z = -1.96$. Thus, for the lower bound,

calculate $x = z\dfrac{\sigma}{\sqrt{n}} + \mu = (-1.96)(0.\overline{5}) + 140 = 138.9\overline{1}$; for the upper bound $(1.96)(0.\overline{5}) + 140 = 138.9\overline{1}$.

Hence, we would expect the sample average to be within $(138.9\overline{1} < \bar{x} < 141.0\overline{8})$ with probability 0.95.

c   **i**   If for all i, x_i is normally distributed with a mean of μ and a standard deviation of σ, the total score is normally distributed.

ii   By the Central Limit Theorem, we know that the total score Σx_i is normally distributed with mean $n\mu = 81(140) = 11,340$ and standard deviation $\sigma\sqrt{n} = 5\sqrt{81} = 45$.

iii   We can calculate the probability of finding the total score between 11,000 and 11,400 (inclusive) as follows: $P(11,000 \le \Sigma x_i \le 11,400 = P(\Sigma x_i < 11,400.5) - P(\Sigma x_i < 10,999.5)$. Then,

$$z = \frac{\Sigma x_i - n\mu}{\sigma\sqrt{n}} = \frac{11,400.5 - 11,340}{45} = 1.34, \text{ so that } P(\Sigma x_i < 11,400.5) = 0.9099, \text{ and}$$

$$z = \frac{\Sigma x_i - n\mu}{\sigma\sqrt{n}} = \frac{10,999.5 - 11,340}{45} = -7.57, \text{ so that } P(\Sigma x_i < 10.999.5) \approx 0. \text{ Hence, the probability that}$$

the total score will be between 11,000 and 11,400 inclusive is 0.9099.

Project 7-B: Test the Nation on CBC

a The mean of the sample proportion of individuals who scored above average is $p = 0.2$ and the standard deviation is $SE(\hat{p}) = \sqrt{\dfrac{pq}{n}} = \sqrt{\dfrac{(0.2)(0.8)}{64}} = 0.05$.

b From the text, we know that the normal distribution will be appropriate if $np > 5$ and $nq > 5$. First, $np = 64(0.2) = 18.2 > 5$, and $nq = 64(0.8) = 51.2 > 5$. This confirms that the distribution of the sample proportion is approximately normal.

c First, calculate $z = \dfrac{\hat{p} - p}{\sqrt{\dfrac{pq}{n}}} = \dfrac{0.18 - 0.20}{0.05} = -0.4$, so that $P(\hat{p} > 18\%) = P(z > -0.4) = 0.6554$.

d To calculate the probability that the sample proportion $\hat{p}$ lies between 19% and 23%, we must first find $P(\hat{p} < 23\%)$ and $P(\hat{p} < 19\%)$. First, calculate $z = \dfrac{\hat{p} - p}{\sqrt{\dfrac{pq}{n}}} = \dfrac{0.23 - 0.20}{0.05} = 0.6$, so that

$P(\hat{p} < 23\%) = P(z < 0.6) = 0.7257$. Also, $z = \dfrac{\hat{p} - p}{\sqrt{\dfrac{pq}{n}}} = \dfrac{0.19 - 0.20}{0.05} = -0.2$, so that

$P(\hat{p} < 19\%) = P(z < -0.2) = 0.4207$.

Thus, $P(19\% < \hat{p} < 23\%) = 0.7257 - 0.4207 = 0.305$.

e Since the normal distribution is a symmetric distribution, we only need to find a $\hat{p}$ such that $P(p < \hat{p}) = 0.005$. The other half must be symmetric. Looking at Table 3, Appendix I, the value of z corresponding to this probability is approximately $z = -2.575$. By symmetry, the other z we need is 2.575.

Thus, for the lower bound, we calculate $\hat{p} = z\sqrt{\dfrac{pq}{n}} + p = (-2.575)(0.05) + 0.20 = 0.07125$, and for the

upper bound, we calculate $\hat{p} = z\sqrt{\dfrac{pq}{n}} + p = (2.575)(0.05) + 0.20 = 0.32875$. Hence, 99% of the time, the

sample proportion $\hat{p}$ will lie between $(0.07125 < \hat{p} < 0.32875)$.

f There are multiple factors that can contribute to a sample proportion as small as 10%. However, the most probable reason for this would be that sampling was not done randomly, leading to a biased $\hat{p}$.

g With a mean of $p = 0.2$ and a standard deviation of $SE(\hat{p}) = 0.05$, we notice that a value of $\hat{p} = 0.35$ is three times the standard deviation away from the mean. When this occurs, we would consider the value of $\hat{p}$ to be an outlier. Therefore, the value of $\hat{p} = 0.35$ would certainly be considered unusual.

Chapter 8: Large-Sample Estimation

8.1 The margin of error in estimation provides a practical upper bound to the difference between a particular estimate and the parameter which it estimates. In this chapter, the margin of error is $1.96 \times$ (standard error of the estimator).

8.3 For the estimate of μ given as $\bar{x}$, the margin of error is $1.96\ SE = 1.96\dfrac{\sigma}{\sqrt{n}}$.

a $1.96\sqrt{\dfrac{0.2}{30}} = 0.160$

b $1.96\sqrt{\dfrac{0.9}{30}} = 0.339$

c $1.96\sqrt{\dfrac{1.5}{30}} = 0.438$

8.5 The margin of error is $1.96\ SE = 1.96\dfrac{\sigma}{\sqrt{n}}$, where σ can be estimated by the sample standard deviation s for large values of n.

a $1.96\sqrt{\dfrac{4}{50}} = 0.554$

b $1.96\sqrt{\dfrac{4}{500}} = 0.175$

c $1.96\sqrt{\dfrac{4}{5000}} = 0.055$

8.7 For the estimate of p given as $\hat{p} = x/n$, the margin of error is $1.96\ SE = 1.96\sqrt{\dfrac{pq}{n}}$.

a $1.96\sqrt{\dfrac{(0.5)(0.5)}{30}} = 0.179$

b $1.96\sqrt{\dfrac{(0.5)(0.5)}{100}} = 0.098$

c $1.96\sqrt{\dfrac{(0.5)(0.5)}{400}} = 0.049$

d $1.96\sqrt{\dfrac{(0.5)(0.5)}{1000}} = 0.031$

8.9 For the estimate of p given as $\hat{p} = x/n$, the margin of error is $1.96\,SE = 1.96\sqrt{\dfrac{pq}{n}}$. Use the estimated value given in the exercise for p.

    a $1.96\sqrt{\dfrac{(0.1)(0.9)}{100}} = 0.0588$

    b $1.96\sqrt{\dfrac{(0.3)(0.7)}{100}} = 0.0898$

    c $1.96\sqrt{\dfrac{(0.5)(0.5)}{100}} = 0.098$

    d $1.96\sqrt{\dfrac{(0.7)(0.3)}{100}} = 0.0898$

    e $1.96\sqrt{\dfrac{(0.9)(0.1)}{100}} = 0.0588$

    f   The largest margin of error occurs when $p = 0.5$.

8.11 The point estimate for p is given as $\hat{p} = \dfrac{x}{n} = \dfrac{655}{900} = 0.728$ and the margin of error is approximately

$$1.96\sqrt{\frac{\hat{p}\hat{q}}{n}} = 1.96\sqrt{\frac{0.728(0.272)}{900}} = 0.029$$

8.13 The point estimate for p is given as $\hat{p} = \dfrac{x}{n} = \dfrac{450}{500} = 0.9$ and the margin of error is approximately

$$1.96\sqrt{\frac{\hat{p}\hat{q}}{n}} = 1.96\sqrt{\frac{0.9(0.1)}{500}} = 0.0263$$

8.15 The point estimate of μ is $\bar{x} = 39.8°$ and the margin of error with $s = 17.2$ and $n = 50$ is

$$1.96\,SE = 1.96\frac{\sigma}{\sqrt{n}} \approx 1.96\frac{s}{\sqrt{n}} = 1.96\frac{17.2}{\sqrt{50}} = 4.768$$

8.17 The point estimate of μ is $\bar{x} = 7.2\%$ and the margin of error with $s = 5.6\%$ and $n = 200$ is

$$1.96\,SE = 1.96\frac{\sigma}{\sqrt{n}} \approx 1.96\frac{s}{\sqrt{n}} = 1.96\frac{5.6}{\sqrt{200}} = 0.776$$

8.19   **a**   Nightly room rates at three hotel chains.

    b   The point estimate of μ for the Marriot hotel is $\bar{x} = 150$ and the margin of error in estimation with $s = 17.2$ and $n = 50$ is

$$1.96\,SE = 1.96\frac{\sigma}{\sqrt{n}} \approx 1.96\frac{s}{\sqrt{n}} = 1.96\frac{17.2}{\sqrt{50}} = 4.7676$$

    c   The point estimate of μ for the Westin hotel is $\bar{x} = 165$ and the margin of error in estimation with $s = 22.5$ and $n = 50$ is

$$1.96\,SE = 1.96\frac{\sigma}{\sqrt{n}} \approx 1.96\frac{s}{\sqrt{n}} = 1.96\frac{22.5}{\sqrt{50}} = 6.2367$$

    d   The point estimate of μ for the Doubletree hotel is $\bar{x} = 125$ and the margin of error in estimation with $s = 12.8$ and $n = 50$ is

$$1.96\,SE = 1.96\frac{\sigma}{\sqrt{n}} \approx 1.96\frac{s}{\sqrt{n}} = 1.96\frac{12.8}{\sqrt{50}} = 3.548$$

e   The graphical comparison of parts **b**, **c**, and **d** is shown below.

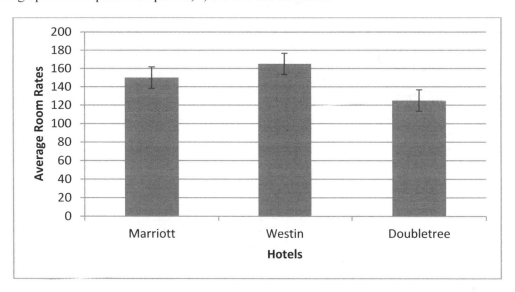

8.21 **a**   The point estimate for the proportion, p, is given as $\hat{p} = \dfrac{x}{n} = 0.69$ and the margin of error is approximately

$$1.96\sqrt{\frac{\hat{p}\hat{q}}{n}} = 1.96\sqrt{\frac{0.69(0.31)}{1275}} = 1.96\sqrt{0.0002} \approx 0.027$$

b   The poll's margin of error does agree with the results of part **a**.

8.23 **a**   This method of sampling would not be random, since only interested viewers (those who were adamant in their approval or disapproval) would reply.

b   The results of such a survey will not be valid, and a margin of error would be useless, since its accuracy is based on the assumption that the sample was random.

8.25 A 95% confidence interval for the population mean μ is given by

$$\bar{x} \pm 1.96 \frac{\sigma}{\sqrt{n}}$$

where σ can be estimated by the sample standard deviation s for large values of n.

a $13.1 \pm 1.96\sqrt{\dfrac{3.42}{36}} = 13.1 \pm 0.604$ or $12.496 < \mu < 13.704$

b $2.73 \pm 1.96\sqrt{\dfrac{0.1047}{64}} = 2.73 \pm 0.079$ or $2.651 < \mu < 2.809$

c   Intervals constructed in this manner will enclose the true value of μ 95% of the time in repeated sampling. Hence, we are fairly confident that these particular intervals will enclose μ.

8.27 **a** $\bar{x} \pm z_{0.005}\dfrac{\sigma}{\sqrt{n}} = \bar{x} \pm 2.58\dfrac{\sigma}{\sqrt{n}} \approx 34 \pm 2.58\sqrt{\dfrac{12}{38}} = 34 \pm 1.450$ or $32.550 < \mu < 35.450$

b $\bar{x} \pm z_{0.05}\dfrac{\sigma}{\sqrt{n}} = \bar{x} \pm 1.645\dfrac{\sigma}{\sqrt{n}} \approx 1049 \pm 1.645\sqrt{\dfrac{51}{65}} = 1049 \pm 1.457$ or $1047.543 < \mu < 1050.457$

c $\bar{x} \pm z_{0.025}\dfrac{\sigma}{\sqrt{n}} = \bar{x} \pm 1.96\dfrac{\sigma}{\sqrt{n}} \approx 66.3 \pm 1.96\sqrt{\dfrac{2.48}{89}} = 66.3 \pm .327$ or $65.973 < \mu < 66.627$

8.29   Calculate $\hat{p} = \dfrac{x}{n} = \dfrac{27}{500} = 0.054$. Then an approximate 95% confidence interval for p is

$$\hat{p} \pm 1.96\sqrt{\frac{\hat{p}\hat{q}}{n}} = 0.054 \pm 1.96\sqrt{\frac{0.054(0.946)}{500}} = 0.054 \pm 0.020 \qquad \text{or} \qquad 0.034 < p < 0.074$$

Notice that the interval is narrower than the one calculated in Exercise 8.28, even though the confidence coefficient is larger <u>and</u> n is larger. This is because the value of p (estimated by $\hat{p}$) is quite close to zero, causing $\sigma_{\hat{p}}$ to be small.

8.31   Refer to Exercise 8.30.

    a   When the sample size is doubled, the width is decreased by $1/\sqrt{2}$.

    b   When the sample size is quadrupled, the width is decreased by $1/\sqrt{4} = 1/2$.

8.33   With $n = 30$, $\bar{x} = 0.145$, and $s = 0.0051$, a 90% confidence interval for μ is approximated by

$$\bar{x} \pm 1.645\frac{s}{\sqrt{n}} = 0.145 \pm 1.645\frac{0.0051}{\sqrt{30}} = 0.145 \pm 0.0015 \text{ or } 0.1435 < \mu < 0.1465$$

8.35   **a**   An approximate 95% confidence interval for p is

$$\hat{p} \pm 1.96\sqrt{\frac{\hat{p}\hat{q}}{n}} = 0.78 \pm 1.96\sqrt{\frac{0.78(0.22)}{1030}} = 0.78 \pm 0.025 \quad \text{or} \quad 0.755 < p < 0.805$$

    b   An approximate 95% confidence interval for p is

$$\hat{p} \pm 1.96\sqrt{\frac{\hat{p}\hat{q}}{n}} = 0.69 \pm 1.96\sqrt{\frac{0.69(0.31)}{1030}} = 0.69 \pm 0.028 \quad \text{or} \quad 0.662 < p < 0.718$$

8.37   The 90% confidence interval for p is

$$\hat{p} \pm 1.645\sqrt{\frac{\hat{p}\hat{q}}{n}} = 0.90 \pm 1.645\sqrt{\frac{0.90(0.10)}{5756}} = 0.90 \pm 0.0065 \quad \text{or} \quad 0.8935 < p < 0.9065$$

8.39   **a**   The time to complete an online order is probably not mound-shaped. The minimum value of x is zero, and there is an average time of $\mu = 4.5$, with a standard deviation of $\sigma = 2.7$. We calculate $\mu - 2\sigma = -0.9$, leaving no possibility for a measurement to fall more than two standard deviations below the mean. For a mound-shaped distribution, approximately 2.5% should fall in that range. The distribution is probably skewed to the right.

    b   Since n is large, the Central Limit Theorem ensures that the sample mean $\bar{x}$ is approximately normal, and the standard normal distribution can be used to construct a confidence interval for μ.

    c   The 95% confidence interval for μ is

$$\bar{x} \pm 1.96\frac{s}{\sqrt{n}} = 4.5 \pm 1.96\frac{2.7}{\sqrt{50}} = 4.5 \pm 0.478 \quad \text{or} \quad 4.022 < \mu < 4.978$$

8.41   **a**   The approximate 90% confidence interval for p is

$$\hat{p} \pm 1.645\sqrt{\frac{\hat{p}\hat{q}}{n}} = 0.55 \pm 1.645\sqrt{\frac{0.55(0.45)}{1006}} = 0.55 \pm 0.0258 \quad \text{or} \quad 0.5242 < p < 0.5758$$

    b   The approximate 90% confidence interval for p is

$$\hat{p} \pm 1.645\sqrt{\frac{\hat{p}\hat{q}}{n}} = 0.54 \pm 1.645\sqrt{\frac{0.54(0.46)}{1006}} = 0.54 \pm 0.0258 \quad \text{or} \quad 0.5142 < p < 0.5658$$

c   Since 19 times out of 20 implies 95% confidence level is used. Thus, the margin of error with 95% confidence will be

$$z_{\alpha/2}\sqrt{\frac{\hat{p}\hat{q}}{n}} = 1.96\sqrt{\frac{0.55(0.45)}{1000}} = 0.0308 \text{ or } 3.1\%$$

Hence, the error margin is calculated correctly.

8.43   **a**   The point estimate of p is $\hat{p} = \frac{x}{n} = \frac{192}{300} = 0.64$, and the approximate 95% confidence interval for p is

$$\hat{p} \pm 1.96\sqrt{\frac{\hat{p}\hat{q}}{n}} = 0.64 \pm 1.96\sqrt{\frac{0.64(0.36)}{300}} = 0.64 \pm 0.054 \qquad \text{or} \quad 0.586 < p < 0.694 \,.$$

       b   Since the possible values for p given in the confidence interval does not includes the value $p = 0.71$, we would disagree with the reported percentage.

       c   The confidence interval in part **a** only estimates the proportion who say they always vote in federal general elections. This is different from the proportion who actually *do* vote in the next federal general election.

8.45   **a**   90% confidence interval for $\mu_1 - \mu_2$ is

$$\left(\bar{x}_1 - \bar{x}_2\right) \pm 1.645\sqrt{\frac{\sigma_1^2}{n_1} + \frac{\sigma_2^2}{n_2}}$$

Estimating σ_1^2 and σ_2^2 with s_1^2 and s_2^2, the approximate interval is

$$\left(2.9 - 5.1\right) \pm 1.645\sqrt{\frac{0.83}{64} + \frac{1.67}{64}} = -2.2 \pm 0.325$$

or $-2.525 < \left(\mu_1 - \mu_2\right) < -1.875$. In repeated sampling, 90% of all intervals constructed in this manner will enclose $\mu_1 - \mu_2$. Hence, we are fairly certain that this particular interval contains $\mu_1 - \mu_2$.

       b   The 99% confidence interval for $\mu_1 - \mu_2$ is approximately

$$\left(\bar{x}_1 - \bar{x}_2\right) \pm 2.58\sqrt{\frac{s_1^2}{n_1} + \frac{s_2^2}{n_2}} = \left(2.9 - 5.1\right) \pm 2.58\sqrt{\frac{0.83}{64} + \frac{1.67}{64}} = -2.2 \pm 0.510$$

or $\quad -2.710 < \left(\mu_1 - \mu_2\right) < -1.690$

Since the value $\mu_1 - \mu_2 = 0$ is not in the confidence interval, it is not likely that $\mu_1 = \mu_2$. There is a difference in the two population means.

8.47   **a**   The point estimate for $\mu_1 - \mu_2$ is $\bar{x}_1 - \bar{x}_2 = 1.5$ and the margin of error with 99% confidence level is

$$2.575\sqrt{\frac{s_1^2}{n_1} + \frac{s_2^2}{n_2}} = 2.575\sqrt{\frac{5.6^2}{500} + \frac{6.8^2}{500}} = 1.014$$

       b   If we combine the point estimate and the margin of error computed in part **a** and construct 99% confidence interval, we can conclude that the means are significantly different since the confidence interval will not contain the value $\mu_1 - \mu_2 = 0$.

8.49   Similar to previous exercises. The 90% confidence interval for $\mu_1 - \mu_2$ is approximately

$$\left(\bar{x}_1 - \bar{x}_2\right) \pm 1.645\sqrt{\frac{s_1^2}{n_1} + \frac{s_2^2}{n_2}} = \left(2.4 - 3.1\right) \pm 1.645\sqrt{\frac{1.44}{100} + \frac{2.64}{100}} = -0.7 \pm 0.332$$

or $\quad -1.032 < \left(\mu_1 - \mu_2\right) < -0.368$

Intervals constructed in this manner will enclose $\mu_1 - \mu_2$ 90% of the time. Hence, we are fairly certain that this particular interval encloses $\left(\mu_1 - \mu_2\right)$.

8.51 Similar to previous exercises. The 95% confidence interval for $\mu_1 - \mu_2$ is approximately

$$\left(\bar{x}_1 - \bar{x}_2\right) \pm 1.96\sqrt{\frac{s_1^2}{n_1} + \frac{s_2^2}{n_2}} = \left(21.3 - 13.4\right) \pm 1.96\sqrt{\frac{(2.6)^2}{30} + \frac{(1.9)^2}{30}} = 7.9 \pm 1.152$$

or $\quad 6.748 < \left(\mu_1 - \mu_2\right) < 9.052$

Intervals constructed in this manner will enclose $\left(\mu_1 - \mu_2\right)$ 95% of the time in repeated sampling. Hence, we are fairly certain that this particular interval encloses $\left(\mu_1 - \mu_2\right)$.

8.53 **a** The 95% confidence interval is approximately

$$\bar{x} \pm 1.96\frac{s}{\sqrt{n}} = 14.06 \pm 1.96\frac{5.65}{\sqrt{376}} = 14.06 \pm 0.571 \quad \text{or} \quad 13.489 < \mu < 14.631$$

b The 95% confidence interval is approximately

$$\bar{x} \pm 1.96\frac{s}{\sqrt{n}} = 12.96 \pm 1.96\frac{5.93}{\sqrt{308}} = 12.96 \pm 0.662 \quad \text{or} \quad 12.298 < \mu < 13.622$$

c The 95% confidence interval for $\mu_1 - \mu_2$ is approximately

$$\left(\bar{x}_1 - \bar{x}_2\right) \pm 1.96\sqrt{\frac{s_1^2}{n_1} + \frac{s_2^2}{n_2}} = \left(14.06 - 12.96\right) \pm 1.96\sqrt{\frac{(5.65)^2}{376} + \frac{(5.93)^2}{308}} = 1.10 \pm 0.875$$

or $\quad 0.225 < \left(\mu_1 - \mu_2\right) < 1.975$

d Since the confidence interval in part **c** has two positive endpoints, it does not contain the value $\mu_1 - \mu_2 = 0$. Hence, it is not likely that the means are equal. It appears that there is a real difference in the mean scores.

8.55 **a** The 99% confidence interval for $\mu_1 - \mu_2$ is approximately

$$\left(\bar{x}_1 - \bar{x}_2\right) \pm 2.58\sqrt{\frac{s_1^2}{n_1} + \frac{s_2^2}{n_2}} = \left(15 - 23\right) \pm 2.58\sqrt{\frac{4^2}{30} + \frac{10^2}{40}} = -8 \pm 4.49$$

or $\quad -12.49 < \left(\mu_1 - \mu_2\right) < -3.51$

b Since the confidence interval in part **a** has two negative endpoints, it does not contain the value $\mu_1 - \mu_2 = 0$. Hence, it is not likely that the means are equal. It appears that there is a real difference in the mean times to completion for the two groups.

8.57 **a** The best estimate of $p_1 - p_2$ is $\hat{p}_1 - \hat{p}_2$ where $\hat{p}_1 = \frac{x_1}{n_1} = \frac{120}{500} = 0.24$ and $\hat{p}_2 = \frac{x_2}{n_2} = \frac{147}{500} = 0.294$.

b The standard error is calculated by estimating p_1 and p_2 with $\hat{p}_1$ and $\hat{p}_2$ in the formula:

$$SE = \sqrt{\frac{p_1 q_1}{n_1} + \frac{p_2 q_2}{n_2}} \approx \sqrt{\frac{\hat{p}_1 \hat{q}_1}{n_1} + \frac{\hat{p}_2 \hat{q}_2}{n_2}} = \sqrt{\frac{0.24(0.76)}{500} + \frac{0.294(0.706)}{500}} = 0.0279$$

c From part **b**, the approximate margin of error is

$$1.96\sqrt{\frac{0.24(0.76)}{500} + \frac{0.294(0.706)}{500}} = 1.96(0.0279) = 0.055$$

8.59 **a** Calculate $\hat{p}_1 = \dfrac{x_1}{n_1} = \dfrac{849}{1265} = 0.671$ and $\hat{p}_2 = \dfrac{x_2}{n_2} = \dfrac{910}{1688} = 0.539$. The approximate 99% confidence interval is

$$(\hat{p}_1 - \hat{p}_2) \pm 2.58\sqrt{\dfrac{\hat{p}_1\hat{q}_1}{n_1} + \dfrac{\hat{p}_2\hat{q}_2}{n_2}} = (0.671 - 0.539) \pm 2.58\sqrt{\dfrac{0.671(0.329)}{1265} + \dfrac{0.539(0.461)}{1688}}$$

$$= 0.132 \pm 0.046 \quad \text{or} \quad 0.086 < (p_1 - p_2) < 0.178$$

In repeated sampling, 99% of all intervals constructed in this manner will enclose $p_1 - p_2$. Hence, we are fairly certain that this particular interval contains $p_1 - p_2$.

b Since the value $p_1 - p_2 = 0$ is not in the confidence interval, it is not likely that $p_1 = p_2$. You should conclude that there is a difference in the two population proportions.

8.61 Calculate $\hat{p}_1 = \dfrac{x_1}{250} = 0.70$ and $\hat{p}_2 = \dfrac{x_2}{250} = 0.86$. The approximate 95% confidence interval is

$$(\hat{p}_1 - \hat{p}_2) \pm 1.96\sqrt{\dfrac{\hat{p}_1\hat{q}_1}{n_1} + \dfrac{\hat{p}_2\hat{q}_2}{n_2}} = (0.70 - 0.86) \pm 1.96\sqrt{\dfrac{0.70(0.30)}{250} + \dfrac{0.86(0.14)}{250}}$$

$$= -0.16 \pm 0.071 \quad \text{or} \quad -0.231 < (p_1 - p_2) < -0.089$$

Since the value $p_1 - p_2 = 0$ is not in the confidence interval, it is not likely that $p_1 = p_2$. You should conclude that there is a difference in the proportion of Conservatives and Liberals who favour the new initiative. It appears that the percentage of Liberal voters is higher than the Conservative percentage.

8.63 **a** Calculate $\hat{p}_1 = \dfrac{390}{430} = 0.907$ and $\hat{p}_2 = \dfrac{100}{570} = 0.175$. The approximate 80% confidence interval is

$$(\hat{p}_1 - \hat{p}_2) \pm 1.28\sqrt{\dfrac{\hat{p}_1\hat{q}_1}{n_1} + \dfrac{\hat{p}_2\hat{q}_2}{n_2}} = (0.907 - 0.175) \pm 1.28\sqrt{\dfrac{0.907(0.093)}{430} + \dfrac{0.175(0.825)}{570}}$$

$$= 0.732 \pm 0.027 \quad \text{or} \quad 0.705 < (p_1 - p_2) < 0.759$$

b Since the value $p_1 - p_2 = 0$ is not in the confidence interval in part **a**, it is not likely that $p_1 = p_2$.

8.65 The following sample information is available:

$$n_1 = n_2 = 200 \qquad \hat{p}_1 = \dfrac{142}{200} = 0.71 \qquad \hat{p}_2 = \dfrac{120}{200} = 0.60$$

The approximate 95% confidence interval is

$$(\hat{p}_1 - \hat{p}_2) \pm 1.96\sqrt{\dfrac{\hat{p}_1\hat{q}_1}{n_1} + \dfrac{\hat{p}_2\hat{q}_2}{n_2}} = (0.71 - 0.60) \pm 1.96\sqrt{\dfrac{0.71(0.29)}{200} + \dfrac{0.60(0.40)}{200}}$$

$$= 0.11 \pm 0.093 \quad \text{or} \quad 0.017 < (p_1 - p_2) < 0.203$$

Intervals constructed in this manner will enclose the true value of $p_1 - p_2$ 95% of the time in repeated sampling. Hence, we are fairly certain that this particular interval encloses $p_1 - p_2$.

8.67 **a** The approximate 98% confidence interval is

$$(\hat{p}_1 - \hat{p}_2) \pm 2.33 \sqrt{\frac{\hat{p}_1 \hat{q}_1}{n_1} + \frac{\hat{p}_2 \hat{q}_2}{n_2}} = (0.20 - 0.26) \pm 2.33 \sqrt{\frac{0.20(0.80)}{500} + \frac{0.26(0.74)}{500}}$$

$$= -0.06 \pm 0.062 \quad \text{or} \quad -0.122 < (p_1 - p_2) < 0.002$$

b Intervals constructed in this manner enclose the true value of $p_1 - p_2$ 98% of the time in repeated sampling. Hence, we are fairly certain that this particular interval encloses $p_1 - p_2$.

c Since the value $p_1 - p_2 = 0$ is in the confidence interval, it is possible that $p_1 = p_2$. You should not conclude that there is a difference in the proportion of men and women who think that space should remain commercial free.

8.69 **a** Calculate $\hat{p}_1 = \frac{x_1}{200} = 0.93$ and $\hat{p}_2 = \frac{x_2}{450} = 0.96$. The approximate 99% confidence interval is

$$(\hat{p}_1 - \hat{p}_2) \pm 2.58 \sqrt{\frac{\hat{p}_1 \hat{q}_1}{n_1} + \frac{\hat{p}_2 \hat{q}_2}{n_2}} = (0.93 - 0.96) \pm 2.58 \sqrt{\frac{0.93(0.07)}{200} + \frac{0.96(0.04)}{450}}$$

$$= -0.03 \pm 0.052 \quad \text{or} \quad -0.082 < (p_1 - p_2) < 0.022$$

b Since the value $p_1 - p_2 = 0$ is in the confidence interval, it is possible that $p_1 = p_2$. You should not conclude that there is a difference in the proportion of people who experience pain relief when using one pain reliever or the other.

8.71 The parameter to be estimated is the population mean μ and the 90% upper confidence bound is calculated using a value $z_\alpha = z_{0.10} = 1.28$.

a The upper bound is approximately

$$\bar{x} + 1.28 \frac{s}{\sqrt{n}} = 75 + 1.28 \sqrt{\frac{65}{40}} = 75 + 1.63 \quad \text{or} \quad \mu < 76.63$$

b The upper bound is approximately

$$\bar{x} + 1.28 \frac{s}{\sqrt{n}} = 1.6 + 1.28 \frac{2.3}{\sqrt{100}} = 1.6 + .29 \quad \text{or} \quad \mu < 1.89$$

8.73 For the difference $\mu_1 - \mu_2$ in the population means for two quantitative populations, the 95% upper confidence bound uses $z_{0.05} = 1.645$ and is calculated as

$$(\bar{x}_1 - \bar{x}_2) + 1.645 \sqrt{\frac{s_1^2}{n_1} + \frac{s_2^2}{n_2}} = (12 - 10) + 1.645 \sqrt{\frac{5^2}{50} + \frac{7^2}{50}}$$

$$= 2 + 2.00 \quad \text{or} \quad (\mu_1 - \mu_2) < 4$$

8.75 For this exercise, $B = 0.04$ for the binomial estimator $\hat{p}$, where $SE(\hat{p}) = \sqrt{\frac{pq}{n}}$. Assuming maximum variation, which occurs if $p = 0.3$ (since we suspect that $0.1 < p < 0.3$) and $z_{0.025} = 1.96$, we have

$$1.96 \sigma_{\hat{p}} \le B \Rightarrow 1.96 \sqrt{\frac{pq}{n}} \le B$$

$$1.96 \sqrt{\frac{0.3(0.7)}{n}} \le 0.04 \Rightarrow \sqrt{n} \ge \frac{1.96 \sqrt{0.3(0.7)}}{0.04} \Rightarrow n \ge 504.21 \quad \text{or} \quad n \ge 505$$

8.77 In this exercise, the parameter of interest is $p_1 - p_2$, $n_1 = n_2 = n$, and $B = 0.05$. Since we have no prior knowledge about p_1 and p_2, we assume the largest possible variation, which occurs if $p_1 = p_2 = 0.5$. Then

$$z_{\alpha/2} \times (\text{std error of } \hat{p}_1 - \hat{p}_2) \le B$$

$$z_{0.01}\sqrt{\frac{p_1 q_1}{n_1} + \frac{p_2 q_2}{n_2}} \le 0.05 \quad \Rightarrow \quad 2.33\sqrt{\frac{(0.5)(0.5)}{n} + \frac{(0.5)(0.5)}{n}} \le 0.05$$

$$\sqrt{n} \ge \frac{2.33\sqrt{0.5}}{0.05} \quad \Rightarrow \quad n \ge 1085.78 \text{ or } n_1 = n_2 = 1086$$

8.79 **a** The sample should be selected randomly. Voter registration lists and telephone listings may provide possible lists from which you might choose. Make sure that your lists do not systematically exclude any segment of the population, which might bias your results.

 b To estimate binomial proportions p in the survey, choose a common value of $p = 0.5$ to maximize the possible error. With $B = 0.01$, solve for n:

$$1.96\sqrt{\frac{pq}{n}} \le 0.01 \quad \Rightarrow \quad 1.96\sqrt{\frac{0.5(0.5)}{n}} \le 0.01 \quad \Rightarrow \quad n \ge 9604$$

8.81 Using $s \approx R/4 = 47/4 = 11.75$:

$$2.58\sqrt{\frac{\sigma_1^2}{n_1} + \frac{\sigma_2^2}{n_2}} \le 2.3 \quad \Rightarrow \quad 2.58\sqrt{\frac{11.75^2}{n} + \frac{11.75^2}{n}} \le 2.3$$

$$\sqrt{n} \ge \frac{2.58\sqrt{276.125}}{2.3} \quad \Rightarrow \quad n > 347.45 \text{ or } n_1 - n_2 = 348$$

8.83 The margin of error in estimation has bound $B = 2$ days. Assuming $\sigma \approx 10$, we must have

$$1.96\frac{\sigma}{\sqrt{n}} \le 2 \quad \Rightarrow \quad 1.96\frac{10}{\sqrt{n}} \le 2$$

$$\sqrt{n} \ge \frac{1.96(10)}{2} = 9.8 \quad \Rightarrow \quad n \ge 96.04 \text{ or } n \ge 97$$

Therefore, we must include 97 hunters in the survey in order to estimate the mean number of days of hunting per hunter to within two days.

8.85 There are now two populations of interest and the parameter to be estimated is $\mu_1 - \mu_2$. The bound on the margin of error is $B = 0.1$, $n_1 = n_2 = n$, and $\sigma_1^2 \approx \sigma_2^2 \approx 0.25$. Then we must have

$$1.645\sqrt{\frac{\sigma_1^2}{n_1} + \frac{\sigma_2^2}{n_2}} \le 0.1 \quad \Rightarrow \quad 1.645\sqrt{\frac{0.25}{n} + \frac{0.25}{n}} \le 0.1$$

$$\sqrt{n} \ge \frac{1.645\sqrt{0.5}}{0.1} \quad \Rightarrow \quad n \ge 135.30$$

or $n_1 = n_2 = 136$ samples should be selected at each location.

8.87 It is given that $n_1 = n_2 = n$ and that $B = 5$. From Exercise 8.48, $s_1 = 24.3$ and $s_2 = 17.6$. Using these values to estimate σ_1 and σ_2, the following inequality must be solved:

$$1.645\sqrt{\frac{\sigma_1^2}{n_1} + \frac{\sigma_2^2}{n_2}} \le 5 \quad \Rightarrow \quad 1.645\sqrt{\frac{24.3^2}{n} + \frac{17.6^2}{n}} \le 5$$

$$n \ge 97.444 \text{ or } n_1 = n_2 = 98$$

8.89   **a**   The point estimate of μ is $\bar{x} = 29.1$ and the margin of error in estimation with $s = 3.9$ and $n = 64$ is

$$1.96\sigma_{\bar{x}} = 1.96\frac{\sigma}{\sqrt{n}} \approx 1.96\frac{s}{\sqrt{n}} = 1.96\left(\frac{3.9}{\sqrt{64}}\right) = 0.9555$$

b   The approximate 90% confidence interval is

$$\bar{x} \pm 1.645\frac{s}{\sqrt{n}} = 29.1 \pm 1.645\frac{3.9}{\sqrt{64}} = 29.1 \pm 0.802 \quad \text{or} \quad 28.298 < \mu < 29.902$$

Intervals constructed in this manner enclose the true value of μ 90% of the time in repeated sampling. Therefore, we are fairly certain that this particular interval encloses μ.

c   The approximate 90% lower confidence bound is

$$\bar{x} - 1.28\frac{s}{\sqrt{n}} = 29.1 - 1.28\frac{3.9}{\sqrt{64}} = 28.48 \quad \text{or} \quad \mu > 28.48$$

d   With B = 0.5, $\sigma \approx 3.9$, and $1 - \alpha = 0.95$, we must solve for n in the following inequality:

$$1.96\frac{\sigma}{\sqrt{n}} \leq B \quad \Rightarrow \quad 1.96\frac{3.9}{\sqrt{n}} \leq 0.5$$

$$\sqrt{n} \geq 15.288 \quad \Rightarrow \quad n \geq 233.723 \quad \text{or} \quad n \geq 234$$

8.91   Refer to Exercise 8.90, with B = 0.2, $1 - \alpha = 0.95$, $n_1 = n_2 = n$, $s_1 = 0.8$, and $s_2 = 1.3$. Using these values to estimate σ_1 and σ_2, the following inequality must be solved:

$$1.96\sqrt{\frac{\sigma_1^2}{n_1} + \frac{\sigma_2^2}{n_2}} \leq 0.2 \quad \Rightarrow \quad 1.96\sqrt{\frac{(0.8)^2}{n} + \frac{(1.3)^2}{n}} \leq 0.2$$

$$\sqrt{n} \geq 14.959 \quad \Rightarrow \quad n \geq 223.77 \quad \text{or} \quad n_1 = n_2 = 224$$

8.93   Assuming maximum variation with $p = 0.5$, solve

$$1.645\sqrt{\frac{pq}{n}} \leq 0.025$$

$$\sqrt{n} \geq \frac{1.645\sqrt{0.5(0.5)}}{0.025} = 32.9 \Rightarrow n \geq 1082.41 \quad \text{or} \quad n \geq 1083$$

8.95   Assuming maximum variation $(p_1 = p_2 = 0.5)$ and $n_1 = n_2 = n$, the inequality to be solved is

$$z_{0.005}\sqrt{\frac{p_1 q_1}{n_1} + \frac{p_2 q_2}{n_2}} \leq 0.06 \quad \Rightarrow \quad 2.58\sqrt{\frac{(0.5)(0.5)}{n} + \frac{(0.5)(0.5)}{n}} \leq 0.06$$

$$\sqrt{n} \geq 30.406 \quad \Rightarrow \quad n \geq 924.5 \quad \text{or} \quad n_1 = n_2 = 925$$

8.97   **a**   Define sample #1 as the sample of 482 women and sample #2 as the sample of 356 men. Then $\hat{p}_1 = 0.5$ and $\hat{p}_2 = 0.75$.

b   The approximate 95% confidence interval is

$$(\hat{p}_1 - \hat{p}_2) \pm 1.96\sqrt{\frac{\hat{p}_1 \hat{q}_1}{n_1} + \frac{\hat{p}_2 \hat{q}_2}{n_2}}$$

$$(0.5 - 0.75) \pm 1.96\sqrt{\frac{0.5(0.5)}{482} + \frac{0.75(0.25)}{356}}$$

$$-0.25 \pm 0.063 \quad \text{or} \quad -0.313 < (p_1 - p_2) < -0.187$$

c   Since the value $p_1 - p_2 = 0$ is not in the confidence interval, it is unlikely that $p_1 = p_2$. You should not conclude that there is a difference in the proportion of women and men on Wall Street who have children. In fact, since all the probable values of $p_1 - p_2$ are negative, the proportion of men of Wall Street who have children appears to be larger than the proportion of women.

8.99   The approximate 90% confidence interval for μ is

$$\bar{x} \pm 1.645 \frac{s}{\sqrt{n}} - 9.7 \pm 1.645 \frac{5.8}{\sqrt{35}} = 9.7 \pm 1.613 \text{ or } 8.087 < \mu < 11.313$$

8.101   Assume that $\sigma = 6$ and the desired bound is 0.5. Then

$$1.96 \frac{\sigma}{\sqrt{n}} \le B \quad \Rightarrow \quad 1.96 \frac{6}{\sqrt{n}} \le 0.5 \quad \Rightarrow \quad n \ge 553.19 \text{ or } n \ge 554$$

8.103   The approximate 95% confidence interval for μ is

$$\bar{x} \pm 1.96 \frac{s}{\sqrt{n}} = 34 \pm 1.96 \frac{3}{\sqrt{100}} = 34 \pm 0.59 \text{ or } 33.41 < \mu < 34.59$$

8.105   **a**   If you use $p = 0.8$ as a conservative estimate for p, the margin of error is approximately

$$\pm 1.96 \sqrt{\frac{0.8(0.2)}{750}} = \pm 0.029$$

b   To reduce the margin of error in part **a** to ± 0.01, solve for n in the equation

$$1.96 \sqrt{\frac{0.8(0.2)}{n}} = 0.01 \quad \Rightarrow \quad \sqrt{n} = \frac{1.96(0.4)}{0.01} = 78.4 \quad \Rightarrow n = 6146.56 \text{ or } n = 6147$$

8.107   **a**   The approximate 95% confidence interval for p is

$$\hat{p} \pm 1.96 \sqrt{\frac{\hat{p}\hat{q}}{n}} = 0.67 \pm 1.96 \sqrt{\frac{0.67(0.33)}{2170}} = 0.67 \pm 0.020 \quad \text{or} \quad 0.65 < p < 0.69$$

b   The approximate 95% confidence interval for p is

$$\hat{p} \pm 1.96 \sqrt{\frac{\hat{p}\hat{q}}{n}} = 0.34 \pm 1.96 \sqrt{\frac{0.34(0.66)}{160}} = 0.34 \pm 0.073 \quad \text{or} \quad 0.267 < p < 0.413.$$

c   The approximate 98% confidence interval for $p_1 - p_2$ is

$$(\hat{p}_1 - \hat{p}_2) \pm 2.33 \sqrt{\frac{\hat{p}_1\hat{q}_1}{n_1} + \frac{\hat{p}_2\hat{q}_2}{n_2}}$$

$$(0.37 - 0.27) \pm 2.33 \sqrt{\frac{0.37(0.63)}{160} + \frac{0.27(0.73)}{(2170-160)}}$$

$$0.10 \pm 0.092 \quad \text{or} \quad 0.008 < (p_1 - p_2) < 0.192$$

8.109   It is assumed that $p = 0.2$ and that the desired bound is 0.01. Hence,

$$1.96 \sqrt{\frac{pq}{n}} \le 0.01 \quad \Rightarrow \quad \sqrt{n} \ge \frac{1.96\sqrt{0.05(0.95)}}{0.01} = 42.72$$

$$n \ge 1824.76 \quad \text{or} \quad n \ge 1825$$

8.111 Ten samples of $n = 400$ printed circuit boards were tested and a $100(1-\alpha)\%$ confidence interval for p was constructed for each of the ten samples. For this exercise, $100(1-\alpha)\% = 90\%$, or $\alpha = 0.10$. The object is to find the probability that exactly one of the intervals will not enclose the true value of p. Hence, the situation descries a binomial experiment with $n = 10$ and

$\qquad p* = $ P(an interval will not contain the true value of p)

$\qquad x = $ number of intervals which do not enclose p

By definition of a 90% confidence interval, it can be said that 90% of the intervals generated in repeated sampling will contain the true value of p; 10% of the intervals will not contain p. Thus, $p* = 0.1$ and the desired probabilities are calculated using the methods of Chapter 4.

1 $\quad P(\text{exactly one of the intervals fails to contain } p) = P(x = 1) = C_1^{10}(0.1)^1(0.9)^9 = 0.3874$

2 $\quad P(\text{at least one}) = 1 - P(x = 0) = 1 - C_0^{10}(0.1)^0(0.9)^{10} = 1 - 0.349 = 0.651$

8.113 **a** The approximate 95% confidence interval for μ is

$$\bar{x} \pm 1.96\frac{s}{\sqrt{n}} = 2.962 \pm 1.96\frac{0.529}{\sqrt{69}} = 2.962 \pm 0.125 \quad \text{or} \quad 2.837 < \mu < 3.087$$

b In order to cut the interval in half, the sample size must increase by 4. If this is done, the new half-width of the confidence interval is

$$1.96\frac{\sigma}{\sqrt{4n}} = \frac{1}{2}\left(1.96\frac{\sigma}{\sqrt{n}}\right)$$

Hence, in this case, the new sample size is $4(69) = 276$.

8.115 The approximate 99% confidence interval for μ is

$$\bar{x} \pm 2.58\frac{s}{\sqrt{n}} = 18,500 \pm 2.58\frac{700}{\sqrt{49}} = 18,500 \pm 258 \text{ or } 18,242 < \mu < 18,758$$

Since $\mu = 17,900$ is not in this interval, it is not possible that the average is as claimed in the exercise. The reported average is contradicted.

8.117 The approximate 98% confidence interval for μ is

$$\bar{x} \pm 2.33\frac{s}{\sqrt{n}} = 2.705 \pm 2.33\frac{0.028}{\sqrt{36}} = 2.705 \pm 0.011 \quad \text{or} \quad 2.694 < \mu < 2.716$$

8.119 Calculate $\hat{p} = \frac{80}{400} = 0.20$. Then the approximate 95% confidence interval for p is

$$\hat{p} \pm 1.96\sqrt{\frac{\hat{p}\hat{q}}{n}} = 0.20 \pm 1.96\sqrt{\frac{0.20(0.80)}{400}} = 0.20 \pm 0.039 \text{ or } 0.161 < p < 0.239$$

8.121 For this exercise, B = 0.08 for the binomial estimator $\hat{p}$, where $SE(\hat{p}) = \sqrt{\frac{pq}{n}}$. If $p = 0.2$, we have

$$1.96\sqrt{\frac{pq}{n}} \le B \Rightarrow 1.96\sqrt{\frac{0.2(0.8)}{n}} \le 0.08$$

$$\Rightarrow \sqrt{n} \ge \frac{1.96\sqrt{0.2(0.8)}}{0.08} \Rightarrow n \ge 9.8 \quad \text{or} \quad n \ge 96.04 \text{ or } n \ge 97$$

Case Study: How Reliable Is That Poll?

1   For the total sample of size $n = 2000$ adults, the margin of error for estimating any sample proportion p is approximately

$$1.96\sqrt{\frac{pq}{n}} \approx 1.96\sqrt{\frac{0.5(0.5)}{2000}} = 0.022$$

Hence, the margin of error is the same as the margin (± 2.2) given by the survey designers. Since the split samples are smaller, the sampling error for these smaller groups will be *larger* than ± 2.2 percentage points. For each of the split samples of $n = 1000$ adults, the margin of error is

$$1.96\sqrt{\frac{pq}{n}} \approx 1.96\sqrt{\frac{0.5(0.5)}{1000}} = 0.031.$$

2   The numbers in the table are the percentages falling in a particular opinion category.

3   Rotating the order of options and the order of questions is done to avoid biases that might be caused by order of presentation.

4   **a**   The approximate 95% confidence interval is

$$\hat{p} \pm 1.96\sqrt{\frac{\hat{p}\hat{q}}{n}} = 0.59 \pm 1.96\sqrt{\frac{0.59(0.41)}{1000}} = 0.59 \pm 0.030 \quad \text{or} \quad 0.56 < p < 0.62$$

   b   The approximate 95% confidence interval is

$$\hat{p} \pm 1.96\sqrt{\frac{\hat{p}\hat{q}}{n}} = 0.30 \pm 1.96\sqrt{\frac{0.30(0.70)}{1000}} = 0.30 \pm 0.028$$

   or $0.272 < p < 0.328$

5   The approximate 95% confidence interval is

$$(\hat{p}_1 - \hat{p}_2) + 1.96\sqrt{\frac{\hat{p}_1\hat{q}_1}{n_1} + \frac{\hat{p}_2\hat{q}_2}{n_2}}$$

$$(0.79 - 0.87) \pm 1.96\sqrt{\frac{0.79(0.21)}{2000} + \frac{0.87(0.13)}{1000}}$$

$$-0.08 \pm 0.027 \quad \text{or} \quad -0.107 < (p_1 - p_2) < -0.053$$

Since zero is not in the interval, it is not possible that $p_1 = p_2$. Yes, the proportion of people who say "multiculturalism makes them proud to be Canadian," and those who say that "the fact that people from different cultural groups in Canada get along and live in peace" are different.

6   Answers will vary from student to student. Responses today will not necessarily be similar to those reported here.

Project 8-A: Saving Time and Making Patients Safer

a   The point estimate for μ_2 is just the sample mean $\bar{x}_2 = 3.1$. The 95% margin of error when $n \geq 30$ is

estimated as $1.96\left(\dfrac{s}{\sqrt{n}}\right) = 1.96\left(\dfrac{\sqrt{1.68}}{\sqrt{100}}\right) = 0.254045$.

b   The 90% confidence interval is $\bar{x}_2 \pm 1.645\left(\dfrac{s}{\sqrt{n}}\right) = 3.1 \pm 1.645\left(\dfrac{\sqrt{1.68}}{\sqrt{100}}\right) = 3.1 \pm 0.213216$. Under repeated

sampling then, the true parameter μ_2 will lie in the interval (2.886784, 3.31322) 90% of the time.

c   No. Since the sample mean before the quality improvement is still higher than the upper boundary of our confidence interval for μ_2, we can conclude that the quality improvement has in fact worked.

d   Yes, the quality control department should be concerned because the waiting time of 2.7 hours falls under the lower boundary of our confidence interval for μ_2.

e   Yes, we can still use the standard normal distribution to construct a confidence internal for μ_2 because the Central Limit Theorem applies in this case.

f   Let us find the sample size n such that the margin of error is equal to 0.5 hours:

$0.5 = 1.96\left(\dfrac{1.7}{\sqrt{n}}\right) \Rightarrow n = \left[\dfrac{1.96(1.7)}{0.5}\right]^2 \approx 44.41$. Thus, a sample of size 45 would be required.

g   The best point estimator for $(\mu_1 - \mu_2)$ is simply $(\bar{x}_1 - \bar{x}_2) = (3.5 - 3.1) = 0.4$.

h   By the Central Limit Theorem, we can invoke approximate normality here. The mean of this normal

distribution will be $(\bar{x}_1 - \bar{x}_2)$, and the standard deviation of this normal distribution will be $\sqrt{\dfrac{s_1^2}{n_1} + \dfrac{s_2^2}{n_2}}$.

The margin of error can be found using $1.96\sqrt{\dfrac{s_1^2}{n_1} + \dfrac{s_2^2}{n_2}} = 1.96\sqrt{\dfrac{2.82}{100} + \dfrac{1.68}{100}} = 0.415779$.

i   A 98% confidence interval for $(\mu_1 - \mu_2)$ can be expressed as $(\bar{x}_1 - \bar{x}_2) \pm 2.33\sqrt{\dfrac{s_1^2}{n_1} + \dfrac{s_2^2}{n_2}}$

$= (3.5 - 3.1) \pm 2.33\sqrt{\dfrac{2.82}{100} + \dfrac{1.68}{100}} = 0.4 \pm 0.4943 = (-0.0943, 0.8943)$

j   No, since zero can be found in the interval, we cannot infer a difference in the true average waiting times.

k   The phrase "98% confident" mean that under repeated sampling, 98% of constructed intervals would contain the true value of the parameter.

Project 8-B: Attitudes of Canadian Women Toward Birthing Centres and Midwife Care for Childbirth

a   The point estimate of p_2 is simply $\hat{p}_2 = 0.31$. The 95% margin of error is given by $1.96\sqrt{\dfrac{\hat{p}_2 \hat{q}_2}{n_2}}$

$$= 1.96\sqrt{\frac{(0.31)(0.69)}{360}} = 0.048, \text{ where } \hat{q}_2 = 1 - \hat{p}_2.$$

b   The point estimate of p_3 is simply $\hat{p}_3 = 0.35$. The 95% margin of error is given by $1.96\sqrt{\dfrac{\hat{p}_3 \hat{q}_3}{n_3}}$

$$= 1.96\sqrt{\frac{(0.35)(0.65)}{169}} = 0.072, \text{ where } \hat{q}_3 = 1 - \hat{p}_3.$$

c   The 99% confidence interval for p_3 is given by $p_3 \pm z_{0.005}\sqrt{\dfrac{\hat{p}_3 \hat{q}_3}{n_3}} = 0.35 \pm 2.58\sqrt{\dfrac{(0.35)(0.65)}{169}}$

$$= 0.35 \pm 0.09466 = (0.25534, 0.44466).$$

Under repeated sampling, 99% of the time the constructed intervals for p_3 will contain the true value of p_3.

d   We need to find a sample of size n_1 such that the 90% margin of error is equal to 0.01. That is, we need

$z_{0.05}\sqrt{\dfrac{\hat{p}_1 \hat{q}_1}{n_1}} = 0.01$, where $z_{0.05} = 1.645$ (for a 90% confidence interval). Solving for n_1 we obtain

$n_1 = \dfrac{z_{0.05}^2 (\hat{p}_1 \hat{q}_1)}{(0.01)^2} = \dfrac{(1.645)^2 (0.28)(0.72)}{(0.01)^2} = 5455.35$. Thus, we would need to sample a minimum of

5456 women if we want the true population proportion to lie within 0.01 of our sample proportion.

e   We need to find a sample of size n_4 such that the 99% margin of error is equal to 0.1. That is, we need

$z_{0.005}\sqrt{\dfrac{\hat{p}_4 \hat{q}_4}{n_4}} = 0.1$, where $z_{0.005} = 2.58$ (for a 99% confidence interval). Solving for n_4, we obtain

$n_4 = \dfrac{z_{0.005}^2 (\hat{p}_4 \hat{q}_4)}{(0.1)^2} = \dfrac{(2.58)^2 (0.30)(0.70)}{(0.1)^2} = 139.78$. Thus, the researcher would need to sample a minimum

of 140 women if he wants the true population proportion to lie within 0.1 of the sample proportion.

f   A 98% confidence interval is $(\hat{p}_2 - \hat{p}_3) \pm z_{0.01}\sqrt{\dfrac{\hat{p}_2 \hat{q}_2}{n_2} + \dfrac{\hat{p}_3 \hat{q}_3}{n_3}}$, where $z_{0.01} = 2.33$. Inputting the required

values yields $(0.31 - 0.35) \pm 2.33\sqrt{\dfrac{(0.31)(0.69)}{360} + \dfrac{(0.35)(0.65)}{169}} = -0.4 \pm 0.1026 = (-0.5026, -0.2974)$. Thus,

we are 98% confident that the true difference in proportions is between -0.5026 and -0.2974.

g   Since zero is not in the interval, we can safely conclude that the two proportions are unequal. That is, there is a real difference in the proportion of women who would like to use a birthing centre between Ontario women and Quebec women.

h   The point estimate of the difference is simply $(\hat{p}_1 - \hat{p}_4) = 0.28 - 0.30 = -0.02$. A 95% margin of error

is $1.96\sqrt{\dfrac{\hat{p}_1\hat{q}_1}{n_1} + \dfrac{\hat{p}_4\hat{q}_4}{n_4}} = 1.96\sqrt{\dfrac{(0.28)(0.72)}{49} + \dfrac{(0.30)(0.70)}{225}} = 0.13925$.

i   It depends on what is meant by "compare." Parameters can be compared to others in different ways. Given the methodology covered in Chapter 8, the answer is likely "no." However, there are more advanced methods, beyond the scope of this text, that would suggest the answer is "yes": it is possible to compare many proportions simultaneously.

Chapter 9: Large-Sample Tests of Hypotheses

9.1 **a** The critical value that separates the rejection and non-rejection regions for a right-tailed test based on a z-statistic will be a value of z (called z_α) such that $P(z > z_\alpha) = \alpha = 0.01$. That is, $z_{0.01} = 2.33$ (see the figure below). The null hypothesis H_0 will be rejected if $z > 2.33$.

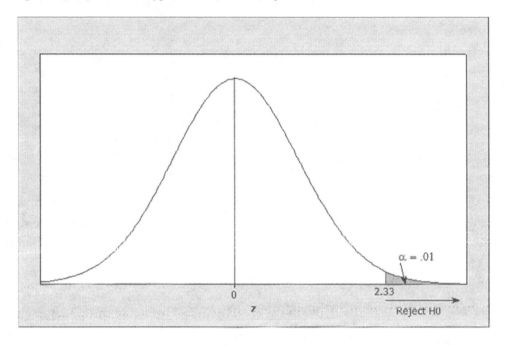

b For a two-tailed test with $\alpha = 0.05$, the critical value for the rejection region cuts off $\alpha/2 = 0.025$ in the two tails of the z distribution in the figure below, so that $z_{0.025} = 1.96$. The null hypothesis H_0 will be rejected if $z > 1.96$ or $z < -1.96$ (which you can also write as $|z| > 1.96$).

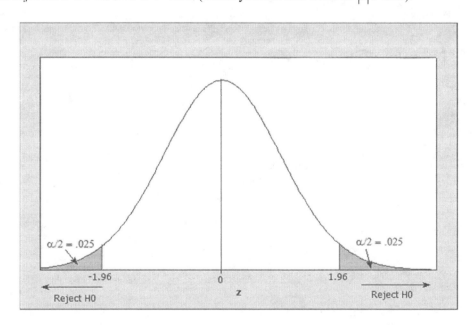

    c   Similar to part **a**, with the rejection region in the lower tail of the z distribution. The null hypothesis H_0 will be rejected if $z < -2.33$.

    d   Similar to part **b**, with $\alpha/2 = 0.005$. The null hypothesis H_0 will be rejected if $z > 2.58$ or $z < -2.58$ (which you can also write as $|z| > 2.58$).

9.3   **a**   Similar to the Exercise 9.1, the critical value that separates the rejection and non-rejection regions for a left-tailed test based on a z-statistic will be a values of z such that $p(z < -z_\alpha) = 0.01$. That is, $z_{0.01} = -2.33$. The null hypothesis H_0 will be rejected if $z < -2.33$.

    b   The critical values that separates the rejection and non-rejection regions for a two-tailed test based on a z-statistic will be a values of z (called z_α) such that $2P(z > |z_\alpha|) = 0.01$. Thus, the critical region is $z > 2.575$ and $z < -2.575$ for tail area $\alpha/2 = 0.005$. The null hypothesis H_0 will be rejected if $z < -2.575$ or $z > 2.575$ (which we can also write as $|z| > 2.575$).

    c   Since $z = -2.41$ does fall in the rejection region, we reject the null hypothesis at $\alpha = 0.01$ for the problem in part **a**. However, for the problem in part **b**, we fail to reject the null hypothesis at $\alpha = 0.01$ since the test statistics value ($z = -2.41$) does not fall in the rejection region.

9.5   Use the guidelines for statistical significance in Section 9.3. The smaller the p-value, the more evidence there is in favour of rejecting H_0. For part **a**, p-value $= 0.1251$ is not statistically significant; H_0 is not rejected. For part **b**, p-value $= 0.0054$ is less than 0.01 and the results are highly significant; H_0 should be rejected. For part **c**, p-value $= 0.0351$ is between 0.01 and 0.05. The results are significant at the 5% level, but not at the 1% level ($P < 0.05$).

9.7   **a**   Since this is a right-tailed test, the p-value is the area under the standard normal distribution to the right of $z = 2.04$:
$$p\text{-value} = P(z > 2.04) = 1 - 0.9793 = 0.0207$$

    b   The p-value, 0.0207, is less than $\alpha = 0.05$, and the null hypothesis is rejected at the 5% level of significance. There is sufficient evidence to indicate that $\mu > 2.3$.

    c   The conclusions reached using the **critical value approach** and the **p-value approach** are identical.

9.9   The null hypothesis to be tested is
$$H_0: \ \mu = 28 \quad \text{versus} \quad H_a: \ \mu \neq 28$$
and the test statistic is
$$z = \frac{\bar{x} - \mu_0}{\sigma/\sqrt{n}} \approx \frac{\bar{x} - \mu_0}{s/\sqrt{n}} = \frac{26.8 - 28}{6.5/\sqrt{100}} = -1.85$$
with p-value $= P(|z| > 1.85) = 2(0.0322) = 0.0644$. To draw a conclusion from the p-value, use the guidelines for statistical significance in Section 9.3. Since the p-value is greater than 0.05, the null hypothesis should not be rejected. There is insufficient evidence to indicate that the mean is different from 28. (Some researchers might report these results as *tending toward significance*.)

9.11   **a**   In order to make sure that the average weight was 1 kilogram, you would test
$$H_0: \ \mu = 1 \quad \text{versus} \quad H_a: \ \mu \neq 1$$

    b–c The test statistic is
$$z = \frac{\bar{x} - \mu_0}{\sigma/\sqrt{n}} \approx \frac{\bar{x} - \mu_0}{s/\sqrt{n}} = \frac{1.01 - 1}{0.02/\sqrt{35}} = 2.96$$
with p-value $= P(|z| > 2.96) = 2(0.0015) = 0.003$. Since the p-value is less than 0.05, the null hypothesis should be rejected. The manager should report that there is sufficient evidence to indicate that the mean is different from 1.

9.13 The theatre chain claims that the average time is no more than 3 minutes. To disprove this claim, you need to show that this average is more than 3 minutes, and you should test

$$H_0: \mu = 3 \quad \text{versus} \quad H_a: \mu > 3$$

with the test statistic

$$z = \frac{\bar{x} - \mu_0}{\sigma/\sqrt{n}} \approx \frac{\bar{x} - \mu_0}{s/\sqrt{n}} = \frac{3.25 - 3}{0.5/\sqrt{50}} = 3.54$$

Since this is a one-tailed test, the rejection region with $\alpha = 0.01$ is set in the right tail of the z-distribution as $z > z_{0.01} = 2.33$ (similar to Exercise 9.1c). Since the observed value $z = 3.54$ falls in the rejection region, H_0 is rejected. There is evidence that the average time is more than claimed by the theatre chain.

9.15 The null hypothesis to be tested is

$$H_0: \mu = 7 \quad \text{versus} \quad H_a: \mu < 7$$

and the test statistic is

$$z = \frac{\bar{x} - \mu_0}{\sigma/\sqrt{n}} \approx \frac{\bar{x} - \mu_0}{s/\sqrt{n}} = \frac{6.7 - 7}{2.7/\sqrt{80}} = -0.992$$

The rejection region with $\alpha = 0.05$ is $z < -1.645$ (similar to Exercise 9.10). The observed value, $z = -0.992$, does not fall in the rejection region and H_0 is not rejected. The data do not provide sufficient evidence to indicate that $\mu < 7$.

9.17   **a**   The null hypothesis to be tested is

$$H_0: \mu = 37 \quad \text{versus} \quad H_a: \mu \neq 37$$

and the test statistic is

$$z = \frac{\bar{x} - \mu_0}{\sigma/\sqrt{n}} \approx \frac{\bar{x} - \mu_0}{s/\sqrt{n}} = \frac{36.81 - 37}{0.73/\sqrt{130}} = -2.97$$

with p-value $= P(z < -2.97) + P(z > 2.97) = 2(0.0015) = 0.003$. Alternatively, we could write p-value $= 2P(z < -2.97) = 2(0.0015) = 0.0030$. With $\alpha = 0.05$, the p-value is less than α and H_0 is rejected. There is sufficient evidence to indicate that the average body temperature for healthy humans is different from 37°C.

b–c   Using the critical value approach, we set the null and alternative hypotheses and calculate the test statistic as in part **a**. The rejection region with $\alpha = 0.05$ is $|z| > 1.96$. The observed value, $z = -2.97$, does fall in the rejection region and H_0 is rejected. The conclusion is the same is in part **a**.

d   How did the doctor record 1 million temperatures in 1868? The technology available at that time makes this a difficult, if not impossible, task. It may also have been that the instruments used for this research were not entirely accurate.

9.19   **a–b**   The null hypothesis of interest is one-tailed:

$$H_0: \mu_1 - \mu_2 = 0 \quad \text{versus} \quad H_a: \mu_1 - \mu_2 > 0$$

c   The test statistic, calculated under the assumption that $\mu_1 - \mu_2 = 0$, is

$$z = \frac{(\bar{x}_1 - \bar{x}_2) - (\mu_1 - \mu_2)}{\sqrt{\dfrac{\sigma_1^2}{n_1} + \dfrac{\sigma_2^2}{n_2}}}$$

with σ_1^2 and σ_2^2 known, or estimated by s_1^2 and s_2^2, respectively. For this exercise,

$$z \approx \frac{(\bar{x}_1 - \bar{x}_2) - 0}{\sqrt{\dfrac{s_1^2}{n_1} + \dfrac{s_2^2}{n_2}}} = \frac{11.6 - 9.7}{\sqrt{\dfrac{27.9}{80} + \dfrac{38.4}{80}}} = 2.09$$

a value that lies slightly more than two standard deviations from the hypothesized difference of zero. This would be a somewhat unlikely observation, if H_0 is true.

d   The *p*-value for this one-tailed test is

$$p\text{-value} = P(z > 2.09) = 1 - 0.9817 = 0.0183$$

Since the *p*-value is not less than $\alpha = 0.01$, the null hypothesis cannot be rejected at the 1% level. There is insufficient evidence to conclude that $\mu_1 - \mu_2 > 0$.

e   Using the critical value approach, the rejection region, with $\alpha = 0.01$, is $z > 2.33$ (see Exercise 9.1a). Since the observed value of z does not fall in the rejection region, H_0 is not rejected. There is insufficient evidence to indicate that $\mu_1 - \mu_2 > 0$, or $\mu_1 > \mu_2$.

9.21   The probability that you are making an incorrect decision is influenced by the fact that if $\mu_1 - \mu_2 = 0$, it is just as likely that $\bar{x}_1 - \bar{x}_2$ will be positive as that it will be negative. Hence, a two-tailed rejection region *must* be used. Choosing a one-tailed region after determining the sign of $\bar{x}_1 - \bar{x}_2$ simply tells us which of the two pieces of the rejection region is being used. Hence,

$$\alpha = P\left(\text{reject } H_0 \text{ when } H_0 \text{ true}\right) = P\left(z > 1.645 \text{ or } z < -1.645 \text{ when } H_0 \text{ true}\right)$$
$$= \alpha_1 + \alpha_2 = 0.05 + 0.05 = 0.10$$

which is twice what the experimenter thinks it is. Hence, one cannot choose the rejection region after the test is performed.

9.23   **a**   The null hypothesis of interest is one-tailed:

$$H_0: \mu_1 - \mu_2 = 0 \quad \text{versus} \quad H_a: \mu_1 - \mu_2 > 0$$

The test statistic, calculated under the assumption that $\mu_1 - \mu_2 = 0$, is

$$z \approx \frac{(\bar{x}_1 - \bar{x}_2) - 0}{\sqrt{\dfrac{s_1^2}{n_1} + \dfrac{s_2^2}{n_2}}} = \frac{33.1 - 28.6}{\sqrt{\dfrac{(11.3)^2}{400} + \dfrac{(12.7)^2}{400}}} = 5.29$$

The rejection region, with $\alpha = 0.01$, is $z > 2.33$ and H_0 is rejected. There is evidence to indicate that $\mu_1 - \mu_2 > 0$, or $\mu_1 > \mu_2$. The average per-capita beef consumption has decreased in the last 10 years. (Alternatively, the *p*-value for this test is the area to the right of $z = 5.29$, which is very close to zero and less than $\alpha = 0.01$.)

b   For the difference $\mu_1 - \mu_2$ in the population means this year and 10 years ago, the 99% lower confidence bound uses $z_{0.01} = 2.33$ and is calculated as

$$(\bar{x}_1 - \bar{x}_2) - 2.33\sqrt{\frac{s_1^2}{n_1} + \frac{s_2^2}{n_2}} = (33.1 - 28.6) - 2.33\sqrt{\frac{11.3^2}{400} + \frac{12.7^2}{400}}$$
$$= 4.5 - 1.98 \quad \text{or} \quad (\mu_1 - \mu_2) > 2.52$$

Since the difference in the means is positive, you can again conclude that there has been a decrease in average per-capita beef consumption over the last 10 years. In addition, it is likely that the average consumption has decreased by more than 2.52 kg per year.

9.25   **a**   The null hypothesis of interest is two-tailed:

$$H_0: \mu_1 - \mu_2 = 0 \quad \text{versus} \quad H_a: \mu_1 - \mu_2 \neq 0$$

and the test statistic, calculated under the assumption that $\mu_1 - \mu_2 = 0$, is

$$z \approx \frac{(\bar{x}_1 - \bar{x}_2) - 0}{\sqrt{\dfrac{s_1^2}{n_1} + \dfrac{s_2^2}{n_2}}} = \frac{40,554 - 38,348}{\sqrt{\dfrac{2225^2}{50} + \dfrac{2375^2}{50}}} = 4.79$$

The rejection region, with $\alpha = 0.05$, is $|z| > 1.96$ and H_0 is rejected. There is evidence to indicate a difference in the means for the graduates in education and the social sciences.

b   The conclusions are the same.

9.27   **a** H_0: $\mu_1 - \mu_2 = 0$ versus H_a: $\mu_1 - \mu_2 \neq 0$

The test statistic is

$$z \approx \frac{(\bar{x}_1 - \bar{x}_2) - 0}{\sqrt{\dfrac{s_1^2}{n_1} + \dfrac{s_2^2}{n_2}}} = \frac{165 - 125}{\sqrt{\dfrac{22.5^2}{50} + \dfrac{12.8^2}{50}}} = 10.926$$

The rejection region, with $\alpha = 0.05$, is $|z| > 1.96$ and H_0 is rejected. There is evidence to indicate that there is a difference in the average room rates for the Westin hotels and Doubletree hotels.

   b   The 95% confidence interval for $\mu_1 - \mu_2$ is approximately

$$(\bar{x}_1 - \bar{x}_2) \pm 1.96 \sqrt{\dfrac{s_1^2}{n_1} + \dfrac{s_2^2}{n_2}}$$

$$(165 - 125) \pm 1.96 \sqrt{\dfrac{22.5^2}{50} + \dfrac{12.8^2}{50}}$$

$$40 \pm 7.1753 \quad \text{or} \quad 32.8247 < \mu_1 - \mu_2 < 47.1753$$

Since the value $\mu_1 - \mu_2 = 0$ does not fall in the interval in part **b**, it is likely that two means are different, confirming the conclusion in part **a**.

9.29   **a**   The null hypothesis of interest is one-tailed:

H_0: $\mu_1 - \mu_2 = 0$ versus H_a: $\mu_1 - \mu_2 < 0$

The test statistic, calculated under the assumption that $\mu_1 - \mu_2 = 0$, is

$$z \approx \frac{(\bar{x}_1 - \bar{x}_2) - 0}{\sqrt{\dfrac{s_1^2}{n_1} + \dfrac{s_2^2}{n_2}}} = \frac{15 - 23}{\sqrt{\dfrac{(4)^2}{30} + \dfrac{(10)^2}{40}}} = -4.59$$

The rejection region, with $\alpha = 0.01$, is $z < -2.33$ and H_0 is rejected. There is evidence to indicate that $\mu_1 - \mu_2 < 0$, or $\mu_1 < \mu_2$. The average time to complete the task was longer for the experimental "rock music" group. (Alternatively, the p-value for this test is the area to the left of $z = -4.59$, which is very close to zero and less than $\alpha = 0.01$.)

   b   For the difference $\mu_1 - \mu_2$ in the population means for the control versus experimental groups, the 99% upper confidence bound uses $z_{0.01} = 2.33$ and is calculated as

$$(\bar{x}_1 - \bar{x}_2) + 2.33 \sqrt{\dfrac{s_1^2}{n_1} + \dfrac{s_2^2}{n_2}} = (15 - 23) + 2.33 \sqrt{\dfrac{4^2}{30} + \dfrac{10^2}{40}}$$

$$-8 + 4.058 \quad \text{or} \quad (\mu_1 - \mu_2) < -3.942$$

Since the difference in the means is negative, you can again conclude that the average time to complete the task was longer for the experimental "rock music" group.

9.31   **a**   The null hypothesis of interest concerns the binomial parameter p and is one-tailed:

H_0: $p = 0.3$ versus H_a: $p < 0.3$

   b   The rejection region is one-tailed, with $\alpha = 0.05$, or $z < -1.645$.

   c   It is given that $x = 279$ and $n = 1000$, so that $\hat{p} = \dfrac{x}{n} = \dfrac{279}{1000} = 0.279$. The test statistic is then

$$z = \frac{\hat{p} - p_0}{\sqrt{\dfrac{p_0 q_0}{n}}} = \frac{0.279 - 0.3}{\sqrt{\dfrac{0.3(0.7)}{1000}}} = -1.449$$

Since the observed value does not fall in the rejection region, H_0 is not rejected. We cannot conclude that $p < 0.3$.

9.33   The null hypothesis of interest is one-tailed:
$$H_0: \ p = 0.5 \quad \text{versus} \quad H_a: \ p > 0.5$$

With $x = 72$ and $n = 120$, so that $\hat{p} = \dfrac{x}{n} = \dfrac{72}{120} = 0.6$, the test statistic is

$$z = \frac{\hat{p} - p_0}{\sqrt{\dfrac{p_0 q_0}{n}}} = \frac{0.6 - 0.5}{\sqrt{\dfrac{0.5(0.5)}{120}}} = 2.19$$

Students may use one of two approaches:

Critical value approach: The rejection region is one-tailed, with $z > 1.645$ with $\alpha = 0.05$ or $z > 2.33$ with $\alpha = 0.01$. Hence, H_0 is rejected at the 5% level, but not at the 1% level. At the 5% significance level, we conclude that $p > 0.5$.

_p_-value approach: Calculate p-value $= P(z > 2.19) = 1 - 0.9857 = 0.0143$. Since this p-value is between 0.01 and 0.05, H_0 is rejected at the 5% level, but not at the 1% level. At the 5% significance level, we conclude that $p > 0.5$.

9.35   **a**   The null hypothesis of interest is two-tailed:
$$H_0: \ p = 0.75 \quad \text{versus} \quad H_a: \ p \neq 0.75$$

b   With $x = 58$ and $n = 100$, so that $\hat{p} = \dfrac{x}{n} = \dfrac{58}{100} = 0.58$, the test statistic is

$$z = \frac{\hat{p} - p_0}{\sqrt{\dfrac{p_0 q_0}{n}}} = \frac{0.58 - 0.75}{\sqrt{\dfrac{0.75(0.25)}{100}}} = -3.93$$

with p-value $= P(|z| > 3.93) < 2(0.0002) = 0.0004$ or p-value ≈ 0. Since this p-value is less than 0.01, H_0 is rejected at the 1% level of significance and the results are declared highly significant. There is evidence that the proportion of red flowered plants is not 0.75.

9.37   **a**   The null hypothesis of interest is one-tailed:
$$H_0: \ p = 0.1 \quad \text{versus} \quad H_a: \ p > 0.1$$

With $\hat{p} = \dfrac{x}{n} = \dfrac{25}{100} = 0.25$, , the test statistic is

$$z = \frac{\hat{p} - p_0}{\sqrt{\dfrac{p_0 q_0}{n}}} = \frac{0.25 - 0.1}{\sqrt{\dfrac{0.1(0.9)}{100}}} = 5$$

with p-value $= P(z > 5) < 1 - 0.9998 = 0.0002$. Since this p-value is less than 0.05, H_0 is rejected at the 5% level of significance. There is evidence that the proportion of infested fields is larger than expected.

b   The most obvious reason for this unusually high proportion of infested fields is that there is contagion at work; that is, the $n = 100$ fields may not be independent, but may be contaminating one another.

9.39 **a** The null hypothesis of interest is

$$H_0:\ p = 0.19 \quad \text{versus} \quad H_a:\ p \neq 0.19$$

With $\hat{p} = \dfrac{x}{n} = \dfrac{20}{90} = 0.22$, the test statistic is

$$z = \frac{\hat{p} - p_0}{\sqrt{\dfrac{p_0 q_0}{n}}} = \frac{0.22 - 0.19}{\sqrt{\dfrac{0.19(0.81)}{90}}} = 0.73$$

The rejection region is two-tailed, $\alpha = 0.05$, or $|z| > 1.96$ and H_0 is not rejected. There is insufficient evidence to indicate that the claim is incorrect.

b The null hypothesis of interest is

$$H_0:\ p = 0.60 \quad \text{versus} \quad H_a:\ p \neq 0.60$$

With $\hat{p} = \dfrac{x}{n} = \dfrac{50}{90} = 0.56$, the test statistic is

$$z = \frac{\hat{p} - p_0}{\sqrt{\dfrac{p_0 q_0}{n}}} = \frac{0.56 - 0.60}{\sqrt{\dfrac{0.60(0.40)}{90}}} = -0.77$$

The rejection region is two-tailed, $\alpha = 0.05$, or $|z| > 1.96$ and H_0 is not rejected. There is insufficient evidence to indicate that the claim is incorrect.

c Unless the experimenter had some preconceived idea that the proportion might be greater or less than claimed, there would be no reason to run a one-tailed test.

9.41 The null hypothesis of interest is

$$H_0:\ p = 0.45 \quad \text{versus} \quad H_a:\ p \neq 0.45$$

With $\hat{p} = \dfrac{x}{n} = \dfrac{140}{300} = 0.47$, the test statistic is

$$z = \frac{\hat{p} - p_0}{\sqrt{\dfrac{p_0 q_0}{n}}} = \frac{0.47 - 0.45}{\sqrt{\dfrac{0.45(0.55)}{300}}} = 0.70$$

The rejection region, with $\alpha = 0.01$, is $|z| > 2.58$ and the null hypothesis is not rejected. (Alternatively, we could calculate p-value $= 2P(z > 0.70) = 2(0.2420) = 0.4840$. Since this p-value is greater than 0.01, the null hypothesis is not rejected.) There is insufficient evidence to indicate that the concerned percentage of Canadians is different from the reported percentage.

9.43 The null hypothesis of interest is

$$H_0:\ p = 0.5 \quad \text{versus} \quad H_a:\ p \neq 0.5$$

With $\hat{p} = \dfrac{x}{n} = \dfrac{114}{300} = 0.38$, the test statistic is

$$z = \frac{\hat{p} - p_0}{\sqrt{\dfrac{p_0 q_0}{n}}} = \frac{0.38 - 0.5}{\sqrt{\dfrac{0.5(0.5)}{300}}} = -4.16$$

with p-value $= 2P(|z| > 4.16) \approx 0$. Since this p-value is smaller than $\alpha = 0.05$, the null hypothesis is rejected. There is thus sufficient evidence to indicate that the proportion of households with at least one pet is different than reported by the Statistics Canada.

9.45 **a–b** If p_1 cannot be larger than p_2, the only alternative to $H_0:\ p_1 - p_2 = 0$ is that $p_1 < p_2$, and the one-tailed alternative is $H_a:\ p_1 - p_2 < 0$.

    c   The rejection region, with $\alpha = 0.05$, is $z < -1.645$ and the observed value of the test statistic is $z = -0.84$. The null hypothesis is not rejected. There is no evidence to indicate that p_1 is smaller than p_2.

9.47   **a**   The null hypothesis of interest is

$$H_0: p_1 - p_2 = 0 \quad \text{versus} \quad H_a: p_1 - p_2 < 0$$

Calculate $\hat{p}_1 = 0.36$, $\hat{p}_2 = 0.60$, and $\hat{p} = \dfrac{n_1\hat{p}_1 + n_2\hat{p}_2}{n_1 + n_2} = \dfrac{18 + 30}{50 + 50} = 0.48$

The test statistic is then

$$z = \frac{\hat{p}_1 - \hat{p}_2}{\sqrt{\hat{p}\hat{q}\left(\dfrac{1}{n_1} + \dfrac{1}{n_2}\right)}} = \frac{0.36 - 0.60}{\sqrt{0.48(0.52)(1/50 + 1/50)}} = -2.40$$

The rejection region, with $\alpha = 0.05$, is $z < -1.645$ and H_0 is rejected. There is evidence of a difference in the proportion of survivors for the two groups.

   b   From Section 8.7, the approximate 95% confidence interval is

$$\left(\hat{p}_1 - \hat{p}_2\right) \pm 1.96\sqrt{\frac{\hat{p}_1\hat{q}_1}{n_1} + \frac{\hat{p}_2\hat{q}_2}{n_2}}$$

$$\left(0.36 - 0.60\right) \pm 1.96\sqrt{\frac{0.36(0.64)}{50} + \frac{0.60(0.40)}{50}}$$

$$-0.24 \pm 0.19 \quad \text{or} \quad -0.43 < \left(p_1 - p_2\right) < -0.05$$

9.49   **a**   The null hypothesis of interest is

$$H_0: p_1 - p_2 = 0 \quad \text{versus} \quad H_a: p_1 - p_2 \neq 0$$

Calculate $\hat{p}_1 = \dfrac{123}{440} = 0.280$, $\hat{p}_2 = \dfrac{145}{560} = 0.259$, and $\hat{p} = \dfrac{x_1 + x_2}{n_1 + n_2} = \dfrac{123 + 145}{440 + 560} = 0.268$

The test statistic is then

$$z = \frac{\hat{p}_1 - \hat{p}_2}{\sqrt{\hat{p}\hat{q}\left(\dfrac{1}{n_1} + \dfrac{1}{n_2}\right)}} = \frac{0.280 - 0.259}{\sqrt{0.268(0.732)(1/440 + 1/560)}} = 0.74$$

The rejection region, with $\alpha = 0.01$, is $|z| > 2.58$ and H_0 is not rejected. There is no evidence of a difference in the proportion of frequent moviegoers in the two demographic groups.

   b   A difference in the proportions might mean that the advertisers would choose different products to advertise before this movie.

9.51   The null hypothesis of interest is

$$H_0: p_1 - p_2 = 0 \quad \text{versus} \quad H_a: p_1 - p_2 > 0$$

Calculate $\hat{p}_1 = \dfrac{40}{2266} = 0.018$, $\hat{p}_2 = \dfrac{21}{2266} = 0.009$, and $\hat{p} = \dfrac{x_1 + x_2}{n_1 + n_2} = \dfrac{40 + 21}{4532} = 0.013$

The test statistic is then

$$z = \frac{\hat{p}_1 - \hat{p}_2}{\sqrt{\hat{p}\hat{q}\left(\dfrac{1}{n_1} + \dfrac{1}{n_2}\right)}} = \frac{0.018 - 0.009}{\sqrt{0.013(0.987)(1/2266 + 1/2266)}} = 2.67$$

The rejection region, with $\alpha = 0.01$, is $z > 2.33$ and H_0 is rejected. There is sufficient evidence to indicate that the risk of dementia is higher for patients using *Prempro*.

9.53   **a**   Since the two treatments were randomly assigned, the randomization procedure can be implemented as each patient becomes available for treatment. Choose a random number between 0 and 9 for each patient. If the patient receives a number between 0 and 4, the assigned drug is *aspirin*. If the patient receives a number between 5 and 9, the assigned drug is clopidogrel.

       b   Assuming $n_1 = 7720$ and $n_2 = 7780$, we are given that $\hat{p}_1 = 0.054$, $\hat{p}_2 = 0.038$ so that

$$\hat{p} = \frac{n_1 \hat{p}_1 + n_2 \hat{p}_2}{n_1 + n_2} = \frac{7720(0.054) + 7780(0.038)}{15,500} = 0.046$$

The test statistic is then

$$z = \frac{\hat{p}_1 - \hat{p}_2}{\sqrt{\hat{p}\hat{q}\left(\dfrac{1}{n_1} + \dfrac{1}{n_2}\right)}} = \frac{0.054 - 0.038}{\sqrt{0.046(0.954)(1/7720 + 1/7780)}} = 4.75$$

with $p\text{-value} = P(|z| > |\,4.75) < 2(0.0002) = 0.0004$. Since the p-value is less than 0.01, the results are statistically significant. There is sufficient evidence to indicate a difference in the proportions for the two treatment groups.

       c   Clopidogrel would be the preferred treatment as long as there are no serious side effects.

9.55   See Section 9.3 of the text.

9.57   The power of the test is $1 - \beta = P(\text{reject } H_0 \text{ when } H_0 \text{ is false})$. As μ gets farther from μ_0, the power of the test increases.

9.59   The objective of this experiment is to make a decision about the binomial parameter p, which is the probability that a customer prefers the first colour. Hence, the null hypothesis will be that a customer has no preference for the first colour, and the alternative will be that the customer does have a preference. If the null hypothesis is true, then

$$H_0: p = P(\text{customer prefers the first colour}) = 1/3$$

If the customer actually has a preference for the first colour, then

$$H_a: p > 1/3$$

       a   The test statistic is calculated with $\hat{p} = \dfrac{400}{1000} - 0.4$ as

$$z = \frac{\hat{p} - p_0}{\sqrt{\dfrac{p_0 q_0}{n}}} = \frac{0.4 - 1/3}{\sqrt{\dfrac{(1/3)(2/3)}{1000}}} = 4.47$$

and the p-value is $p\text{-value} = P(z > 4.47) < 1 - 0.9998 = 0.0002$, since $P(z > 4.47)$ is surely less than $P(z > 3.49)$, the largest value in Table 3, Appendix I.

       b   Since $\alpha = 0.05$ is larger than the p-value, which is less than 0.0002, H_0 can be rejected. We conclude that customers have a preference for the first colour.

9.61   **a–b**   Since it is necessary to prove that the average pH level is less than 7.5, the null hypothesis to be tested is one-tailed:

$$H_0: \mu = 7.5 \quad \text{versus} \quad H_a: \mu < 7.5$$

       c   Answers will vary.

       d   The test statistic is $z = \dfrac{\bar{x} - \mu}{\sigma/\sqrt{n}} \approx \dfrac{\bar{x} - \mu}{s/\sqrt{n}} = \dfrac{-0.2}{0.2/\sqrt{30}} = -5.477$

and the rejection region, with $\alpha = 0.05$, is $z < -1.645$. The observed value, $z = -5.477$, falls in the rejection region and H_0 is rejected. We conclude that the average pH level is less than 7.5.

9.63   **a–b**   Since there is no prior knowledge as to which mean should be larger, the null hypothesis of interest is two-tailed:

$$H_0: \mu_1 - \mu_2 = 0 \quad \text{versus} \quad H_a: \mu_1 - \mu_2 \neq 0$$

   c   The test statistic is

$$z \approx \frac{(\bar{x}_1 - \bar{x}_2) - 0}{\sqrt{\dfrac{s_1^2}{n_1} + \dfrac{s_2^2}{n_2}}} = \frac{908 - 976}{\sqrt{\dfrac{347^2}{40} + \dfrac{293^2}{40}}} = -0.947$$

The rejection region, with $\alpha = 0.05$, is two-tailed or $|z| > 1.96$. The null hypothesis is not rejected. There is insufficient evidence to indicate a difference in the two means.

9.65   Let p_1 be the proportion of defectives produced by machine A, and p_2 be the proportion of defectives produced by machine B. The null hypothesis to be tested is

$$H_0: p_1 - p_2 = 0 \quad \text{versus} \quad H_a: p_1 - p_2 \neq 0$$

Calculate $\hat{p}_1 = \dfrac{16}{200} = 0.08$, $\hat{p}_2 = \dfrac{8}{200} = 0.04$, and $\hat{p} = \dfrac{x_1 + x_2}{n_1 + n_2} = \dfrac{16 + 8}{200 + 200} = 0.06$

The test statistic is then

$$z = \frac{\hat{p}_1 - \hat{p}_2}{\sqrt{\hat{p}\hat{q}\left(\dfrac{1}{n_1} + \dfrac{1}{n_2}\right)}} = \frac{0.08 - 0.04}{\sqrt{0.06(0.94)(1/200 + 1/200)}} = 1.684$$

The rejection region, with $\alpha = 0.05$, is $|z| > 1.96$, and H_0 is not rejected. There is insufficient evidence to indicate that the machines are performing differently in terms of the percentage of defectives being produced.

9.67   **a**   The null hypothesis to be tested is

$$H_0: p_1 - p_2 = 0 \quad \text{versus} \quad H_a: p_1 - p_2 > 0$$

Calculate $\hat{p}_1 = \dfrac{136}{200} = 0.68$, $\hat{p}_2 = \dfrac{124}{200} = 0.62$, and $\hat{p} = \dfrac{x_1 + x_2}{n_1 + n_2} = \dfrac{136 + 124}{200 + 200} = 0.65$

The test statistic is then

$$z = \frac{\hat{p}_1 - \hat{p}_2}{\sqrt{\hat{p}\hat{q}\left(\dfrac{1}{n_1} + \dfrac{1}{n_2}\right)}} = \frac{0.68 - 0.62}{\sqrt{0.65(0.35)(1/200 + 1/200)}} = 1.26$$

and the p-value is $P(z \geq 1.26) = 1 - 0.8962 = 0.1038$

   b   Since the observed p-value, 0.1038, is greater than $\alpha = 0.05$, H_0 cannot be rejected. There is insufficient evidence to support the researcher's belief.

9.69   The null hypothesis to be tested is

$$H_0: \mu_1 - \mu_2 = 0 \quad \text{versus} \quad H_a: \mu_1 - \mu_2 > 0$$

and the test statistic is

$$z \approx \frac{(\bar{x}_1 - \bar{x}_2) - 0}{\sqrt{\dfrac{s_1^2}{n_1} + \dfrac{s_2^2}{n_2}}} = \frac{4.54 - 3.63}{\sqrt{\dfrac{1.95}{40} + \dfrac{2.59}{40}}} = 2.70$$

The rejection region, with $\alpha = 0.05$, is one-tailed or $z > 1.645$ and the null hypothesis is rejected. There is sufficient evidence to indicate a difference in the two means. Hence, we conclude that diet I has a greater mean weight loss than diet II.

9.71 The null hypothesis to be tested is
$$H_0: \mu_1 - \mu_2 = 0 \quad \text{versus} \quad H_a: \mu_1 - \mu_2 \neq 0$$
and the test statistic is
$$z \approx \frac{(\overline{x}_1 - \overline{x}_2) - 0}{\sqrt{\dfrac{s_1^2}{n_1} + \dfrac{s_2^2}{n_2}}} = \frac{1925 - 1905}{\sqrt{\dfrac{40^2}{100} + \dfrac{30^2}{100}}} = 4$$

The rejection region, with $\alpha = 0.05$, is two-tailed or $|z| > 1.96$ and the null hypothesis is rejected. There is difference in mean breaking strengths for the two cables.

9.73 **a** The null hypothesis to be tested is
$$H_0: \mu_1 - \mu_2 = 0 \quad \text{versus} \quad H_a: \mu_1 - \mu_2 > 0$$
and the test statistic is
$$z \approx \frac{(\overline{x}_1 - \overline{x}_2) - 0}{\sqrt{\dfrac{s_1^2}{n_1} + \dfrac{s_2^2}{n_2}}} = \frac{109 - 103}{\sqrt{\dfrac{445}{200} + \dfrac{372}{200}}} = 2.97$$

The rejection region, with $\alpha = 0.05$, is one-tailed or $z > 1.645$ and the null hypothesis is rejected. There is a difference in mean yield for the two types of spray.

b An approximate 95% confidence interval for $\mu_1 - \mu_2$ is
$$(\overline{x}_1 - \overline{x}_2) \pm 1.96 \sqrt{\frac{s_1^2}{n_1} + \frac{s_2^2}{n_2}}$$
$$(109 - 103) \pm 1.96 \sqrt{\frac{445}{200} + \frac{372}{200}}$$
$$6 \pm 3.96 \quad \text{or} \quad 2.04 < (\mu_1 - \mu_2) < 9.96$$

9.75 **a** The null hypothesis to be tested is
$$H_0: \mu = 2.71 \quad \text{versus} \quad H_a: \mu \neq 2.71$$
The test statistic is
$$z \approx \frac{\overline{x} - \mu}{s/\sqrt{n}} = \frac{2.71 - 2.71}{0.54/\sqrt{100}} = 0$$
and the p-value is
$$p\text{-value} = 2P(z > 0) = 2(0.5) = 1$$

H_0 cannot be rejected. There is insufficient evidence to indicate that the average GPA score for all Black applicants is different from the overall average.

b The null hypothesis to be tested is
$$H_0: \mu = 142 \quad \text{versus} \quad H_a: \mu \neq 142.$$
The test statistic is
$$z \approx \frac{\overline{x} - \mu}{s/\sqrt{n}} = \frac{150 - 142}{30/\sqrt{100}} = 2.67$$
and the p-value is
$$p\text{-value} = 2P(z < -1) = 2(0.0038) = 0.0076$$

Since the p-value, 0.0076, is smaller than $\alpha = 0.05$, H_0 is rejected and we can conclude that the average LSAT score for all Black applicants in the class of 2005 is different from the national average.

c Since the same students are used to measure GPA and LSAT scores, there would not be two independent samples, and the two-sample z-test would not be appropriate.

9.77 The null hypothesis to be tested is
$$H_0:\ \mu = 5 \quad \text{versus} \quad H_a:\ \mu > 5$$
and the test statistic is
$$z = \frac{\bar{x} - \mu_0}{\sigma/\sqrt{n}} \approx \frac{\bar{x} - \mu_0}{s/\sqrt{n}} = \frac{7.2 - 5}{6.2/\sqrt{38}} = 2.19$$
The rejection region, with $\alpha = 0.01$, is $z > 2.33$. The observed value, $z = 2.19$, does not fall in the rejection region and H_0 is not rejected. The data do not provide sufficient evidence to indicate that the mean ppm of PCBs in the population of game birds exceeds the FDA's recommended limit of 5 ppm.

9.79 The null hypothesis of interest is
$$H_0:\ p = 0.68 \quad \text{versus} \quad H_a:\ p \neq 0.68$$
with $\hat{p} = \dfrac{x}{n} = \dfrac{65}{100} = 0.65$, the test statistic is
$$z = \frac{\hat{p} - p_0}{\sqrt{\dfrac{p_0 q_0}{n}}} = \frac{0.65 - 0.68}{\sqrt{\dfrac{0.68(0.32)}{100}}} = -0.64$$
The rejection region, with $\alpha = 0.05$, is two-tailed or $|z| > 1.96$ and the null hypothesis is not rejected. There is insufficient evidence to indicate that the percentage reported by survey is incorrect.

9.81 The null hypothesis to be tested is
$$H_0:\ p_1 - p_2 = 0 \quad \text{versus} \quad H_a:\ p_1 - p_2 \neq 0$$
Calculate $\hat{p}_1 = 0.30$, $\hat{p}_2 = 0.33$, and $\hat{p} = \dfrac{x_1 + x_2}{n_1 + n_2} = \dfrac{247(0.30) + 753(0.33)}{1000} = 0.323$

The test statistic is then
$$z = \frac{\hat{p}_1 - \hat{p}_2}{\sqrt{\hat{p}\hat{q}\left(\dfrac{1}{n_1} + \dfrac{1}{n_2}\right)}} = \frac{0.30 - 0.33}{\sqrt{0.323(0.677)(1/247 + 1/753)}} = -0.87$$

The rejection region for $\alpha = 0.01$ is $|z| > 2.58$ and the null hypothesis is not rejected. There is insufficient evidence to indicate that the percentage of Quebecers who said "too many" differ from the opinion of the rest of Canada.

9.83 **a** An approximate 99% confidence interval for $\mu_1 - \mu_2$ is
$$(\bar{x}_1 - \bar{x}_2) \pm 2.58 \sqrt{\frac{s_1^2}{n_1} + \frac{s_2^2}{n_2}}$$
$$(9017 - 5853) \pm 2.58 \sqrt{\frac{7162^2}{130} + \frac{1961^2}{80}}$$
$$3164 \pm 1716.51 \quad \text{or} \quad 1447.49 < (\mu_1 - \mu_2) < 4880.51$$

b Pure breaststroke swimmers swim between 1447 and 4881 more metres per week than to individual medley swimmers. This would be reasonable, since swimmers in the individual medley have three other strokes to practice—freestyle, backstroke, and butterfly.

Case Study: Cure for the Cold—Pooling Data: Making Sense or Folly?

1   Let p_1 be the proportion of patients who have laboratory confirmed influenza among the hypothetical population of all people who could be treated with 200 mg of ginseng extract, and let p_2 be the proportion of patients who have laboratory confirmed influenza among the hypothetical population of all people who could be treated with a placebo. The null hypothesis to be tested is

$$H_0: p_1 - p_2 = 0 \quad \text{versus} \quad H_a: p_1 - p_2 < 0$$

Trial 1

Calculate $\hat{p}_1 = \dfrac{0}{40} = 0$, $\hat{p}_2 = \dfrac{3}{49} = 0.0612244898$, and $\hat{p} = \dfrac{x_1 + x_2}{n_1 + n_2} = \dfrac{0+3}{40+49} = 0.0337078652$. The test

statistic is then $z = \dfrac{\hat{p}_1 - \hat{p}_2}{\sqrt{\hat{p}\hat{q}\left(\dfrac{1}{n_1} + \dfrac{1}{n_2}\right)}} = \dfrac{0 - 0.0612244898}{\sqrt{0.033707865(0.966292134)(1/40 + 1/49)}} = -1.59$, which is not

significant at $\alpha \le 0.05$, with *p*-value 0.0559.

Trial 2

Calculate $\hat{p}_1 = \dfrac{1}{57} = 0.0175438596$, $\hat{p}_2 = \dfrac{6}{52} = 0.1153846154$, and $\hat{p} = \dfrac{x_1 + x_2}{n_1 + n_2} = \dfrac{1+6}{57+52} = 0.0642201835$.

The test statistic is then $z = \dfrac{\hat{p}_1 - \hat{p}_2}{\sqrt{\hat{p}\hat{q}\left(\dfrac{1}{n_1} + \dfrac{1}{n_2}\right)}} = \dfrac{0.0175438596 - 0.1153846154}{\sqrt{0.0642201835(0.9357798165)(1/57 + 1/52)}} = -2.08$, which

is significant at $\alpha = 0.05$, but not significant at $\alpha = 0.01$, with *p*-value 0.0188.

Note that both studies are not significant at $\alpha = 0.01$.

2   The null hypothesis to be tested is

$$H_0: p_1 - p_2 = 0 \quad \text{versus} \quad H_a: p_1 - p_2 < 0$$

Calculate $\hat{p}_1 = \dfrac{1}{97} = 0.0103092784$, $\hat{p}_2 = \dfrac{9}{101} = 0.0891089109$, and

$\hat{p} = \dfrac{x_1 + x_2}{n_1 + n_2} = \dfrac{1+9}{97+101} = 0.0505050505$. The test statistic is then

$z = \dfrac{\hat{p}_1 - \hat{p}_2}{\sqrt{\hat{p}\hat{q}\left(\dfrac{1}{n_1} + \dfrac{1}{n_2}\right)}} = \dfrac{0.0103092784 - 0.0891089109}{\sqrt{0.0505050505(0.9494949495)(1/97 + 1/101)}} = -2.53$, which is significant, with

p-value 0.0057.

3   The answers will vary.

Project 9-A: Proportion of "Cured" Cancer Patients: How Does Canada Compare with Europe?

a   **i**   The null hypothesis to be tested is H_0: $p = 0.32$ versus H_a: $p \neq 0.32$.

The test statistic is $z = \dfrac{\hat{p} - p_0}{\sqrt{\dfrac{p_0 q_0}{n}}} = \dfrac{0.36 - 0.32}{\sqrt{\dfrac{(0.32)(0.68)}{75}}} \approx 0.7426$.

Since $z = 0.7426$ is in the acceptance region (i.e. is between -1.96 and 1.96 for a 2-sided $\alpha = 5\%$ test), we fail to reject the null hypothesis H_0: $p = 0.32$.

ii   The p-value is equal to $P(z > 0.7426) + P(z < -0.7426) = 0.2296 + 0.2296 = 0.4592$. The p-value is greater than the specified 5% significance level, and therefore the null hypothesis $H_0 : p_1 = 0.32$ is not rejected. Assuming H_0 were true, there would be a 0.4592 probability of observing sample proportions (of size 75) at least as large as 0.04 away from $p = 0.32$.

iii   A 95% confidence interval is $\hat{p} \pm z_{0.025} \sqrt{\dfrac{\hat{p}\hat{q}}{n}} = 0.36 \pm 1.96 \sqrt{\dfrac{(0.36)(0.64)}{75}} = (0.2514, 0.4686)$.

iv   If we wish to test if a specific proportion, p_A say, is equal to p_0 or not, we can simply check if p_A is in this confidence interval. If it is, then we cannot reject the null hypothesis that they are equal. Note that this will only work for two-sided tests, at 5% significance.

b   **i**   The null hypothesis should be $H_0 : p_1 = p_2$ or $H_0 : (p_1 - p_2) = 0$, versus the alternative $H_a : p_1 \neq p_2$ or $H_a : (p_1 = p_2) = 0$.

ii   A Type II error: the probability of accepting the null hypothesis when it is in reality false.

iii   The standard error, using the pooled estimate, is $\sqrt{\hat{p}\hat{q}\left(\dfrac{1}{n_1} + \dfrac{1}{n_2}\right)} = \sqrt{(0.294)(0.706)\left(\dfrac{1}{150} + \dfrac{1}{1000}\right)} =$

0.0399, since $\hat{p} = \dfrac{x_1 + x_2}{n_1 + n_2} = \dfrac{338}{1150} = 0.294$ (using the notation from the text).

iv   The null hypothesis to be tested is $H_0 : p_1 = p_2$ versus $H_a : p_1 \neq p_2$. Next, find

$$z = \dfrac{\hat{p}_1 - \hat{p}_2}{\sqrt{\hat{p}\hat{q}\left(\dfrac{1}{n_1} + \dfrac{1}{n_2}\right)}} = \dfrac{0.313 - 0.291}{\sqrt{(0.294)(0.706)\left(\dfrac{1}{150} + \dfrac{1}{1000}\right)}} = 0.5515.$$

Since the z-score is low, it is relatively safe to conclude that we have a likely observation. That is, $H_0 : p_1 = p_2$ may very well be true.

v   Thus, p-value $= P(z > 0.5515) + P(z < -0.5515) = (1 - 0.7088) + (0.2912) = 0.5824$.

Since the p-value is substantially larger than 1% (the significance level), $H_0 : p_1 = p_2$ is not rejected.

vi   For $\alpha = 0.01$, the rejection region is where $z > z_{0.005} = 2.58$ or where $z < -z_{0.005} = -2.58$. Since our test statistic (from part **iv** above) is $z = 0.5515$ and is not in the rejection region, our test shows no difference between the two proportions.

vii   A 95% confidence interval for the difference $(p_1 - p_2)$ is given by

$$\left(\hat{p}_1 - \hat{p}_2\right) \pm z_{0.025} \sqrt{\dfrac{\hat{p}_1 \hat{q}_1}{n_1} + \dfrac{\hat{p}_2 \hat{q}_2}{n_2}} = (0.313 - 0.291) \pm 1.96 \sqrt{\dfrac{(0.313)(0.687)}{150} + \dfrac{(0.291)(0.709)}{1000}}$$

$$= 0.022 \pm 0.079$$

This implies that $-0.06 < (p_1 - p_2) < 0.10$, with probability 0.95. Since zero is contained in the interval, there is no statistical evidence that the two proportions are unequal at the 5% significance level.

c

i   The null hypothesis is $H_0 : p_1 = 0.10$ versus $H_a : p_1 > 0.10$.

ii   The test statistic is $z = \dfrac{\hat{p} - p_0}{\sqrt{\dfrac{p_0 q_0}{n}}} = \dfrac{0.078 - 0.10}{\sqrt{\left(\dfrac{(0.10)(0.90)}{500} \right)}} = -1.64$

iii   The p-value $= P(z > -1.64) = 0.9495$. Thus, based on the very large p-value, there is strong evidence that we should not reject H_0 in favour of the alternative. That is, it is very unlikely that the cure rate in Spain is actually greater than 10%.

Project 9-B: Walking and Talking: My Favourite Sport

a   **i**   The null hypothesis test is $H_0 : \mu = 4.8$ vs $H_a : \mu < 4.8$ and the test statistic is

$$z = \frac{\overline{x} - \mu_0}{s / \sqrt{n}} = \frac{4.5 - 4.8}{0.4 / \sqrt{40}} = -4.74$$

Assuming $\alpha = 0.01$ for this one-sided test, the critical value is $z_{0.01} = -2.33$. Thus, the null hypothesis can be rejected since $z < -0.233$.

ii   By changing $\alpha = 0.01$ to $\alpha = 0.20$, the critical value would then be $z_{0.20} = -0.84$. Hence, we would have the same conclusion as in the first question.

ii*   The p-value $= P(z < -4.74) \approx 0$. Therefore, we reject H_0 as before.

iii   For this problem, a Type I error will occur if we reject $H_0 : \mu = 4.8$ in favour of $H_a : \mu < 4.8$ when in fact $H_0 : \mu = 4.8$ is true. A Type II error will occur if we fail to reject $H_0 : \mu = 4.8$ when it is actually false.

iv   For this solution, we will mimic the wording, sequence, and logic of Example 9.8 from the text.

The acceptance region is the area to the right of $\mu_0 + 2.33\left(\dfrac{s}{\sqrt{n}}\right) = 4.8 + 2.33\left(\dfrac{0.4}{\sqrt{40}}\right) = 4.95$.

The probability of accepting H_0, given that $\mu = 4.7$, is equal to the area under the sampling distribution when the values are greater than 4.95.

The z-value that corresponds to 4.95 is $z = \dfrac{\overline{x} - \mu}{s / \sqrt{n}} = \dfrac{4.95 - 4.7}{0.4 / \sqrt{40}} = 3.95$.

Then, $\beta = P(\text{accept } H_0 \text{ when } \mu = 4.7) = P(z > 3.95) = 0.00004$. Hence, the power of the test is $(1 - \beta) = 1 - 0.00004 = 0.99996$. The probability of correctly rejecting the null hypothesis, given that $\mu = 4.7$, is virtually certain.

v   Answers will vary.

b   **i**   The test is $H_0 : (\mu_1 - \mu_2) = 0$ versus $H_a : (\mu_1 - \mu_2) \neq 0$, and the test statistic is

$$z = \frac{(\overline{x}_1 - \overline{x}_2) - D_0}{\sqrt{\dfrac{s_1^2}{n_1} + \dfrac{s_2^2}{n_2}}} = \frac{(4.9 - 5.4) - 0}{\sqrt{\dfrac{0.5^2}{81} + \dfrac{0.2^2}{64}}} = -8.21$$

The p-value corresponding to this test statistic is basically zero. In any case, using any reasonable α, we would reject the null hypothesis and conclude that there is a difference between the average walking speed of men and women.

ii   The 99% lower confidence bound is given by

$$(\overline{x}_1 - \overline{x}_2) - 2.33\left(\sqrt{\dfrac{s_1^2}{n_1} + \dfrac{s_2^2}{n_2}}\right) = (4.9 - 5.4) - 2.33\left(\sqrt{\dfrac{0.5^2}{81} + \dfrac{0.2^2}{64}}\right) = (-0.5) - 0.142 = -0.642$$

The lower confidence bound does not really confirm our conclusion from the previous question, since it is only on one side, but it is consistent with our conclusions from part **i**. As stated in the text, "a 95% lower one-sided confidence bound will help you find the lowest likely value for the difference." This is therefore the additional information that is provided.

Chapter 10: Inference from Small Samples

10.1 Refer to Table 4, Appendix I, indexing df along the left or right margin and t_α across the top.

a $t_{0.05} = 2.015$ with 5 df

b $t_{0.025} = 2.306$ with 8 df

c $t_{0.10} = 1.330$ with 18 df

d $t_{0.025} \approx 1.96$ with 30 df

10.3 a The p-value for a two-tailed test is defined as
$$p\text{-value} = P\left(|t| > 2.43\right) = 2P\left(t > 2.43\right)$$

so that $P\left(t > 2.43\right) = \dfrac{1}{2} p\text{-value}$

Refer to Table 4, Appendix I, with $df = 12$. The exact probability, $P\left(t > 2.43\right)$ is unavailable; however, it is evident that $t = 2.43$ falls between $t_{0.025} = 2.179$ and $t_{0.01} = 2.681$. Therefore, the area to the right of $t = 2.43$ must be between 0.01 and 0.025. Since

$$0.01 < \frac{1}{2} p\text{-value} < 0.025$$

the p value can be approximated as
$$0.02 < p\text{-value} < 0.05$$

b For a right-tailed test, $p\text{-value} = P\left(t > 3.21\right)$ with $df = 16$. Since the value $t = 3.21$ is larger than $t_{0.005} = 2.921$, the area to its right must be less than 0.005 and you can bound the p-value as
$$p\text{-value} < 0.005$$

c For a two-tailed test, $p\text{-value} = P\left(|t| > 1.19\right) = 2P\left(t > 1.19\right)$, so that $P\left(t > 1.19\right) = \dfrac{1}{2} p\text{-value}$. From Table 4 with $df = 25$, $t = 1.19$ is smaller than $t_{0.10} = 1.316$ so that

$$\frac{1}{2} p\text{-value} > 0.10 \quad \text{and} \quad p\text{-value} > 0.20$$

d For a left-tailed test, $p\text{-value} = P\left(t < -8.77\right) = P\left(t > 8.77\right)$ with $df = 7$. Since the value $t = 8.77$ is larger than $t_{0.005} = 3.499$, the area to its right must be less than 0.005 and you can bound the p-value as
$$p\text{-value} < 0.005$$

10.5 a Using the formulas given in Chapter 2, calculate $\sum x_i = 70.5$ and $\sum x_i^2 = 499.27$. Then

$$\bar{x} = \frac{\sum x_i}{n} = \frac{70.5}{10} = 7.05$$

$$s^2 = \frac{\sum x_i^2 - \dfrac{\left(\sum x_i\right)^2}{n}}{n-1} = \frac{499.27 - \dfrac{\left(70.5\right)^2}{10}}{9} = 0.249444 \quad \text{and} \quad s = 0.4994$$

b With $df = n - 1 = 9$, the appropriate value of t is $t_{0.01} = 2.821$ (from Table 4, Appendix I) and the 99% upper one-sided confidence bound is

$$\bar{x} + t_{0.01} \frac{s}{\sqrt{n}} \quad \Rightarrow \quad 7.05 + 2.821 \sqrt{\frac{0.249444}{10}} \quad \Rightarrow \quad 7.05 + 0.446$$

or $\mu < 7.496$. Intervals constructed using this procedure will enclose μ 99% of the time in repeated sampling. Hence, we are fairly certain that this particular interval encloses μ.

c The null hypothesis to be tested is
$$H_0: \mu = 7.5 \quad \text{versus} \quad H_a: \mu < 7.5$$
and the test statistic is
$$t = \frac{\bar{x} - \mu}{s/\sqrt{n}} = \frac{7.05 - 7.5}{\sqrt{\dfrac{0.249444}{10}}} = -2.849$$

The rejection region with $\alpha = 0.01$ and $n - 1 = 9$ degrees of freedom is located in the lower tail of the t distribution and is found from Table 4 as $t < -t_{0.01} = -2.821$. Since the observed value of the test statistic falls in the rejection region, H_0 is rejected and we conclude that μ is less than 7.5.

d Notice that the 99% upper one-sided confidence bound for μ does not include the value $\mu = 7.5$. This would confirm the results of the hypothesis test in part **c**, in which we concluded that μ is less than 7.5.

10.7 Similar to previous exercises. The null hypothesis to be tested is
$$H_0: \mu = 5 \quad \text{versus} \quad H_a: \mu < 5$$
Calculate
$$\bar{x} = \frac{\sum x_i}{n} = \frac{29.6}{6} = 4.933$$

$$s^2 = \frac{\sum x_i^2 - \dfrac{(\sum x_i)^2}{n}}{n-1} = \frac{146.12 - \dfrac{(29.6)^2}{6}}{5} = 0.01867 \quad \text{and} \quad s = 0.1366$$

The test statistic is
$$t = \frac{\bar{x} - \mu}{s/\sqrt{n}} = \frac{4.933 - 5}{\dfrac{0.1366}{\sqrt{6}}} = -1.195$$

The critical value of t with $\alpha = 0.05$ and $n - 1 = 5$ degrees of freedom is $t_{0.05} = 2.015$ and the rejection region is $t < -2.015$. Since the observed value does not fall in the rejection region, H_0 is not rejected. There is no evidence to indicate that the dissolved oxygen content is less than 5 parts per million.

10.9 a Similar to previous exercises. The null hypothesis to be tested is
$$H_0: \mu = 100 \quad \text{versus} \quad H_a: \mu < 100$$
Calculate
$$\bar{x} = \frac{\sum x_i}{n} = \frac{1797.095}{20} = 89.8547$$

$$s^2 = \frac{\sum x_i^2 - \dfrac{(\sum x_i)^2}{n}}{n-1} = \frac{165,697.7081 - \dfrac{(1797.095)^2}{20}}{19} = 222.1150605 \quad \text{and} \quad s = 14.9035$$

The test statistic is
$$t = \frac{\bar{x} - \mu}{s/\sqrt{n}} = \frac{89.8547 - 100}{\dfrac{14.9035}{\sqrt{20}}} = -3.044$$

The critical value of t with $\alpha = 0.01$ and $n - 1 = 19$ degrees of freedom is $t_{0.01} = 2.539$ and the rejection region is $t < -2.539$. H_0 is rejected and we conclude that μ is less than 100 DL.

b The 95% upper one-sided confidence bound, based on $n - 1 = 19$ degrees of freedom, is
$$\bar{x} + t_{0.05}\frac{s}{\sqrt{n}} \Rightarrow 89.8547 + 2.539\frac{14.9035}{\sqrt{20}} \Rightarrow \mu < 98.316$$

This confirms the results of part **a** in which we concluded that the mean is less than 100 DL.

10.11 Calculate

$$\bar{x} = \frac{\sum x_i}{n} = \frac{37.82}{10} = 3.782$$

$$s^2 = \frac{\sum x_i^2 - \frac{\left(\sum x_i\right)^2}{n}}{n-1} = \frac{143.3308 - \frac{(37.82)^2}{10}}{9} = 0.03284 \quad \text{and} \quad s = 0.1812$$

The 95% confidence interval based on $df = 9$ is

$$\bar{x} \pm t_{0.025}\frac{s}{\sqrt{n}} \Rightarrow 3.782 \pm 2.262\frac{0.1812}{\sqrt{10}} \Rightarrow 3.782 \pm 0.130 \quad \text{or} \quad 3.652 < \mu < 3.912$$

10.13　**a**　The null hypothesis to be tested is

$$H_0: \mu = 25 \quad \text{versus} \quad H_a: \mu < 25$$

The test statistic is

$$t = \frac{\bar{x} - \mu_0}{s/\sqrt{n}} = \frac{20.3 - 25}{\frac{5}{\sqrt{21}}} = -4.31$$

The critical value of t with $\alpha = 0.05$ and $n - 1 = 20$ degrees of freedom is $t_{0.05} = 1.725$ and the rejection region is $t < -1.725$. Since the observed value does fall in the rejection region, H_0 is rejected, and we conclude that pre-treatment mean is less than 25.

b　The 95% confidence interval based on $df = 20$ is

$$\bar{x} \pm t_{0.025}\frac{s}{\sqrt{n}} \Rightarrow 26.6 \pm 2.086\frac{7.4}{\sqrt{21}} \Rightarrow 26.6 \pm 3.37 \text{ or } 23.23 < \mu < 29.97$$

c　The pre-treatment mean looks considerably smaller than the other two means.

10.15　**a**　The t test of the null hypothesis

$$H_0 : \mu = 1 \quad \text{versus} \quad H_a : \mu \ne 1$$

is not significant, since the p-value $= 0.113$ associated with the test statistic

$$t = \frac{\bar{x} - \mu}{s/\sqrt{n}} = \frac{1.05222 - 1}{0.16565/\sqrt{27}} = 1.64$$

is greater than 0.10. There is insufficient evidence to indicate that the mean weight per package is different from 1 kilogram.

b　In fact, the 95% confidence limits for the average weight per package are

$$\bar{x} \pm t_{0.025}\frac{s}{\sqrt{n}} \Rightarrow 1.05222 \pm 2.056\frac{0.16565}{\sqrt{27}} \Rightarrow 1.05222 \pm 0.06554 \text{ or } 0.98668 < \mu < 1.11776$$

These values agree (except in the last decimal place) with those given in the printout. Remember that you used the rounded values of $\bar{x}$ and s from the printout, causing a small rounding error in the results.

10.17　Refer to Exercise 10.16. If we use the large-sample method of Chapter 8, the large-sample confidence interval is

$$\bar{x} \pm z_{0.025}\frac{s}{\sqrt{n}} \Rightarrow 246.96 \pm 1.96\frac{46.8244}{\sqrt{50}} \Rightarrow 246.96 \pm 12.98 \text{ or } 233.98 < \mu < 259.94$$

The intervals are fairly similar, which is why we choose to approximate the sampling distribution of $\frac{\bar{x} - \mu}{s/\sqrt{n}}$ with a z distribution when $n > 30$.

10.19 **a** $s^2 = \dfrac{(n_1-1)s_1^2+(n_2-1)s_2^2}{n_1+n_2-2} = \dfrac{9(3.4)+3(4.9)}{10+4-2} = 3.775$

b $s^2 = \dfrac{(n_1-1)s_1^2+(n_2-1)s_2^2}{n_1+n_2-2} = \dfrac{11(18)+20(23)}{12+21-2} = 21.2258$

10.21 **a** The null hypothesis to be tested is
$$H_0: \mu_1-\mu_2=0 \quad \text{versus} \quad H_a: \mu_1-\mu_2 \neq 0$$

b The rejection region is two-tailed, based on $df = n_1+n_2-2 = 16+13-2 = 27$ degrees of freedom. With $\alpha=0.01$, from Table 4, Appendix I, the rejection region is $|t| > t_{0.005} = 2.771$.

c The pooled estimator of σ^2 is calculated as
$$s^2 = \dfrac{(n_1-1)s_1^2+(n_2-1)s_2^2}{n_1+n_2-2} = \dfrac{15(4.8)+12(5.9)}{16+13-2} = 5.2889$$
and the test statistic is
$$t = \dfrac{(\bar{x}_1-\bar{x}_2)-0}{\sqrt{s^2\left(\dfrac{1}{n_1}+\dfrac{1}{n_2}\right)}} = \dfrac{34.6-32.2}{\sqrt{5.2889\left(\dfrac{1}{16}+\dfrac{1}{13}\right)}} = 2.795$$

d The *p*-value is
$$p\text{-value} = P(|t|>2.795) = 2P(t>2.795), \text{ so that } P(t>2.795) = \frac{1}{2}p\text{-value}.$$

From Table 4 with $df=27$, $t=2.795$ is greater than the largest tabulated value ($t_{0.005}=2.771$). Therefore, the area to the right of $t=2.795$ must be less than 0.005 so that
$$\frac{1}{2}p\text{-value} < 0.005 \quad \text{and} \quad p\text{-value} < 0.01$$

e Comparing the observed $t=2.795$ to the critical value $t_{0.005}=2.771$ or comparing the *p*-value (<0.01) to $\alpha=0.01$, H_0 is rejected and we conclude that $\mu_1 \neq \mu_2$.

10.23 **a** If you check the ratio of the two variances using the rule of thumb given in this section you will find:
$$\frac{\text{larger } s^2}{\text{smaller } s^2} = \frac{(4.67)^2}{(4.00)^2} = 1.36$$
which is less than 3. Therefore, it is reasonable to assume that the two population variances are equal.

b From the *MINITAB* printout, the test statistic is $t=0.06$ with *p*-value $=0.95$.

c The value of $s=4.38$ is labelled "Pooled StDev" in the printout, so that $s^2 = (4.38)^2 = 19.1844$.

d Since the *p*-value $=0.95$ is greater than 0.10, the results are not significant. There is insufficient evidence to indicate a difference in the two population means.

e A 95% confidence interval for $(\mu_1-\mu_2)$ is given as
$$(\bar{x}_1-\bar{x}_2) \pm t_{0.025}\sqrt{s^2\left(\frac{1}{n_1}+\frac{1}{n_2}\right)}$$
$$(29-28.86) \pm 2.201\sqrt{19.1844\left(\frac{1}{6}+\frac{1}{7}\right)}$$
$$0.14 \pm 5.363 \quad \text{or} \quad -5.223 < (\mu_1-\mu_2) < 5.503$$

Since the value $\mu_1-\mu_2=0$ falls in the confidence interval, it is possible that the two population means are the same. There insufficient evidence to indicate a difference in the two population means.

10.25 **a** If the antiplaque rinse is effective, the plaque buildup should be less for the group using the antiplaque rinse. Hence, the null hypothesis to be tested is

$$H_0: \mu_1 - \mu_2 = 0 \quad \text{versus} \quad H_a: \mu_1 - \mu_2 > 0$$

b The pooled estimator of σ^2 is calculated as

$$s^2 = \frac{(n_1 - 1)s_1^2 + (n_2 - 1)s_2^2}{n_1 + n_2 - 2} = \frac{6(0.32)^2 + 6(0.32)^2}{7 + 7 - 2} = 0.1024$$

and the test statistic is

$$t = \frac{(\bar{x}_1 - \bar{x}_2) - 0}{\sqrt{s^2 \left(\frac{1}{n_1} + \frac{1}{n_2} \right)}} = \frac{1.26 - 0.78}{\sqrt{0.1024 \left(\frac{1}{7} + \frac{1}{7} \right)}} = 2.806$$

The rejection region is one-tailed, based on $n_1 + n_2 - 2 = 12$ degrees of freedom. With $\alpha = 0.05$, from Table 4, Appendix I, the rejection region is $t > t_{0.05} = 1.782$ and H_0 is rejected. There is evidence to indicate that the rinse is effective.

c The p-value is

$$p\text{-value} = P(t > 2.806)$$

From Table 4 with $df = 12$, $t = 2.806$ is between two tabled entries $t_{0.005} = 3.055$ and $t_{0.01} = 2.681$, we can conclude that

$$0.005 < p\text{-value} < 0.01$$

10.27 **a** The null hypothesis to be tested is

$$H_0: \mu_1 - \mu_2 = 0 \quad \text{versus} \quad H_a: \mu_1 - \mu_2 \neq 0$$

where μ_1 is the average compartment pressure for runners, and μ_2 is the average compartment pressure for cyclists. The pooled estimator of σ^2 is calculated as

$$s^2 = \frac{(n_1 - 1)s_1^2 + (n_2 - 1)s_2^2}{n_1 + n_2 - 2} = \frac{9(3.92)^2 + 9(3.98)^2}{18} = 15.6034$$

and the test statistic is

$$t = \frac{(\bar{x}_1 - \bar{x}_2) - 0}{\sqrt{s^2 \left(\frac{1}{n_1} + \frac{1}{n_2} \right)}} = \frac{14.5 - 11.1}{\sqrt{15.6034 \left(\frac{1}{10} + \frac{1}{10} \right)}} = 1.92$$

The rejection region is two-tailed, based on $df = 18$ degrees of freedom. With $\alpha = 0.05$, from Table 4, Appendix I, the rejection region is $|t| > t_{0.025} = 2.101$. We do not reject H_0; there is insufficient evidence to indicate a difference in the means.

b Calculate

$$s^2 = \frac{(n_1 - 1)s_1^2 + (n_2 - 1)s_2^2}{n_1 + n_2 - 2} = \frac{9(3.49)^2 + 9(4.95)^2}{18} = 18.3413$$

A 95% confidence interval for $(\mu_1 - \mu_2)$ is given as

$$(\bar{x}_1 - \bar{x}_2) \pm t_{0.025} \sqrt{s^2 \left(\frac{1}{n_1} + \frac{1}{n_2} \right)}$$

$$(12.2 - 11.5) \pm 2.101 \sqrt{18.3413 \left(\frac{1}{10} + \frac{1}{10} \right)}$$

$$0.7 \pm 4.02 \quad \text{or} \quad -3.32 < (\mu_1 - \mu_2) < 4.72$$

   c   Check the ratio of the two variances using the rule of thumb given in this section:

$$\frac{\text{larger } s^2}{\text{smaller } s^2} = \frac{(16.9)^2}{(4.47)^2} = 14.29$$

which is greater than 3. Therefore, it is not reasonable to assume that the two population variances are equal. You should use the unpooled t test with Satterthwaite's approximation to the degrees of freedom.

10.29 **a** Use your scientific calculator or the computing formulas to find:

$$\bar{x}_1 = 0.0125 \qquad s_1^2 = 0.000002278 \qquad s_1 = 0.001509$$
$$\bar{x}_2 = 0.0138 \qquad s_2^2 = 0.000003733 \qquad s_2 = 0.001932$$

Since the ratio of the variances is less than 3, you can use the pooled t test, calculating

$$s^2 = \frac{(n_1-1)s_1^2 + (n_2-1)s_2^2}{n_1 + n_2 - 2} = \frac{9(0.000002278) + 9(0.000003733)}{18} = 0.000003006$$

and the test statistic is

$$t = \frac{(\bar{x}_1 - \bar{x}_2) - 0}{\sqrt{s^2\left(\dfrac{1}{n_1} + \dfrac{1}{n_2}\right)}} = \frac{0.0125 - 0.0138}{\sqrt{s^2\left(\dfrac{1}{10} + \dfrac{1}{10}\right)}} = -1.68$$

For a two-tailed test with $df = 18$, the p-value can be bounded using Table 4, Appendix I, so that

$$0.05 < \frac{1}{2}\,p\text{-value} < 0.10 \quad \text{or} \quad 0.10 < p\text{-value} < 0.20$$

Since the p-value is greater than 0.10, H_0: $\mu_1 - \mu_2 = 0$ is not rejected. There is insufficient evidence to indicate that there is a difference in the mean titanium contents for the two methods.

   b A 95% confidence interval for $(\mu_1 - \mu_2)$ is given as

$$(\bar{x}_1 - \bar{x}_2) \pm t_{0.025}\sqrt{s^2\left(\frac{1}{n_1} + \frac{1}{n_2}\right)}$$

$$(0.0125 - 0.0138) \pm 2.101\sqrt{s^2\left(\frac{1}{10} + \frac{1}{10}\right)}$$

$$-0.0013 \pm 0.0016 \quad \text{or} \quad -0.0029 < (\mu_1 - \mu_2) < 0.0003$$

Since $\mu_1 - \mu_2 = 0$ falls in the confidence interval, the conclusion of part **a** is confirmed. This particular data set is very susceptible to rounding error. You need to carry as much accuracy as possible to obtain accurate results.

10.31 **a** The null hypothesis of interest is

$$H_0: \mu_1 - \mu_2 = 0 \quad \text{versus} \quad H_a: \mu_1 - \mu_2 > 0$$

and the preliminary calculations are as follows:

Sample 1 (Above)	Sample 2 (Below)
$\sum x_{1i} = 25$	$\sum x_{2i} = 24.3$
$\sum x_{1i}^2 = 125.1$	$\sum x_{2i}^2 = 118.15$
$n_1 = 5$	$n_2 = 5$

Then

$$s^2 = \frac{\sum x_{1i}^2 - \frac{\left(\sum x_{1i}\right)^2}{n_1} + \sum x_{2i}^2 - \frac{\left(\sum x_{2i}\right)^2}{n_2}}{n_1 + n_2 - 2}$$

$$= \frac{125.1 - \frac{(25)^2}{5} + 118.15 - \frac{(24.3)^2}{5}}{5 + 5 - 2} = \frac{0.1 + 0.052}{8} = 0.019$$

Also,

$$\overline{x}_1 = \frac{25}{5} = 5 \qquad \text{and} \qquad \overline{x}_2 = \frac{24.3}{5} = 4.86$$

The test statistic is

$$t = \frac{\left(\overline{x}_1 - \overline{x}_2\right) - 0}{\sqrt{s^2\left(\frac{1}{n_1} + \frac{1}{n_2}\right)}} = \frac{5 - 4.86}{\sqrt{0.019\left(\frac{1}{5} + \frac{1}{5}\right)}} = 1.606$$

For a one-tailed test with $df = 8$ and $\alpha = 0.05$, the rejection region is $t > t_{0.05} = 1.86$, and H_0 is not rejected. There is insufficient evidence to indicate that the mean content of oxygen below town is less than the mean content above.

b A 95% confidence interval for $\left(\mu_1 - \mu_2\right)$ is given as

$$\left(\overline{x}_1 - \overline{x}_2\right) \pm t_{0.025}\sqrt{s^2\left(\frac{1}{n_1} + \frac{1}{n_2}\right)}$$

$$(5 - 4.86) \pm 2.306\sqrt{0.019\left(\frac{1}{5} + \frac{1}{5}\right)}$$

$$0.14 \pm 0.201 \quad \text{or} \quad -0.061 < \left(\mu_1 - \mu_2\right) < 0.341$$

10.33 Refer to Exercise 10.32. A 95% lower one-sided confidence bound for $\left(\mu_1 - \mu_2\right)$ is given as

$$\left(\overline{x}_1 - \overline{x}_2\right) - t_{.05}\sqrt{s^2\left(\frac{1}{n_1} + \frac{1}{n_2}\right)}$$

$$(59.646 - 59.627) - 1.734\sqrt{.03124722\left(\frac{1}{10} + \frac{1}{10}\right)}$$

$$0.019 - 0.137 \quad \text{or} \quad \left(\mu_1 - \mu_2\right) > -0.118$$

Since the value $\mu_1 - \mu_2 = 0$ is in the interval, it is possible that the two means might be equal. We do not have enough evidence to indicate that there is a difference in the means.

10.35 **a** If you check the ratio of the two variances using the rule of thumb given in this section, you will find:

$$\frac{\text{larger } s^2}{\text{smaller } s^2} = \frac{44.029}{23.333} = 1.89$$

which is less than 3. Therefore, it is reasonable to assume that the two population variances are equal.

b The null hypothesis of interest is

$$H_0: \mu_1 - \mu_2 = 0 \quad \text{versus} \quad H_a: \mu_1 - \mu_2 \neq 0$$

From the *Excel* printout, the test statistic is $t = -3.47$. The rejection region, based on 29 *df* and $\alpha = 0.05$ is $|t| > t_{0.025} = 2.045$ and the null hypothesis is rejected. There is thus sufficient evidence to indicate that the average number of completed passes is different for Aaron Rodgers and Drew Brees.

c From the *Excel* printout, the two tailed *p-value* = 0.002. Since the *p-value* is less than 5% level of significance, we reject the null hypothesis in part **b**.

d A 95% confidence interval for $(\mu_1 - \mu_2)$ is given as

$$(\bar{x}_1 - \bar{x}_2) \pm t_{0.025} \sqrt{s^2\left(\frac{1}{n_1} + \frac{1}{n_2}\right)}$$

$$(28.667 - 28.286) \pm 2.045 \sqrt{33.324\left(\frac{1}{15} + \frac{1}{16}\right)}$$

$$-7.2 \pm 4.243 \quad \text{or} \quad -11.443 < (\mu_1 - \mu_2) < -2.957$$

Since the value $\mu_1 - \mu_2 = 0$ does not fall in the confidence interval, it is unlikely that the two population means are equal. Thus, we have sufficient evidence to indicate a difference in the two population means, confirming the results in part **b**.

10.37 a The test statistic is

$$t = \frac{\bar{d} - \mu_d}{s_d / \sqrt{n}} = \frac{0.3 - 0}{\sqrt{\dfrac{0.16}{10}}} = 2.372$$

with $n - 1 = 9$ degrees of freedom. The p-value is then

$$P(|t| > 2.372) = 2P(t > 2.372) \quad \text{so that} \quad P(t > 2.372) = \frac{1}{2} p\text{-value}$$

Since the value $t = 2.372$ falls between two tabled entries for $df = 9$ ($t_{0.025} = 2.262$ and $t_{0.01} = 2.821$), you can conclude that

$$0.01 < \frac{1}{2} p\text{-value} < 0.025$$

$$0.02 < p\text{-value} < 0.05$$

Since the p-value is less than $\alpha = 0.05$, the null hypothesis is rejected and we conclude that there is a difference in the two population means.

b A 95% confidence interval for $\mu_1 - \mu_2 = \mu_d$ is

$$\bar{d} \pm t_{0.025} \frac{s_d}{\sqrt{n}} \quad \Rightarrow \quad 3 \pm 2.262 \sqrt{\frac{0.16}{10}} \quad \Rightarrow \quad 0.3 \pm 0.286 \text{ or } 0\,0.014 < (\mu_1 - \mu_2) < 0.586$$

c Using $s_d^2 = 0.16$ and B $= 0.1$, the inequality to be solved is approximately

$$1.96 \frac{s_d}{\sqrt{n}} \le 0.1$$

$$\sqrt{n} \ge \frac{1.96\sqrt{0.16}}{0.1} = 7.84 \quad \Rightarrow \quad n \ge 61.47 \quad \text{or} \quad n = 62$$

Since this value of n is greater than 30, the sample size, $n = 62$ pairs, will be valid.

10.39 a It is necessary to use a paired-difference test, since the two samples are not random and independent. The null hypothesis of interest is

$$H_0: \mu_1 - \mu_2 = 0 \quad \text{or} \quad H_0: \mu_d = 0$$

versus

$$H_a: \mu_1 - \mu_2 \ne 0 \quad \text{or} \quad H_a: \mu_d \ne 0$$

The table of differences, along with the calculation of $\bar{d}$ and s_d^2, is presented below.

d_i	0.1	0.1	0	0.2	-0.1	$\sum d_i = 0.3$
d_i^2	0.01	0.01	0.00	0.04	0.01	$\sum d_i^2 = 0.07$

$$\bar{d} = \frac{\sum d_i}{n} = \frac{0.3}{5} = 0.06 \text{ and } s_d^2 = \frac{\sum d_i^2 - \frac{\left(\sum d_i\right)^2}{n}}{n-1} = \frac{0.07 - \frac{(0.3)^2}{5}}{4} = 0.013$$

The test statistic is

$$t = \frac{\bar{d} - \mu_d}{s_d / \sqrt{n}} = \frac{0.06 - 0}{\sqrt{\frac{0.013}{5}}} = 1.177$$

with $n - 1 = 4$ degrees of freedom. The rejection region with $\alpha = 0.05$ is $|t| > t_{0.025} = 2.776$, and H_0 is not rejected. We cannot conclude that the means are different.

b The *p*-value is

$$P\left(|t| > 1.177\right) = 2P\left(t > 1.177\right) > 2(0.10) = 0.20$$

c A 95% confidence interval for $\mu_1 - \mu_2 = \mu_d$ is

$$\bar{d} \pm t_{0.025} \frac{s_d}{\sqrt{n}} \quad \Rightarrow \quad 0.06 \pm 2.776\sqrt{\frac{0.013}{5}} \quad \Rightarrow \quad 0.06 \pm 0.142$$

or $-0.082 < \left(\mu_1 - \mu_2\right) < 0.202$.

d In order to use the paired-difference test, it is necessary that the *n* paired observations be randomly selected from normally distributed populations.

10.41 **a** The null hypothesis of interest is $H_0: \mu_1 - \mu_2 = 0$ versus $H_a: \mu_1 - \mu_2 \neq 0$ for the two independent samples of runners and cyclists before exercise. Since the ratio of the sample variances is greater than 3, the population variances cannot be assumed to be equal and you must use the unpooled *t* test with Satterthwaite's approximate *df*. Calculate

$$t = \frac{\left(\bar{x}_1 - \bar{x}_2\right) - 0}{\sqrt{\frac{s_1^2}{n_1} + \frac{s_2^2}{n_2}}} = \frac{255.63 - 173.8}{\sqrt{\frac{(115.48)^2}{10} + \frac{(60.69)^2}{10}}} = 1.984$$

which has a *t* distribution with $df = \dfrac{\left(\dfrac{s_1^2}{n_1} + \dfrac{s_2^2}{n_2}\right)^2}{\dfrac{\left(\dfrac{s_1^2}{n_1}\right)^2}{n_1 - 1} + \dfrac{\left(\dfrac{s_2^2}{n_2}\right)^2}{n_2 - 1}} = 13.619 \approx 13$

A two-tailed rejection region is then $|t| > t_{0.025} = 2.160$ and H_0 is not rejected. A 95% confidence interval for $\mu_1 - \mu_2$ is given as

$$\left(\bar{x}_1 - \bar{x}_2\right) \pm t_{0.025} \sqrt{\frac{s_1^2}{n_1} + \frac{s_2^2}{n_2}}$$

$$\left(255.63 - 173.8\right) \pm 2.160\sqrt{\frac{(115.48)^2}{10} + \frac{(60.69)^2}{10}}$$

$$81.83 \pm 89.11 \text{ or } -7.28 < \left(\mu_1 - \mu_2\right) < 170.94$$

b Similar to part **a**. The null hypothesis of interest is $H_0: \mu_1 - \mu_2 = 0$ versus $H_a: \mu_1 - \mu_2 \neq 0$ for the two independent samples of runners and cyclists after exercise. Since the ratio of the sample variances is greater than 3, you must again use the unpooled *t* test with Satterthwaite's approximate *df*. Calculate

$$t = \frac{\left(\bar{x}_1 - \bar{x}_2\right) - 0}{\sqrt{\frac{s_1^2}{n_1} + \frac{s_2^2}{n_2}}} = \frac{284.75 - 177.1}{\sqrt{\frac{(132.64)^2}{10} + \frac{(64.53)^2}{10}}} = 2.307$$

which has a t distribution with $df = \dfrac{\left(\dfrac{s_1^2}{n_1} + \dfrac{s_2^2}{n_2}\right)^2}{\dfrac{\left(\dfrac{s_1^2}{n_1}\right)^2}{n_1 - 1} + \dfrac{\left(\dfrac{s_2^2}{n_2}\right)^2}{n_2 - 1}} = 13.046 \approx 13$

A two-tailed rejection region is then $|t| > t_{0.025} = 2.160$ and H_0 is rejected. A 95% confidence interval for $\mu_1 - \mu_2$ is given as

$$\left(\bar{x}_1 - \bar{x}_2\right) \pm t_{0.025}\sqrt{\dfrac{s_1^2}{n_1} + \dfrac{s_2^2}{n_2}}$$

$$\left(284.75 - 177.1\right) \pm 2.160\sqrt{\dfrac{\left(132.64\right)^2}{10} + \dfrac{\left(64.53\right)^2}{10}}$$

$$107.65 \pm 100.783 \quad\text{or}\quad 6.867 < \left(\mu_1 - \mu_2\right) < 208.433$$

c To test the difference between runners before and after exercise, you use a paired-difference test, and the null hypothesis of interest is

$H_0: \mu_1 - \mu_2 = 0$ or $H_0: \mu_d = 0$

versus

$H_a: \mu_1 - \mu_2 \neq 0$ or $H_a: \mu_d \neq 0$

It is given that $\bar{d} = 29.13$ and $s_d = 21.01$, so that the test statistic is

$$t = \dfrac{\bar{d} - \mu_d}{s_d/\sqrt{n}} = \dfrac{29.13 - 0}{\dfrac{21.01}{\sqrt{10}}} = 4.38$$

The rejection region with $\alpha = 0.05$ and $n - 1 = 9$ df is $|t| > t_{0.025} = 2.262$, and H_0 is rejected. We can conclude that the means are different.

d The difference in mean CPK values for the 10 cyclists before and after exercise uses $\bar{d} = 3.3$ with $s_d = 6.85$. The 95% confidence interval for $\mu_1 - \mu_2 = \mu_d$ is

$$\bar{d} \pm t_{0.05}\dfrac{s_d}{\sqrt{n}} \quad\Rightarrow\quad 3.3 \pm 2.262\dfrac{6.85}{\sqrt{10}} \quad\Rightarrow\quad 3.3 \pm 4.90$$

or $-1.6 < \left(\mu_1 - \mu_2\right) < 8.2$. Since the interval contains the value $\mu_1 - \mu_2 = 0$, we cannot conclude that there is a significant difference between the means.

10.43 **a** Each driver was presented with both signs in a random order. If the driver's reaction time in general is high, both responses will be high. Similarly, if the driver's reaction time in general is low, both responses will be low. The large variability from subject to subject will mask the variability due to the difference in sign types. The paired difference design will eliminate this subject to subject variability.

b The null hypothesis of interest is

$H_0: \mu_1 - \mu_2 = 0$ or $H_0: \mu_d = 0$

versus

$H_a: \mu_1 - \mu_2 \neq 0$ or $H_a: \mu_d \neq 0$

Using the *Excel* printout, the test statistic is

$$t = \dfrac{\bar{d} - \mu_d}{s_d/\sqrt{n}} = 9.15$$

Since our test is two-tailed, the p-value from the *Excel* printout is 0.00000746. This p-value is very small and the null hypothesis is rejected at any reasonable level of significance, and thus we conclude that the means are different.

10.45   **a**   A paired-difference test is used, since the two samples are not random and independent (at any location, the ground and air temperatures are related). The null hypothesis of interest is

$$H_0: \mu_1 - \mu_2 = 0 \quad \text{versus} \quad H_a: \mu_1 - \mu_2 \neq 0$$

The table of differences, along with the calculation of $\bar{d}$ and s_d^2, is presented below.

Location	1	2	3	4	5	Totals
d_i	−0.4	−2.7	−1.6	−1.7	−1.5	−7.9

$$\bar{d} = \frac{\sum d_i}{n} = \frac{-7.9}{5} = -1.58$$

$$s_d^2 = \frac{\sum d_i^2 - \dfrac{\left(\sum d_i\right)^2}{n}}{n-1} = \frac{15.15 - \dfrac{(-7.9)^2}{5}}{4} = 0.667 \quad \text{and} \quad s_d = 0.8167$$

and the test statistic is

$$t = \frac{\bar{d} - \mu_d}{s_d / \sqrt{n}} = \frac{-1.58 - 0}{\dfrac{0.8167}{\sqrt{5}}} = -4.326$$

A rejection region with $\alpha = 0.05$ and $df = n - 1 = 4$ is $|t| > t_{0.025} = 2.776$, and H_0 is rejected at the 5% level of significance. We conclude that the air-based temperature readings are biased.

   b   The 95% confidence interval for $\mu_1 - \mu_2 = \mu_d$ is

$$\bar{d} \pm t_{0.025} \frac{s_d}{\sqrt{n}} \quad \Rightarrow \quad -1.58 \pm 2.776 \frac{0.8167}{\sqrt{5}} \quad \Rightarrow \quad -1.58 \pm 1.014 \quad \text{or} \quad -2.594 < (\mu_1 - \mu_2) < -0.566$$

   c   The inequality to be solved is

$$t_{\alpha/2} SE \leq B$$

We need to estimate the difference in mean temperatures between ground-based and air-based sensors to within 0.2 degrees centigrade with 95% confidence. Since this is a paired experiment, the inequality becomes

$$t_{0.025} \frac{s_d}{\sqrt{n}} \leq 0.2$$

With $s_d = 0.8167$ and n represents the number of pairs of observations, consider the sample size obtained by replacing $t_{0.025}$ by $z_{0.025} = 1.96$.

$$1.96 \frac{0.8167}{\sqrt{n}} \leq 0.2$$

$$\sqrt{n} \geq 8.0019 \quad \Rightarrow \quad n = 64.03 \quad \text{or} \quad n = 65$$

Since the value of n is greater than 30, the use of $z_{\alpha/2}$ for $t_{\alpha/2}$ is justified.

10.47   **a**   Use the *MINITAB* printout given in the text. The null hypothesis of interest is

$$H_0: \mu_A - \mu_B = 0 \quad \text{versus} \quad H_a: \mu_A - \mu_B > 0$$

and the test statistic is

$$t = \frac{\bar{d} - \mu_d}{s_d / \sqrt{n}} = \frac{1.4875 - 0}{\dfrac{1.49134}{\sqrt{8}}} = 2.82$$

The *p*-value shown in the printout is *p*-value = 0.013. Since the *p*-value is less than 0.05, H_0 is rejected at the 5% level of significance. We conclude that assessor A gives higher assessments than assessor B.

b   A 95% lower one-sided confidence bound for $\mu_1 - \mu_2 = \mu_d$ is

$$\bar{d} - t_{0.05} \frac{s_d}{\sqrt{n}} \quad \Rightarrow \quad 1.4875 - 1.895 \frac{1.49134}{\sqrt{8}} \quad \Rightarrow \quad 1.4875 - 0.999 \text{ or } \left(\mu_1 - \mu_2 \right) > 0.4885$$

c   In order to apply the paired-difference test, the eight properties must be randomly and independently selected and the assessments must be normally distributed.

d   Yes. If the individual assessments are normally distributed, then the mean of four assessments will be normally distributed. Hence, the difference $x_A - \bar{x}$ will be normally distributed and the *t* test on the differences is valid as in part **c**.

10.49   A paired-difference analysis must be used. The null hypothesis of interest is

$$H_0: \mu_1 - \mu_2 = 0 \quad \text{or} \quad H_0: \mu_d = 0$$

versus

$$H_a: \mu_1 - \mu_2 > 0 \quad \text{or} \quad H_a: \mu_d > 0$$

The table of differences is presented below. Use your scientific calculator to find $\bar{d}$ and s_d.

d_i	3	3	−2	1	−1	3	−1

Calculate $\bar{d} = 0.857$, $s_d = 2.193$, and the test statistic is

$$t = \frac{\bar{d} - \mu_d}{s_d / \sqrt{n}} = \frac{0.857 - 0}{\dfrac{2.193}{\sqrt{7}}} = 1.03$$

Since $t = 1.03$ with $df = n - 1 = 6$ is smaller than the smallest tabled value $t_{0.10}$, *p*-value > 0.10 for this one-tailed test and H_0 is not rejected. We cannot conclude that the average time outside the office is less when music is piped in.

10.51   For this exercise, $s^2 = 0.3214$ and $n = 15$.

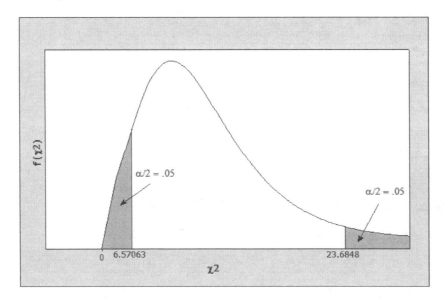

A 90% confidence interval for σ^2 will be

$$\frac{(n-1)s^2}{\chi_{\alpha/2}^2} < \sigma^2 < \frac{(n-1)s^2}{\chi_{(1-\alpha/2)}^2}$$

where $\chi_{\alpha/2}^2$ represents the value of χ^2 such that 5% of the area under the curve (shown in the figure above) lies to its right. Similarly, $\chi_{(1-\alpha/2)}^2$ will be the χ^2 value such that an area 0.95 lies to its right. Hence, we have located one-half of α in each tail of the distribution. Indexing $\chi_{0.05}^2$ and $\chi_{0.95}^2$ with $n-1=14$ degrees of freedom in Table 5, Appendix I, yields

$$\chi_{0.05}^2 = 23.6848 \quad \text{and} \quad \chi_{0.95}^2 = 6.57063$$

and the confidence interval is

$$\frac{14(0.3214)}{23.6848} < \sigma^2 < \frac{14(0.3214)}{6.57063} \quad \text{or} \quad 0.190 < \sigma^2 < 0.685$$

10.53   The null hypothesis of interest is

$$H_0: \sigma = 0.7 \quad \text{versus} \quad H_a: \sigma > 0.7$$

or equivalently $H_0: \sigma^2 = 0.49$ versus $H_a: \sigma^2 > 0.49$

Calculate

$$s^2 = \frac{\sum x_i^2 - \frac{(\sum x_i)^2}{n}}{n-1} = \frac{36 - \frac{(10)^2}{4}}{3} = 3.6667$$

The test statistic is

$$\chi^2 = \frac{(n-1)s^2}{\sigma_0^2} = \frac{3(3.6667)}{0.49} = 22.449$$

The one-tailed rejection region with $\alpha = 0.05$ and $n-1 = 3$ degrees of freedom is $\chi^2 > \chi_{0.05}^2 = 7.81$ and H_0 is rejected. There is sufficient evidence to indicate that σ^2 is greater than 0.49.

10.55   **a**   The null hypothesis to be tested is

$$H_0: \mu = 5 \quad \text{versus} \quad H_a: \mu \neq 5$$

Calculate

$$\bar{x} = \frac{\sum x_i}{n} = \frac{19.96}{4} = 4.99 \qquad s^2 = \frac{\sum x_i^2 - \frac{(\sum x_i)^2}{n}}{n-1} = \frac{99.6226 - \frac{(19.96)^2}{4}}{3} = 0.0074$$

and the test statistic is

$$t = \frac{\bar{x} - \mu_0}{s/\sqrt{n}} = \frac{4.99 - 5}{\sqrt{\frac{0.0074}{4}}} = -0.232$$

The rejection region with $\alpha = 0.05$ and $n-1 = 3$ degrees of freedom is found from Table 4, Appendix I, as $|t| > t_{0.025} = 3.182$. Since the observed value of the test statistic does not fall in the rejection region, H_0 is not rejected. There is insufficient evidence to show that the mean differs from 5 mg/cc.

b   The manufacturer claims that the range of the potency measurements will equal 0.2. Since this range is given to equal 6σ, we know that $\sigma \approx 0.0333$. Then

$$H_0: \sigma^2 = (0.0333)^2 = 0.0011 \quad \text{versus} \quad H_a: \sigma^2 > 0.0011$$

The test statistic is

$$\chi^2 = \frac{(n-1)s^2}{\sigma_0^2} = \frac{3(0.0074)}{0.0011} = 20.18$$

and the one-tailed rejection region with $\alpha = 0.05$ and $n - 1 = 3$ degrees of freedom is

$$\chi^2 > \chi_{0.05}^2 = 7.81$$

H_0 is rejected; there is sufficient evidence to indicate that the range of the potency will exceed the manufacturer's claim.

10.57 **a** The force transmitted to a wearer, X, is known to be normally distributed with $\mu = 363$ and $\sigma = 18.1$. Hence,

$$P(X > 454) = P\left(z > \frac{454 - 363}{18.1}\right) = P(z > 5.03) \approx 0$$

It is highly improbable that any particular helmet will transmit a force in excess of 454 kilograms.

  b Since $n = 40$, a large sample test will be used to test

$$H_0: \mu = 454 \quad \text{versus} \quad H_a: \mu > 454$$

The test statistic is

$$z = \frac{\bar{x} - \mu_0}{s/\sqrt{n}} = \frac{374 - 454}{\sqrt{\dfrac{1070}{40}}} = -15.47$$

and the rejection region with $\alpha = 0.05$ is $z > 1.645$. H_0 is not rejected and we conclude that the mean force transmitted by the helmets does not exceed 454 kilograms. [Note: Here the p-value ≈ 1.00]

10.59 The null hypothesis of interest is

$$H_0: \sigma = 150 \quad \text{versus} \quad H_a: \sigma < 150$$

Calculate

$$(n-1)s^2 = \sum x_i^2 - \frac{\left(\sum x_i\right)^2}{n} = 92{,}305{,}600 - \frac{(42{,}812)^2}{20} = 662{,}232.8$$

and the test statistic is $\chi^2 = \dfrac{(n-1)s^2}{\sigma_0^2} = \dfrac{662{,}232.8}{150^2} = 29.433$. The one-tailed rejection region with $\alpha = 0.01$

and $n - 1 = 19$ degrees of freedom is $\chi^2 < \chi_{0.99}^2 = 7.63273$, and H_0 is not rejected. There is insufficient evidence to indicate that the manufacturer is meeting its goal.

10.61 Refer to Exercise 10.60. From Table 6, Appendix I, $F_{df_1, df_2} = 2.62$ and $F_{df_2, df_1} \approx 2.76$. The 95% confidence interval for σ_1^2 / σ_2^2 is

$$\frac{s_1^2}{s_2^2} \frac{1}{F_{df_1, df_2}} < \frac{\sigma_1^2}{\sigma_2^2} < \frac{s_1^2}{s_2^2} F_{df_2, df_1}$$

$$\frac{55.7}{31.4}\left(\frac{1}{2.62}\right) < \frac{\sigma_1^2}{\sigma_2^2} < \frac{55.7}{31.4}(2.76) \quad \text{or} \quad 0.667 < \frac{\sigma_1^2}{\sigma_2^2} < 4.896$$

10.63 The null hypothesis of interest is

$$H_0: \sigma_1^2 = \sigma_2^2 \quad \text{versus} \quad H_a: \sigma_1^2 \neq \sigma_2^2$$

and the test statistic is

$$F = \frac{s_1^2}{s_2^2} = \frac{0.71^2}{0.69^2} = 1.059$$

The critical values of F for various values of α are given on the next page using $df_1 = 14$ and $df_2 = 14$.

α	0.10	0.05	0.025	0.01	0.005
F_α	2.02	2.48	2.97	3.70	4.30

Hence, $p\text{-value} = 2P(F > 1.059) > 2(0.10) = 0.20$

Since the p-value is so large, H_0 is not rejected. There is no evidence to indicate that the variances are different.

10.65 Refer to Exercise 10.64. Noting that $F_{df_1, df_2} \approx 2.01$, the 90% confidence interval for σ_1^2 / σ_2^2 is

$$\frac{s_1^2}{s_2^2} \frac{1}{F_{df_1, df_2}} < \frac{\sigma_1^2}{\sigma_2^2} < \frac{s_1^2}{s_2^2} F_{df_2, df_1}$$

$$\frac{12,996}{10,609}\left(\frac{1}{2.01}\right) < \frac{\sigma_1^2}{\sigma_2^2} < \frac{12,996}{10,609}(2.01) \quad \text{or} \quad 0.609 < \frac{\sigma_1^2}{\sigma_2^2} < 2.462$$

10.67 **a** The null hypothesis of interest is

$H_0: \sigma_1^2 = \sigma_2^2$ versus $H_a: \sigma_1^2 \neq \sigma_2^2$

Calculate

$$s_1^2 = \frac{\sum x_i^2 - \frac{(\sum x_i)^2}{n}}{n-1} = \frac{7106 - \frac{(312)^2}{15}}{14} = 44.0286 \quad \text{and similarly } s_2^2 = \frac{4982 - \frac{(240)^2}{12}}{11} = 16.5455$$

and the test statistic is

$$F = \frac{s_1^2}{s_2^2} = \frac{44.0286}{16.5455} = 2.66$$

The rejection region is two-tailed with $\alpha = 0.01$ and $df_1 = 14$ and $df_2 = 11$. The upper tail of this rejection region is approximated using $df_1 = 12$ and $df_2 = 11$ as $F > F_{0.025} = 5.24$. Since the observed value of the test statistic does not fall in the rejection region, H_0 is not rejected. There is thus not enough evidence to indicate a difference in the variability for the two quarterbacks.

b Since the F test did not show any reasons to doubt the equality of variance assumption, it is appropriate to use the two sample t test, which assumes equal variances.

10.69 **a** The null hypothesis of interest is

$H_0: \sigma_1^2 = \sigma_2^2$ versus $H_a: \sigma_1^2 \neq \sigma_2^2$

and the test statistic is

$$F = \frac{s_1^2}{s_2^2} = \frac{0.273}{0.094} = 2.904$$

The upper portion of the rejection region with $\alpha = 2(0.005) = 0.01$ is $F > F_{0.005} = 6.54$ (from Table 6, Appendix I) and H_0 is not rejected. There is insufficient evidence to indicate that the supplier's shipments differ in variability.

b The 99% confidence interval for σ_2^2 is

$$\frac{(n_2 - 1)s^2}{\chi_{0.005}^2} < \sigma_2^2 < \frac{(n_2 - 1)s^2}{\chi_{0.995}^2}$$

$$\frac{9(.094)}{23.5893} < \sigma_2^2 < \frac{9(.094)}{1.734926} \quad \text{or} \quad 0.036 < \sigma_2^2 < 0.488$$

Intervals constructed in this manner enclose σ_2^2, 99% of the time. Hence, we are fairly certain that σ_2^2 is between 0.036 and 0.488.

10.71 As in the case of the single population mean, random samples must be independently drawn from two populations that possess normal distributions with a common variance, σ^2. Consequently, it is natural that information in the two sample variances, s_1^2 and s_2^2, should be pooled in order to give the best estimate of the common variance, σ^2. In this way, all of the sample information is being utilized to its best advantage.

10.73 **a** Upper one-tailed rejection region with 11 *df* is $t > t_{0.05} = 1.796$.

      b A two-tailed rejection region with 7 *df* is $|t| > t_{0.025} = 2.365$.

      c A lower one-tailed rejection region with 15 *df* is $t < -t_{0.01} = -2.602$.

10.75 The null hypothesis to be tested is

$$H_0: \mu = 48 \quad \text{versus} \quad H_a: \mu \neq 48$$

and the test statistic is

$$t = \frac{\bar{x} - \mu_0}{s/\sqrt{n}} = \frac{47.1 - 48}{\dfrac{2.168}{\sqrt{12}}} = -1.438$$

Using the *critical value approach*, the rejection region with $\alpha = 0.05$ and $n - 1 = 11$ degrees of freedom is located in both tails of the *t*-distribution and is found from Table 4, Appendix I, as $|t| > t_{0.205} = 2.201$. Since the observed value of the test statistic does not fall in the rejection region, H_0 is not rejected and we cannot conclude that the population mean is different than 48.

10.77 The 90% confidence interval is

$$\bar{x} \pm t_{0.05} \frac{s}{\sqrt{n}} \Rightarrow 25 \pm 1.746 \frac{7}{\sqrt{17}} \Rightarrow 25 \pm 2.96 \text{ or } 22.04 < \mu < 27.96$$

10.79 Since it is necessary to determine whether the injected rats drink more water than non-injected rates, the null hypothesis to be tested is

$$H_0: \mu = 22.0 \quad \text{versus} \quad H_a: \mu > 22.0$$

and the test statistic is

$$t = \frac{\bar{x} - \mu_0}{s/\sqrt{n}} = \frac{31.0 - 22.0}{\dfrac{6.2}{\sqrt{17}}} = 5.985$$

Using the *critical value approach*, the rejection region with $\alpha = 0.05$ and $n - 1 = 16$ degrees of freedom is located in the upper tail of the *t*-distribution and is found from Table 4, Appendix I, as $t > t_{0.05} = 1.746$.

Since the observed value of the test statistic falls in the rejection region, H_0 is rejected and we conclude that the injected rats do drink more water than the non-injected rats. The 90% confidence interval is

$$\bar{x} \pm t_{0.05} \frac{s}{\sqrt{n}} \Rightarrow 31.0 \pm 1.746 \frac{6.2}{\sqrt{17}} \Rightarrow 31.0 \pm 2.625 \text{ or } 28.375 < \mu < 33.625$$

10.81 The null hypothesis of interest is

$$H_0: \sigma_1^2 = \sigma_2^2 \quad \text{versus} \quad H_a: \sigma_1^2 < \sigma_2^2$$

and the test statistic is

$$F = \frac{s_2^2}{s_1^2} = \frac{(28.2)^2}{(15.6)^2} = 3.268$$

The critical values of *F* for various values of α are given below using $df_1 = 30$ (since there are no tabled values for $df_1 = 29$) and $df_2 = 29$.

α	0.10	0.05	0.025	0.01	0.005
F_α	1.62	1.85	2.09	2.41	2.66

Hence, p-value $= P(F > 3.268) < 0.005$. Since the p-value is so small, H_0 is rejected. There is evidence to indicate that increased maintenance of the older system is needed.

10.83 From Exercise 10.82, the best estimate for σ is $s = 21.5$. Then, with $B = 5$, solve for n in the following inequality:

$$t_{0.025}\frac{s}{\sqrt{n}} \le 5$$

which is approximately

$$1.96\frac{21.5}{\sqrt{n}} \le 5 \quad \Rightarrow \quad \sqrt{n} \ge \frac{1.96(21.5)}{5} = 8.428$$

$$n \ge 71.03 \quad \text{or} \quad n \ge 72$$

Since n is greater than 30, the sample size, $n = 72$, is valid.

10.85 Use the computing formulas or your scientific calculator to calculate

$$\bar{x} = \frac{\sum x_i}{n} = \frac{322.1}{13} = 24.777$$

$$s^2 = \frac{\sum x_i^2 - \dfrac{(\sum x_i)^2}{n}}{n-1} = \frac{8114.59 - \dfrac{(322.1)^2}{13}}{12} = 11.1619$$

$s = 3.3409$ and the 95% confidence interval is

$$\bar{x} \pm t_{0.025}\frac{s}{\sqrt{n}} \quad \Rightarrow \quad 24.777 \pm 2.179\frac{3.3409}{\sqrt{13}} \quad \Rightarrow \quad 24.777 \pm 2.019 \text{ or } 22.578 < \mu < 26.796$$

10.87 **a** The inequality to be solved is $t_{\alpha/2} \times (\text{std error of estimator}) \le B$. In this exercise, it is necessary to estimate the difference in means to within 1 minute with 95% confidence. The inequality is then

$$t_{0.025}\sqrt{s^2\left(\frac{1}{n_1} + \frac{1}{n_2}\right)} \le 1$$

We assume that $n_1 = n_2 = n$ and $s^2 = 17.64$ from Exercise 10.86. Consider the sample size obtained by replacing $t_{0.025}$ by $z_{0.025} = 1.96$.

$$1.96\sqrt{17.64\left(\frac{1}{n} + \frac{1}{n}\right)} \le 1 \quad \Rightarrow \quad \sqrt{n} \ge 1.96\sqrt{35.28}$$

$$n \ge 135.53 \quad \text{or} \quad n \ge 136$$

Since the value of n is greater than 30, the sample size is valid.

b Consider the inequality from part **a**,

$$t_{\alpha/2}\sqrt{s^2\left(\frac{1}{n_1} + \frac{1}{n_2}\right)} \le 1$$

When $n_1 = n_2 = n$, this becomes

$$t_{\alpha/2}\sqrt{s^2\left(\frac{2}{n}\right)} \le 1 \quad \Rightarrow \quad \sqrt{n} \ge t_{\alpha/2}\sqrt{2s^2}$$

To reduce the sample size necessary to achieve this inequality, we must reduce the quantity

$$t_{\alpha/2}\sqrt{2s^2}$$

If we are willing to lower the level of confidence (or equivalently increase the value of α), the value of $t_{\alpha/2}$ will be smaller. This will decrease the size of n, but at the price of decreased confidence. The only other quantity in the expression which is not fixed is s^2. If this variable can be made smaller, the required sample size will also be reduced. From the definition of s^2, it can be seen that s^2 includes the variability associated with the difference in drugs A and B as well as the variability in absorption rates among the people in the experiment. The experiment could be run a bit differently by using the same people for both drugs. Each person would receive a dose of drug A and drug B. The difference in absorption rates for the two drugs would be observed within each individual. Such a design would eliminate the variability in absorption rates from person to person. The value of s^2 would be reduced and a smaller sample size would be required. The resulting experiment would be analyzed as a paired-difference experiment, as discussed in Section 10.5.

10.89 **a** The range of the first sample is 47, while the range of the second sample is only 16. There is probably a difference in the variances.

b The null hypothesis of interest is

$$H_0: \sigma_1^2 = \sigma_2^2 \quad \text{versus} \quad H_a: \sigma_1^2 \neq \sigma_2^2$$

Calculate $s_1^2 = \dfrac{177,294 - \dfrac{(838)^2}{4}}{3} = 577.6667 \qquad s_2^2 = \dfrac{192,394 - \dfrac{(1,074)^2}{6}}{5} = 29.6$

and the test statistic is

$$F = \frac{s_1^2}{s_2^2} = \frac{577.6667}{29.6} = 19.516$$

The critical values with $df_1 = 3$ and $df_2 = 5$ are shown below from Table 6, Appendix I.

α	0.10	0.05	0.025	0.01	0.005
F_α	3.62	5.41	7.76	12.06	16.53

Hence, $p\text{-value} = 2P(F > 19.516) < 2(0.005) = 0.01$. Since the p-value is smaller than 0.01, H_0 is rejected at the 1% level of significance. There is a difference in variability.

c Since the Student's t test requires the assumption of equal variance, it would be inappropriate in this instance. You should use the unpooled t test with Satterthwaite's approximation to the degrees of freedom.

10.91 **a** The leaf measurements probably come from mound-shaped, or approximately normal populations, since their length, width, thickness, and so on can be thought of as being a composite sum of many factors that affect their growth (see the Central Limit Theorem). The values of the sample variances are not very different, and we would not question the assumption of equal variances. Finally, since the plants were all given the same experimental treatment, they can be considered random and independent samples within a treatment group.

b The null hypothesis to be tested is

$$H_0: \mu_1 - \mu_2 = 0 \quad \text{versus} \quad H_a: \mu_1 - \mu_2 \neq 0$$

Since the ratio of the variances is less than 3, you can use the pooled t test. The pooled estimator of σ^2 is calculated as

$$s^2 = \frac{(n_1 - 1)s_1^2 + (n_2 - 1)s_2^2}{n_1 + n_2 - 2} = \frac{15(43)^2 + 14(41.7)^2}{29} = 1795.8434$$

and the test statistic is

$$t = \frac{(\bar{x}_1 - \bar{x}_2) - 0}{\sqrt{s^2\left(\dfrac{1}{n_1} + \dfrac{1}{n_2}\right)}} = \frac{128 - 78.7}{\sqrt{1795.8434\left(\dfrac{1}{16} + \dfrac{1}{15}\right)}} = 3.237$$

The two-tailed p-value with $df = 29$ can be bounded as $p\text{-value} < 2(0.005) = 0.01$. H_0 is rejected. There is a difference in the means.

c The null hypothesis to be tested is

$$H_0: \mu_1 - \mu_2 = 0 \qquad \text{versus} \qquad H_a: \mu_1 - \mu_2 \neq 0$$

Since the ratio of the variances is slightly greater than 3, you should use the pooled t test with the test statistic

$$t = \frac{(\bar{x}_1 - \bar{x}_2) - 0}{\sqrt{\dfrac{s_1^2}{n_1} + \dfrac{s_2^2}{n_2}}} = \frac{46.8 - 8.1}{\sqrt{\dfrac{(2.21)^2}{16} + \dfrac{(1.26)^2}{15}}} = 60.36$$

The p-value is two-tailed, based on

$$df = \frac{\left(\dfrac{s_1^2}{n_1} + \dfrac{s_2^2}{n_2}\right)^2}{\dfrac{\left(\dfrac{s_1^2}{n_1}\right)^2}{n_1 - 1} + \dfrac{\left(\dfrac{s_2^2}{n_2}\right)^2}{n_2 - 1}} \approx 25 \text{ degrees of freedom}$$

and is bounded as p-value $< 2(0.005) = 0.01$. The results are highly significant and H_0 is rejected. There is a difference in the means.

10.93 A paired-difference test is used, since the two samples are not random and independent. The null hypothesis of interest is

$$H_0: \mu_1 - \mu_2 = 0 \quad \text{versus} \quad H_a: \mu_1 - \mu_2 > 0$$

and the table of differences, along with the calculation of $\bar{d}$ and s_d^2, is presented below.

Pair	1	2	3	4	Totals
d_i	−1	5	11	7	22

$$\bar{d} = \frac{\sum d_i}{n} = \frac{22}{4} = 5.5$$

$$s_d^2 = \frac{\sum d_i^2 - \dfrac{(\sum d_i)^2}{n}}{n-1} = \frac{196 - \dfrac{(22)^2}{4}}{3} = 25 \text{ and } s_d = 5$$

and the test statistic is

$$t = \frac{\bar{d} - \mu_d}{s_d / \sqrt{n}} = \frac{5.5 - 0}{\dfrac{5}{\sqrt{4}}} = 2.2$$

The one-tailed p-value with $df = 3$ can be bounded between 0.05 and 0.10. Since this value is greater than 0.10, H_0 is not rejected. The results are not significant; there is insufficient evidence to indicate that lack of school experience has a depressing effect on IQ scores.

10.95 A paired-difference analysis is used. The null hypothesis of interest is

$$H_0: \mu_1 - \mu_2 = 0 \quad \text{versus} \quad H_a: \mu_1 - \mu_2 \neq 0$$

and the differences are shown below.

156, 447, −3, 42

Calculate

$$\bar{d} = \frac{\sum d_i}{n} = \frac{642}{4} = 160.5$$

$$s_d = \sqrt{\frac{\sum d_i^2 - \dfrac{(\sum d_i)^2}{n}}{n-1}} = \sqrt{\frac{225918 - \dfrac{(642)^2}{4}}{3}} = 202.3833$$

and the test statistic is

$$t = \frac{\bar{d} - \mu_d}{s_d/\sqrt{n}} = \frac{160.5 - 0}{\frac{202.3833}{\sqrt{4}}} = 1.586$$

The two-tailed p-value with $df = 3$ is greater than $2(0.10) = 0.20$. Since this value is greater than 0.05, H_0 is not rejected. The results are not significant; there is insufficient evidence to indicate a difference in the average cost of repair for the Honda Civic and the Hyundai Elantra.

10.97 The object is to determine whether or not there is a difference between the mean responses for the two different stimuli to which the people have been subjected. The samples are independently and randomly selected, and the assumptions necessary for the t test of Section 10.4 are met. The hypothesis to be tested is

$$H_0: \mu_1 - \mu_2 = 0 \quad \text{versus} \quad H_a: \mu_1 - \mu_2 \neq 0$$

and the preliminary calculations are as follows:

$$\bar{x}_1 = \frac{15}{8} = 1.875 \quad \text{and} \quad \bar{x}_2 = \frac{21}{8} = 2.625$$

$$s_1^2 = \frac{33 - \frac{(15)^2}{8}}{7} = 0.69643 \quad \text{and} \quad s_2^2 = \frac{61 - \frac{(21)^2}{8}}{7} = 0.83929$$

Since the ratio of the variances is less than 3, you can use the pooled t test. The pooled estimator of σ^2 is calculated as

$$s^2 = \frac{(n_1 - 1)s_1^2 + (n_2 - 1)s_2^2}{n_1 + n_2 - 2} = \frac{4.875 + 5.875}{14} = 0.7679$$

and the test statistic is

$$t = \frac{(\bar{x}_1 - \bar{x}_2) - 0}{\sqrt{s^2\left(\frac{1}{n_1} + \frac{1}{n_2}\right)}} = \frac{1.875 - 2.625}{\sqrt{0.7679\left(\frac{1}{8} + \frac{1}{8}\right)}} = -1.712$$

The two-tailed rejection region with $\alpha = 0.05$ and $df = 14$ is $|t| > t_{0.025} = 2.145$, and H_0 is not rejected. There is insufficient evidence to indicate that there is a difference in means.

10.99 Refer to Exercise 10.97 and 10.98. For the unpaired design, the 95% confidence interval for $(\mu_1 - \mu_2)$ is

$$(\bar{x}_1 - \bar{x}_2) \pm t_{0.025}\sqrt{s^2\left(\frac{1}{n_1} + \frac{1}{n_2}\right)}$$

$$-0.75 \pm 2.145\sqrt{0.7679\left(\frac{1}{8} + \frac{1}{8}\right)}$$

$$-0.75 \pm 0.94 \quad \text{or} \quad -1.69 < (\mu_1 - \mu_2) < 0.19$$

while for the paired design, the 95% confidence interval is

$$\bar{d} \pm t_{0.025}\frac{s_d}{\sqrt{n}} \Rightarrow -0.75 \pm 2.365\frac{0.88641}{\sqrt{8}} \Rightarrow -0.75 \pm 0.74 \text{ or } -1.49 < (\mu_1 - \mu_2) < -0.01$$

Although the width of the confidence interval has decreased slightly, it does not appear that blocking has increased the amount of information by much.

10.101 a Note that the experiment has been designed so that two cake pans, one containing batter A and one containing batter B, were placed side by side at each of six different locations in an oven. The two samples are therefore not independent, and a paired-difference analysis must be used. To test $H_0: \mu_2 - \mu_1 = 0$ versus $H_a: \mu_2 - \mu_1 \neq 0$, calculate the differences:

$$-0.006, 0.018, 0.014, 0.011, 0.004, 0.019$$

Then $\bar{d} = \dfrac{\sum d_i}{n} = \dfrac{0.06}{6} = 0.01$

$$s_d^2 = \frac{\sum d_i^2 - \dfrac{\left(\sum d_i\right)^2}{n}}{n-1} = \frac{0.001054 - \dfrac{(0.06)^2}{6}}{5} = 0.0000908 \text{ and } s_d = 0.009529$$

and the test statistic is

$$t = \frac{\bar{d} - \mu_d}{s_d / \sqrt{n}} = \frac{0.06 - 0}{\dfrac{0.009529}{\sqrt{6}}} = 2.5706$$

For a two-tailed test with $df = 5$, the p-value is bounded as

$$2(0.025) < p\text{-value} < 20(.05) \quad \text{or} \quad 0.05 < p\text{-value} < 0.10$$

Since the p-value is greater than 0.10, H_0 is not rejected. There is insufficient evidence to indicate a difference between mean densities for batters A and B.

b The 95% confidence interval is

$$\bar{d} \pm t_{0.025}\frac{s_d}{\sqrt{n}} \quad \Rightarrow \quad 0.01 \pm 2.571\frac{0.009529}{\sqrt{6}} \quad \Rightarrow \quad 0.01 \pm 0.010 \text{ or } 0.000 < (\mu_1 - \mu_2) < 0.020$$

10.103 It is possible to test the null hypothesis $H_0: \sigma_1^2 = \sigma_2^2$ against any one of three alternative hypotheses:

$$\text{(1)} \ \ H_a: \sigma_1^2 \neq \sigma_2^2 \qquad \text{(2)} \ \ H_a: \sigma_1^2 < \sigma_2^2 \qquad \text{(3)} \ \ H_a: \sigma_1^2 > \sigma_2^2$$

a The first alternative would be preferred by the manager of the dairy. The manager does not know anything about the variability of the two machines and would wish to detect departures from equality of the type $\sigma_1^2 < \sigma_2^2$ or $\sigma_1^2 > \sigma_2^2$. These alternatives are implied in (1).

b The sales representative for company A would prefer that the experimenter select the second alternative. Rejection of the null hypothesis would imply that the company A machine had smaller variability. Moreover, even if the null hypothesis were not rejected, there would be no evidence to indicate that the variability of the company A machine was greater than the variability of the company B machine.

c The sales representative for company B would prefer the third alternative for a similar reason.

10.105 a The manufacturer claims that the range of the random variable x (purity of his product) is no more than 2%. In terms of the standard deviation σ, it is claiming that $\sigma \leq 0.5$ since

$$Range \approx 4\sigma = 2 \quad \Rightarrow \quad \sigma = 0.5$$

Hence, the null hypothesis to be tested is

$$H_0: \sigma = 0.5 \quad \text{versus} \quad H_a: \sigma > 0.5 \quad \text{or equivalently}$$

$$H_0: \sigma^2 = 0.25 \quad \text{versus} \quad H_a: \sigma^2 > 0.25$$

Calculate

$$s^2 = \frac{47{,}982.56 - \dfrac{(489.8)^2}{5}}{4} = 0.438$$

and the test statistic is

$$\chi^2 = \frac{(n-1)s^2}{\sigma_0^2} = \frac{4(0.438)}{0.25} = 7.088$$

The one-tailed p-value with $n-1 = 4$ degrees of freedom is $p\text{-value} > 0.10$ and H_0 is not rejected. There is insufficient evidence to contradict the manufacturer's claim.

b Indexing $\chi_{0.05}^2$ and $\chi_{0.95}^2$ with $n-1 = 4$ degrees of freedom in Table 5 yields

$$\chi_{0.05}^2 = 9.48773 \quad \text{and} \quad \chi_{0.95}^2 = 0.710721$$

and the confidence interval is

$$\frac{4(0.438)}{9.48773} < \sigma^2 < \frac{4(0.438)}{0.710721} \quad \text{or} \quad 0.185 < \sigma^2 < 2.465$$

10.107 A paired-difference analysis is used. To test $H_0: \mu_1 - \mu_2 = 0$ versus $H_a: \mu_1 - \mu_2 > 0$, where μ_2 is the mean reaction time after injection and μ_1 is the mean reaction time before injection, calculate the differences $(x_2 - x_1)$: 6, 1, 6, 1

Then $\bar{d} = \dfrac{\sum d_i}{n} = \dfrac{14}{4} = 3.5$

$$s_d^2 = \frac{\sum d_i^2 - \dfrac{(\sum d_i)^2}{n}}{n-1} = \frac{74 - \dfrac{(14)^2}{4}}{3} = 8.33 \text{ and } s_d = 2.88675$$

and the test statistic is

$$t = \frac{\bar{d} - \mu_d}{s_d/\sqrt{n}} = \frac{3.5 - 0}{\dfrac{2.88675}{\sqrt{4}}} = 2.425$$

For a one-tailed test with $df = 3$, the rejection region with $\alpha = 0.05$ is $t > t_{0.05} = 2.353$, and H_0 is rejected. We conclude that the drug significantly increases with reaction time.

10.109 The null hypothesis to be tested is

$$H_0: \mu_1 - \mu_2 = 0 \quad \text{versus} \quad H_a: \mu_1 - \mu_2 \neq 0$$

and the preliminary calculations are as follows:

$$\bar{x}_1 = \frac{0.6}{6} = 0.1 \text{ and } \bar{x}_2 = \frac{0.83}{6} = 0.1383$$

$$s_1^2 = \frac{0.0624 - \dfrac{(0.6)^2}{6}}{5} = 0.00048 \quad \text{and} \quad s_2^2 = \frac{0.1175 - \dfrac{(0.83)^2}{6}}{5} = 0.00053667$$

Since the ratio of the variances is less than 3, you can use the pooled t test. The pooled estimator of σ^2 is calculated as

$$s^2 = \frac{(n_1 - 1)s_1^2 + (n_2 - 1)s_2^2}{n_1 + n_2 - 2} = \frac{0.0024 + 0.00268}{10} = 0.0005083$$

and the test statistic is

$$t = \frac{(\bar{x}_1 - \bar{x}_2) - 0}{\sqrt{s^2\left(\dfrac{1}{n_1} + \dfrac{1}{n_2}\right)}} = \frac{-0.0383}{\sqrt{0.0005083\left(\dfrac{1}{6} + \dfrac{1}{6}\right)}} = -2.945$$

The p-value for a one-tailed test with 10 degrees of freedom is bounded as $0.005 < p\text{-value} < 0.010$. Hence, the null hypothesis H_0 is rejected. There is sufficient evidence to indicate that $\mu_1 < \mu_2$.

10.111 The underlying populations are ratings and can only take on the finite number of values, 1, 2, …, 9, 10. Neither population has a normal distribution, but both are discrete. Further, the samples are not independent, since the same person is asked to rank each car design. Hence, two of the assumptions required for the Student's t test have been violated.

10.113 The null hypothesis to be tested is $H_0: \mu_1 - \mu_2 = 0$ versus $H_a: \mu_1 - \mu_2 \neq 0$, and the test statistic using the *Excel* printout is

$$t = \frac{\bar{d} - \mu_d}{s_d/\sqrt{n}} = 1.862$$

with two-tailed p-value $= 0.112$. Since this p-value is greater than 0.10, we fail to reject H_0. There is insufficient evidence to indicate a greater demand for one of the two entries.

10.115 The *MINITAB* printout below shows the summary statistics for the two samples:

```
Descriptive Statistics: Method 1, Method 2
Variable   N    Mean   SE Mean   StDev
Method 1   5   137.00    4.55    10.17
Method 2   5   147.20    3.29     7.36
```

Since the ratio of the two sample variances is less than 3, you can use the pooled t test to compare the two methods of measurement, using the remainder of the *MINITAB* printout below:

```
Two-Sample T-Test and CI: Method 1, Method 2
Difference = mu (Method 1) - mu (Method 2)
Estimate for difference:  -10.2000
95% CI for difference:  (-23.1506, 2.7506)
T-Test of difference = 0 (vs not =): T-Value = -1.82  P-Value = 0.107  DF = 8
Both use Pooled StDev = 8.8798
```

The test statistic is $t = -1.82$ with p-value $= 0.107$ and the results are not significant. There is insufficient evidence to declare a difference in the two population means.

10.117 a   Calculate $\bar{x} = \dfrac{\sum x_i}{n} = \dfrac{68.5}{10} = 6.85$

$$s^2 = \frac{\sum x_i^2 - \dfrac{\left(\sum x_i\right)^2}{n}}{n-1} = \frac{478.375 - \dfrac{\left(68.5\right)^2}{10}}{9} = 1.016667 \quad \text{and} \quad s = 1.0083$$

The 99% confidence interval based on $df = 9$ is

$$\bar{x} \pm t_{0.005} \frac{s}{\sqrt{n}} \Rightarrow 6.85 \pm 3.25 \frac{1.0083}{\sqrt{10}} \Rightarrow 6.85 \pm 1.036 \text{ or } 5.814 < \mu < 7.886$$

b   The sample must have been randomly selected from a normal population.

10.119 a   A paired-difference test is used. To test $H_0: \mu_1 - \mu_2 = 0$ versus $H_a: \mu_1 - \mu_2 \neq 0$, where μ_1 is the mean in 2008 and μ_2 is the mean price in 2010, calculate the differences:

       $61, -171, 186, 449, 148, 72, -357$

Then $\bar{d} = \dfrac{\sum d_i}{n} = \dfrac{388}{7} = 55.42857, \quad s_d^2 = \dfrac{423{,}696 - \dfrac{\left(388\right)^2}{7}}{6} = 60{,}031.61805,$ and $s_d = 258.90465$

and the test statistic is

$$t = \frac{\bar{d} - \mu_d}{s_d / \sqrt{n}} = \frac{55.42857 - 0}{\dfrac{258.90465}{\sqrt{7}}} = 0.566$$

For a two-tailed test with $df = 6$, the rejection region with $\alpha = 0.01$ is $|t| > t_{0.005} = 3.707$, and H_0 is not rejected. There is thus insufficient evidence to indicate the mean prices in 2008 are different than the prices in 2010.

b   The 98% confidence interval is

$$\bar{d} \pm t_{0.01} \frac{s_d}{\sqrt{n}} \Rightarrow 55.42857 \pm 3.143 \frac{258.90465}{\sqrt{7}} \Rightarrow 55.42857 \pm 307.5638$$

or $-252.135 < \left(\mu_1 - \mu_2\right) < 362.992$

10.121   **a**   The null hypothesis of interest is

$$H_0: \sigma_1^2 = \sigma_2^2 \quad \text{versus} \quad H_a: \sigma_1^2 \neq \sigma_2^2$$

and the test statistic is

$$F = \frac{s_1^2}{s_2^2} = \frac{22^2}{20^2} = 1.21$$

The upper portion of the two-tailed rejection region with $\alpha = 0.05$ is $F > F_{19,19} \approx F_{20,19} = 2.51$ and H_0 is not rejected. There is insufficient evidence to indicate that the population variances are different.

b   The null hypothesis to be tested is

$$H_0: \mu_1 - \mu_2 = 0 \quad \text{versus} \quad H_a: \mu_1 - \mu_2 \neq 0$$

Based on the results of part **a**, you can use the pooled t test. The pooled estimator of σ^2 is calculated

as $s^2 = \dfrac{(n_1 - 1)s_1^2 + (n_2 - 1)s_2^2}{n_1 + n_2 - 2} = \dfrac{19(22^2) + 19(20^2)}{38} = 442$

and the test statistic is

$$t = \frac{(\bar{x}_1 - \bar{x}_2) - 0}{\sqrt{s^2\left(\dfrac{1}{n_1} + \dfrac{1}{n_2}\right)}} = \frac{78 - 67}{\sqrt{442\left(\dfrac{1}{20} + \dfrac{1}{20}\right)}} = 1.65$$

The rejection region with $\alpha = 0.05$ and $df = 20 + 20 - 2 = 38$ (approximated with $df = 29$) is $|t| > 2.045$ and H_0 is not rejected. There is insufficient evidence to indicate a difference in the two populaton means.

Case Study: How Does Bait Type Affect the Visit of the American Marten in Ontario?

1   A two sampled t test is used to test H_0: $\mu_1 - \mu_2 = 0$ versus H_a: $\mu_1 - \mu_2 < 0$, where μ_1 is the mean number of days until a track box with jam-lard-fish oil mixture bait was visited, and μ_2 is the mean number of days until a track box with chicken bait was visited. Using *MINITAB* to perform the two sampled t test, we obtain the following printout.

```
Two-Sample T-Test and CI: Jam, Chicken
Two-sample T for Jam vs Chicken
          N   Mean   StDev   SE Mean
Jam       5   3.80   1.79    0.80
Chicken   5   4.40   1.67    0.75

Difference = mu (Jam) - mu (Chicken)
Estimate for difference:  -0.60
95% upper bound for difference:  1.48
T-Test of difference = 0 (vs <): T-Value = -0.55  P-Value = 0.300  DF = 7
```

The test statistic of $t = -0.55$ with p-value $= 0.300$ indicates that the results are not significant. There is not enough evidence to indicate that jam-lard-fish oil mixture attracts the martens more efficiently than chicken.

2   A two sampled t test is used to test H_0: $\mu_1 - \mu_2 = 0$ versus H_a: $\mu_1 - \mu_2 < 0$, where μ_1 is the mean number of days until a track box with peanut butter bait was visited, and μ_2 is the mean number of days until a track box with control was visited. Using *MINITAB* to perform the two sampled t test, we obtain the following printout.

```
Two-Sample T-Test and CI: Peanut, Control
Two-sample T for Peanut vs Control
          N   Mean   StDev   SE Mean
Peanut    5   5.00   1.41    0.63
Control   5   5.60   1.14    0.51

Difference = mu (Peanut) - mu (Control)
Estimate for difference:  -0.600
95% upper bound for difference:  0.939
T-Test of difference = 0 (vs <): T-Value = -0.74  P-Value = 0.242  DF = 7
```

The test statistic of $t = -0.74$ with p-value $= 0.242$ indicates that the results are not significant. There is not enough evidence to indicate that American martens have a better taste for peanut butter.

3   From the printout below, the 95% confidence interval for the difference in days taken for the marten to visit a chicken track box and a peanut butter track box is $-2.917 < \mu_1 - \mu_2 < 1.717$.

```
Two-Sample T-Test and CI: Chicken, Peanut
Two-sample T for Chicken vs Peanut
          N   Mean   StDev   SE Mean
Chicken   5   4.40   1.67    0.75
Peanut    5   5.00   1.41    0.63

Difference = mu (Chicken) - mu (Peanut)
Estimate for difference:  -0.600
95% CI for difference:  (-2.917, 1.717)
T-Test of difference = 0 (vs not =): T-Value = -0.61  P-Value = 0.560  DF = 7
```

Based on this interval, which contains the value $\mu_1 - \mu_2 = 0$, there is no evidence to indicate the significant difference.

4   Based on the analysis of these variables, no bait seems significantly more effective than the other.

Project 10: Watch Your Sugar Level!

a   **i**   To test whether the blood glucose level is higher than 7.0 mmol/L, we have the following null and alternative hypotheses:
$$H_0: \mu = 7.0 \quad \text{versus} \quad H_a: \mu > 7.0$$

        ii   Since we have a small sample size ($n = 7$), we use a t test statistic to test our hypotheses. Specifically, we have

$$t_{test} = \frac{\overline{x} - \mu}{\frac{s}{\sqrt{n}}} = \frac{7.014286 - 7}{\frac{0.4913538}{\sqrt{7}}} = 0.07692308$$

where

$$\overline{x} = \frac{1}{n}\sum_{i=1}^{n} x_i = 7.014286$$

$$s^2 = \frac{1}{n-1}\sum_{i=1}^{n}\left(x_i - \overline{x}\right)^2 = 0.2414286$$

        Our degrees of freedom for this test are $n - 1 = 7 - 1 = 6$.

        iii   Using Table 4 in Appendix I, we find that the approximate p-value for this test is $P(t > 0.07692308) > 0.10$. At the $\alpha = 0.05$ level, we would fail to reject the null hypothesis. There is insufficient evidence to suggest that the blood glucose level is higher than 7.0 mmol/L. The test fails to support the alternative hypothesis.

        iv   A 95% confidence interval is calculated as

$$\overline{x} \pm t_{\frac{\alpha}{2}, n-1} \frac{s}{\sqrt{n}}$$

$$7.014286 \pm 2.447 \frac{0.4913538}{\sqrt{7}}$$

which gives us an interval of (6.559859, 7.468712). Since our interval covers the null-hypothesized value of 7.0mmol/L, we do not have sufficient evidence to reject the null hypothesis.

b   **i**   To test whether the blood glucose level is higher than 7.0 mmol/L, we have the following null and alternative hypotheses:
$$H_0: \sigma^2 = 0.8 \quad \text{versus} \quad H_a: \sigma^2 < 0.8$$

        ii   To test the null hypothesis, we calculate a χ^2 test statistic. Specifically,

$$\chi^2_{test} = \frac{(n-1)s^2}{\sigma_0^2} = \frac{6.02414286}{0.8} = 1.810714$$

        The test is rejected if our test statistic exceeds χ^2 on $n - 1 = 6$ degrees of freedom (with $\alpha = 0.05$). Thus, we reject the null hypothesis in favour of the alternative if our test statistic exceeds 12.59159. Since our test statistic is less than the critical value, we do not reject the null hypothesis. There is insufficient evidence to suggest the variance is less than 0.8.

        iii   The p-value is determined using Table 5 in Appendix I. On 6 degrees of freedom, the p-value would be $P(\chi^2 > 1.810714) > 0.10$.

        iv   A confidence interval for the population variance is

$$\frac{(n-1)s^2}{\chi^2_{\frac{\alpha}{2}, n-1}} < \sigma^2 < \frac{(n-1)s^2}{\chi^2_{1-\frac{\alpha}{2}, n-1}}$$

$$\frac{6 \cdot 0.2414286}{12.59159} < \sigma^2 < \frac{6 \cdot 0.2414286}{1.635383}$$

$$0.1150428 < \sigma^2 < 0.885769$$

        v   Yes.

c   **i**   To compare the treatments (placebo vs. treatment), we can assume that the population variances are the same. This is the case since the ratio of the sample variances is less than 3 (i.e., $0.21/0.17 < 3$).

ii   The null and alternative hypothesis are

$H_0: \mu_1 = \mu_2$ or $\mu_1 - \mu_2 = 0$ versus $H_a: \mu_1 > \mu_2$ or $\mu_1 - \mu_2 > 0$

Here μ_1 represents the population mean for the placebo group, and μ_2 represents the population mean for the treatment group. To test the null hypothesis, we calculate an independent samples t test statistic. Since we have assumed equal variances, we calculate the pooled estimate of variance. Specifically, we have

$$s_p^2 = \frac{(n_1 - 1)s_1^2 + (n_2 - 1)s_2^2}{n_1 + n_2 - 2} = \frac{9 \cdot 0.21 + 9 \cdot 0.17}{10 + 10 - 2} = 0.19$$

And thus our test statistic is

$$t_{test} = \frac{\overline{x_1} - \overline{x_2}}{\sqrt{s_p^2\left(\frac{1}{n_1} + \frac{1}{n_2}\right)}} = \frac{6.5 - 5.4}{\sqrt{0.19\left(\frac{1}{10} + \frac{1}{10}\right)}} = 5.642881$$

The critical t value on $n_1 + n_2 - 2 = 18$ degrees of freedom (with $\alpha = 0.05$) is 1.734064. Our decision rule is to reject the null hypothesis if our test statistic exceeds the critical value. Since our test statistic $5.642881 > 1.734064$, we reject the null hypothesis. There is sufficient evidence to suggest that the strict diet plan lowers the blood glucose level.

iii   The approximate p-value for this test is obtained from Table 4 of Appendix I. With 18 degrees of freedom we have $P(t > 5.642881) < 0.005$.

iv   Since our p-value < 0.005 is less than $\alpha = 0.10$, we would reject the null hypothesis. That is, the blood glucose levels following treatment are significantly lower than the blood glucose levels for the placebo group.

v   A 95% confidence interval for the difference in the two means is

$$\overline{x_1} - \overline{x_2} \pm t_{\frac{\alpha}{2}, n_1 + n_2 - 2}\sqrt{s_p^2\left(\frac{1}{n_1} + \frac{1}{n_2}\right)}$$

$$1.1 \pm 2.101\sqrt{0.19\left(\frac{1}{10} + \frac{1}{10}\right)}$$

which gives (0.6904549, 1.5095451). Since the interval does not cover zero, we can say there is a significant difference between the two means. Further, since the interval for the difference between the placebo and treatment groups is positive, there is significant evidence to suggest that the placebo group has a higher blood glucose reading than the treatment group.

d   **i**   To test the equality of the variances we perform an F test. Our hypotheses are

$H_0: \sigma_1^2 = \sigma_2^2$ versus $H_a: \sigma_1^2 > \sigma_2^2$

where σ_1^2 represents the population variance for the placebo group, and σ_2^2 represents the population variance for the treatment group. Our F test statistic is

$$F_{test} = \frac{s_1^2}{s_2^2} = \frac{0.21}{0.17} = 1235294$$

The decision to reject the null hypothesis will be made if the test statistic exceeds the critical F value on $n_1 - 1 = 9$ and $n_2 - 1 = 9$ degrees of freedom. Using Table 6 from Appendix I, our critical F value with $\alpha = 0.10$ is 2.44. Since our test statistic is less than 2.440340, we do not reject the null hypothesis. There is insufficient evidence to suggest that the variances are different.

ii   A 90% confidence interval for the ratio of the two population variances is

$$\left(\frac{s_2^1}{s_2^2}\right)\frac{1}{F_{\frac{\alpha}{2}, df 1, df 2}} < \frac{\sigma_1^2}{\sigma_2^2} < \left(\frac{s_2^1}{s_2^2}\right)F_{\frac{\alpha}{2}, df 2, df 1}$$

$$\frac{1.235294}{3.18} < \frac{\sigma_1^2}{\sigma_2^2} < 1.235294 \cdot 3.18$$

$$0.388 < \frac{\sigma_1^2}{\sigma_2^2} < 3.927$$

iii Since the interval covers 1, we have insufficient evidence to suggest that the ratio of the variances is 1. Hence, we can assume that the variances are not significantly different.

e **i** The samples are not independent since the readings made after medication will depend on the pre-treatment results. With this in mind, performing a paired-difference t test would be valid (assuming the data comes from a normal distribution).

ii The null and alternative hypotheses are thus based on the differences before and after medication. Specifically, we have

$H_0: \mu_d = 0$ versus $H_a: \mu_d > 0$, where $\mu_d = \mu_{before} - \mu_{after}$

iii To calculate the test statistic, we need to determine the sample mean and sample variance of the differences. Our differences are

1.2, 1.8, 0.4, 3.0, 2.2, 3.2, 4.0, 2.3, 2.9, 2.4

for each of the adults respectively. The sample mean and sample variance are

$$\overline{x}_d = \frac{1}{n} \sum_{i=1}^{n} x_i = \frac{1}{10}(1.2 + 1.8 + \ldots + 2.4) = 2.34$$

$$s_d^2 = \frac{1}{n-1} \sum_{i=1}^{n} (x_i - \overline{x}_d)^2 = \frac{1}{9}\left((1.2 - 2.34)^2 + (1.8 - 2.34)^2 + \ldots + (2.4 - 2.34)^2\right) = 1.069333$$

where $n = 10$, the number of differences.

iv The test statistic is

$$t_{test} = \frac{\overline{x}_d - \mu_d}{\dfrac{s_d}{\sqrt{n}}} = \frac{2.34}{\dfrac{1.034086}{\sqrt{10}}} = 7.155817$$

v Given the one-sided alternative, we find the critical t value from Table 4 in Appendix I. With $n - 1 = 9$ degrees of freedom, and $\alpha = 0.05$, we will reject the null hypothesis if our test statistic is greater than 1.833.

vi Since our test statistic is greater than the critical value, we reject the null hypothesis in favour of the alternative. There is sufficient evidence to suggest that the blood glucose levels are lower after treatment with medication.

vii The approximate p-value can be determined using Table 4 in Appendix I. In this case, with 9 degrees of freedom, we obtain a p-value $= P(t > 7.155817) < 0.005$.

viii A 90% confidence interval for the differences in blood glucose level between the two groups is

$$\overline{x}_d \pm t_{\frac{\alpha}{2}, n-1} \frac{s_d}{\sqrt{n}}$$

$$2.34 \pm 1.833 \frac{1.034086}{\sqrt{10}}$$

which gives an interval of (1.740560, 2.939440). Since this interval does not cover zero, there is evidence to suggest that there is a significant difference in the average blood glucose levels between the two groups. This is consistent with the findings of the hypothesis test.

Chapter 11: The Analysis of Variance

11.1   In comparing 6 populations, there are $k-1$ degrees of freedom for treatments and $n=6(10)=60$. The ANOVA table is shown below.

Source	df
Treatments	5
Error	54
Total	59

11.3   Refer to Exercise 11.2.

a $\bar{x}_1 \pm t_{0.025}\sqrt{\dfrac{MSE}{n_1}} \Rightarrow 3.07 \pm 1.96\sqrt{\dfrac{0.3}{10}} \Rightarrow 3.07 \pm 0.339$

or $2.731 < \mu_1 < 3.409$

b $(\bar{x}_1 - \bar{x}_2) \pm t_{0.025}\sqrt{MSE\left(\dfrac{1}{n_1}+\dfrac{1}{n_2}\right)}$

$(3.07 - 2.52) \pm 1.96\sqrt{0.3\left(\dfrac{2}{10}\right)}$

0.55 ± 0.480 or $0.07 < \mu_1 - \mu_2 < 1.03$

11.5   **a**   Refer to Exercise 11.4. The given sums of squares are inserted and missing entries found by subtraction. The mean squares are found as $MS - SS/df$.

Source	df	SS	MS	F
Treatments	3	339.8	113.267	16.98
Error	20	133.4	6.67	
Total	23	473.2		

b   The F statistic, $F = MST/MSE$, has $df_1 = 3$ and $df_2 = 20$ degrees of freedom.

c   With $\alpha = 0.05$ and degrees of freedom from **b**, H_0 is rejected if $F > F_{0.05} = 3.10$.

d   Since $F = 16.98$ falls in the rejection region, the null hypothesis is rejected. There is a difference among the means.

e   The critical values of F with $df_1 = 3$ and $df_2 = 20$ (Table 6) for bounding the p-value for this one-tailed test are shown below.

α	0.10	0.05	0.025	0.01	0.005
F_α	2.38	3.10	3.86	4.94	5.82

Since the observed value $F = 16.98$ is greater than $F_{0.005}$, p-value < 0.005 and H_0 is rejected as in part **d**.

11.7   The following preliminary calculations are necessary:

$T_1 = 14 \quad T_2 = 19 \quad T_3 = 5 \quad G = 38$

a $CM = \dfrac{\left(\sum x_{ij}\right)^2}{n} = \dfrac{(38)^2}{14} = 103.142857$

Total $SS = \sum x_{ij}^2 - CM = 3^2 + 2^2 + \cdots + 2^2 + 1^2 - CM = 130 - 103.142857 = 26.8571$

b $\text{SST} = \sum \dfrac{T_i^2}{n_i} - \text{CM} = \dfrac{14^2}{5} + \dfrac{19^2}{5} + \dfrac{5^2}{4} - \text{CM} = 117.65 - 103.142857 = 14.5071$

and $\text{MST} = \dfrac{\text{SST}}{k-1} = \dfrac{14.5071}{2} = 7.2536$

c   By subtraction, $\text{SSE} = \text{Total SS} - \text{SST} = 26.8571 - 14.5071 = 12.3500$ and the degrees of freedom, by subtraction, are $13 - 2 = 11$. Then

$$\text{MSE} = \dfrac{\text{SSE}}{11} = \dfrac{12.3500}{11} = 1.1227$$

d   The information obtained in parts **a–c** is consolidated in an ANOVA table.

Source	df	SS	MS
Treatments	2	14.5071	7.2536
Error	11	12.3500	1.1227
Total	13	26.8571	

e   The null hypothesis to be tested is

$H_0: \mu_1 = \mu_2 = \mu_3$ versus H_a: at least one pair of means are different

f   The rejection region for the test statistic $F = \dfrac{\text{MST}}{\text{MSE}} = \dfrac{7.2536}{1.1227} = 6.46$ is based on an F-distribution with

2 and 11 degrees of freedom. The critical values of F for bounding the p-value for this one-tailed test are shown below.

α	0.10	0.05	0.025	0.01	0.005
F_α	2.86	3.98	5.26	7.21	8.91

Since the observed value $F = 6.46$ is between $F_{0.01}$ and $F_{0.025}$, $0.01 < p\text{-value} < 0.025$ and H_0 is rejected at the 5% level of significance. There is a difference among the means.

11.9   **a**   The 90% confidence interval for μ_1 is

$$\overline{x}_1 \pm t_{0.05} \sqrt{\dfrac{\text{MSE}}{n_1}} \;\Rightarrow\; 2.8 \pm 1.796 \sqrt{\dfrac{1.1227}{5}} \;\Rightarrow\; 2.8 \pm 0.85$$

or $1.95 < \mu_1 < 3.65$

b   The 90% confidence interval for $\mu_1 - \mu_3$ is

$$\left(\overline{x}_1 - \overline{x}_3\right) \pm t_{0.05} \sqrt{\text{MSE}\left(\dfrac{1}{n_1} + \dfrac{1}{n_3}\right)}$$

$$\left(2.8 - 1.25\right) \pm 1.796 \sqrt{1.1227\left(\dfrac{1}{5} + \dfrac{1}{4}\right)}$$

1.55 ± 1.28 or $0.27 < \mu_1 - \mu_3 < 2.83$

11.11   **a**   The 95% confidence interval for μ_A is

$$\overline{x}_A \pm t_{0.025} \sqrt{\dfrac{\text{MSE}}{n_A}} \;\Rightarrow\; 76 \pm 2.306 \sqrt{\dfrac{62.333}{5}} \;\Rightarrow\; 76 \pm 8.142 \text{ or } 67.86 < \mu_A < 84.14$$

b   The 95% confidence interval for μ_B is

$$\overline{x}_B \pm t_{0.025} \sqrt{\dfrac{\text{MSE}}{n_B}} \;\Rightarrow\; 66.33 \pm 2.306 \sqrt{\dfrac{62.333}{3}} \;\Rightarrow\; 66.33 \pm 10.51 \text{ or } 55.82 < \mu_B < 76.84$$

c   The 95% confidence interval for $\mu_A - \mu_B$ is

$$\left(\bar{x}_A - \bar{x}_B\right) \pm t_{0.025}\sqrt{\mathrm{MSE}\left(\frac{1}{n_A} + \frac{1}{n_B}\right)}$$

$$(76 - 66.33) \pm 2.306\sqrt{62.333\left(\frac{1}{5} + \frac{1}{3}\right)}$$

$$9.667 \pm 13.296 \quad \text{or} \quad -3.629 < \mu_A - \mu_B < 22.963$$

d   Note that these three confidence intervals cannot be jointly valid because all three employ the same value of $s = \sqrt{\mathrm{MSE}}$ and are dependent.

11.13   **a**   We would be reasonably confident that the data satisfied the normality assumption because each measurement represents the average of 10 continuous measurements. The Central Limit Theorem assures us that this mean will be approximately normally distributed.

        b   We have a completely randomized design with four treatments, each containing six measurements. The analysis of variance table is given in the *MINITAB* printout. The F test is

$$F = \frac{\mathrm{MST}}{\mathrm{MSE}} = \frac{6.580}{0.115} = 57.38$$

with p-value $= 0.000$ (in the column marked "P"). Since the p-value is very small (less than 0.01), H_0 is rejected. There is a significant difference in the mean leaf length among the four locations with $P < 0.01$ or even $P < 0.001$.

        c   The null hypothesis to be tested is $H_0: \mu_1 = \mu_4$ versus $H_a: \mu_1 \neq \mu_4$ and the test statistic is

$$t = \frac{x_1 - \bar{x}_4}{\sqrt{\mathrm{MSE}\left(\frac{1}{n_1} + \frac{1}{n_4}\right)}} = \frac{6.0167 - 3.65}{\sqrt{0.115\left(\frac{1}{6} + \frac{1}{6}\right)}} = 12.09$$

The p-value with $df = 20$ is $2P(t > 12.09)$ is bounded (using Table 4) as p-value $< 2(0.005) = 0.01$ and the null hypothesis is rejected. We conclude that there is a difference between the means.

        d   The 99% confidence interval for $\mu_1 - \mu_4$ is

$$\left(\bar{x}_1 - \bar{x}_4\right) \pm t_{0.005}\sqrt{\mathrm{MSE}\left(\frac{1}{n_1} + \frac{1}{n_4}\right)}$$

$$(6.0167 - 3.65) \pm 2.845\sqrt{0.115\left(\frac{1}{6} + \frac{1}{6}\right)}$$

$$2.367 \pm 0.557 \quad \text{or} \quad 1.810 < \mu_1 - \mu_4 < 2.924$$

        e   When conducting the t tests, remember that the stated confidence coefficients are based on random sampling. If you looked at the data and only compared the largest and smallest sample means, the randomness assumption would be disturbed.

11.15   The design is completely randomized with three treatments and five replications per treatment. The *MINITAB* printout below shows the analysis of variance for this experiment.

```
One-way ANOVA: Calcium versus Method
Source   DF        SS          MS        F       P
Method    2   0.0000041   0.0000021   16.38   0.000
Error    12   0.0000015   0.0000001
Total    14   0.0000056

S = 0.0003545    R-Sq = 73.19%    R-Sq(adj) = 68.72%
```

```
           Individual 95% CIs For Mean Based on
                                Pooled StDev
Level  N    Mean      StDev    -+---------+---------+---------+--------
1      5  0.027620  0.000421                        (------*------)
2      5  0.026780  0.000396    (------*------)
3      5  0.028040  0.000207                          (------*------)
                                -+---------+---------+---------+--------
                              0.02650   0.02700   0.02750   0.02800
Pooled StDev = 0.000354
```

The test statistic, $F = 16.38$, with p-value $= 0.000$ indicates the results are highly significant; there is a difference in the mean calcium contents for the three methods. All assumptions appear to have been satisfied.

11.17   **a**   The design is a completely randomized design (four independent samples).

   b   The following preliminary calculations are necessary:

$$T_1 = 1211 \quad T_2 = 1074 \quad T_3 = 1158 \quad T_4 = 1243 \quad G = 4686$$

$$CM = \frac{\left(\sum x_{ij}\right)^2}{n} = \frac{(4686)^2}{20} = 1{,}097{,}929.8 \quad \text{Total SS} = \sum x_{ij}^2 - CM = 1{,}101{,}862 - CM = 3932.2$$

$$SST = \sum \frac{T_i^2}{n_i} - CM = \frac{1211^2}{5} + \frac{1074^2}{5} + \frac{1158^2}{5} + \frac{1243^2}{5} - CM = 3272.2$$

Calculate $MS = SS/df$ and consolidate the information in an ANOVA table.

Source	df	SS	MS
Treatments	3	3272.2	1090.7333
Error	16	660	41.25
Total	19	3932.2	

   c   The null hypothesis to be tested is

   $H_0: \mu_1 = \mu_2 = \mu_3 = \mu_4$ versus H_a: at least one pair of means are different

and the F test to detect a difference in average prices is

$$F = \frac{MST}{MSE} = 26.44$$

The rejection region with $\alpha = 0.05$ and 3 and 16 df is approximately $F > 3.24$ and H_0 is rejected. There is enough evidence to indicate a difference in the average prices for the four provinces.

11.19   Sample means must be independent and based upon samples of equal size.

11.21   **a** $\omega = q_{0.05}(4,12)\frac{s}{\sqrt{5}} = 4.20\frac{s}{\sqrt{5}} = 1.878s$

   b $\omega = q_{0.01}(6,12)\frac{s}{\sqrt{8}} = 6.10\frac{s}{\sqrt{8}} = 2.1567s$

11.23   With $k = 4$, $df = 20$, $n_t = 6$,

$$\omega = q_{0.01}(4,20)\sqrt{\frac{MSE}{n_t}} = 5.02\sqrt{\frac{0.115}{6}} = 0.69$$

The ranked means are shown below.

6.0167	5.65	5.35	3.65
$\overline{x}_1$	$\overline{x}_2$	$\overline{x}_3$	$\overline{x}_4$

11.25 The design is completely randomized with three treatments and five replications per treatment. The *MINITAB* printout below shows the analysis of variance for this experiment.

```
One-way ANOVA: mg/dl versus Lab
Source  DF    SS    MS     F      P
Lab      2  42.6  21.3   0.60   0.562
Error   12 422.5  35.2
Total   14 465.0

S = 5.933   R-Sq = 9.15%   R-Sq(adj) = 0.00%

                                Individual 95% CIs For Mean Based on
                                Pooled StDev
Level  N    Mean   StDev   --+---------+---------+---------+-------
1      5  108.86   7.47                   (-------------*--------------)
2      5  105.04   6.01     (--------------*-------------)
3      5  105.60   3.70       (-------------*-------------)
                            --+---------+---------+---------+-------
                            100.0      104.0     108.0     112.0
Pooled StDev = 5.93
Tukey 95% Simultaneous Confidence Intervals
All Pairwise Comparisons among Levels of Lab
Individual confidence level = 97.94%

Lab = 1 subtracted from:
Lab    Lower   Center   Upper    +---------+---------+---------+---------
2    -13.824  -3.820   6.184     (-----------  --*-------------)
3    -13.264   3.260   6.744     (--      ----*--------------)
                                 +---------+---------+---------+---------
                                -14.0     -7.0       0.0       7.0

Lab = 2 subtracted from:
Lab    Lower   Center   Upper    +---------+---------+---------+---------
3     -9.444   0.560  10.564                (-    -----*-          --)
                                 +---------+---------+---------+---------
                                -14.0     -7.0       0.0       7.0
```

a The analysis of variance F test for $H_0: \mu_1 = \mu_2 = \mu_3$ is $F = 0.60$ with p-value $= 0.562$. The results are not significant and H_0 is not rejected. There is insufficient evidence to indicate a difference in the treatment means.

b Since the treatment means are not significantly different, there is no need to use Tukey's test to search for the pairwise differences. Notice that all three intervals generated by *MINITAB* contain zero, indicating that the pairs cannot be judged different.

11.27 The following preliminary calculations are necessary:
$$T_1 = 2835 \quad T_2 = 3300 \quad T_3 = 2724 \quad G = 8859$$

$$\text{CM} = \frac{\left(\sum x_{ij}\right)^2}{n} = \frac{(8859)^2}{15} = 5232125.4 \quad \text{Total SS} = \sum x_{ij}^2 - \text{CM} = 5,295,693 - \text{CM} = 63567.6$$

$$\text{SST} = \sum \frac{T_i^2}{n_i} - \text{CM} = \frac{2835^2}{5} + \frac{3300^2}{5} + \frac{2724^2}{5} - \text{CM} = 37354.8$$

Calculate $\text{MS} = \text{SS}/df$ and consolidate the information in an ANOVA table.

Source	*df*	SS	MS
Treatments	2	37354.8	18677.4
Error	12	26212.8	2184.4
Total	14	63567.6	

a The hypothesis to be tested is
$$H_0: \mu_1 = \mu_2 = \mu_3 \quad \text{versus} \quad H_a: \text{at least one pair of means are different}$$

and the F test to detect a difference in average scores is

$$F = \frac{\text{MST}}{\text{MSE}} = 8.55$$

The rejection region with $\alpha = 0.05$ and 2 and 12 df is approximately $F > 3.89$ and H_0 is rejected. There is evidence of a difference in the average scores for the three graduate programs.

b The 95% confidence interval for $\mu_1 - \mu_2$ is

$$\left(\overline{x}_1 - \overline{x}_2 \right) \pm t_{0.025} \sqrt{\text{MSE} \left(\frac{1}{n_1} + \frac{1}{n_2} \right)}$$

$$\left(\frac{2835}{5} - \frac{3300}{5} \right) \pm 2.179 \sqrt{2184.4 \left(\frac{1}{5} + \frac{1}{5} \right)}$$

$$-93 \pm 64.41 \quad \text{or} \quad -157.41 < \mu_1 - \mu_2 < -28.59$$

c With $k = 3$, $df = 12$, $n_t = 5$,

$$\omega = q_{0.05}(3,12) \frac{\sqrt{\text{MSE}}}{\sqrt{n_t}} = 3.77 \sqrt{\frac{2184.4}{5}} = 78.80$$

The ranked means are shown below.

$$\begin{array}{ccc} 544.8 & 567 & 660 \\ \overline{x}_3 & \overline{x}_1 & \overline{x}_2 \end{array}$$

There is no significant difference between programs 1 and 3, but programs 1 and 2, and 2 and 3 are different from each other.

11.29 Refer to Exercise 11.28. The given sums of squares are inserted and missing entries found by subtraction. The mean squares are found as $\text{MS} = \text{SS}/df$.

Source	df	SS	MS	F
Treatments	2	11.4	5.70	4.01
Blocks	5	17.1	3.42	2.41
Error	10	14.2	1.42	
Total	17	42.7		

11.31 The 95% confidence interval for $\mu_A - \mu_B$ is then

$$\left(\overline{x}_A - \overline{x}_B \right) \pm t_{0.025} \sqrt{\text{MSE} \left(\frac{2}{b} \right)}$$

$$\left(21.9 - 24.2 \right) \pm 2.228 \sqrt{1.42 \left(\frac{2}{6} \right)}$$

$$-2.3 \pm 1.533 \quad \text{or} \quad -3.833 < \mu_A - \mu_B < -0.767$$

11.33 Use *MINITAB* to obtain an ANOVA printout, or use the following calculations:

$$\text{CM} = \frac{\left(\sum x_{ij} \right)^2}{n} = \frac{(113)^2}{12} = 1064.08333$$

$$\text{Total SS} = \sum x_{ij}^2 - \text{CM} = 6^2 + 10^2 + \cdots + 14^2 - \text{CM} = 1213 - \text{CM} = 148.91667$$

$$\text{SST} = \sum \frac{T_j^2}{3} - \text{CM} = \frac{22^2 + 34^2 + 27^2 + 30^2}{3} - \text{CM} = 25.58333$$

$$\text{SSB} = \sum \frac{B_i^2}{4} - \text{CM} = \frac{33^2 + 25^2 + 55^2}{4} - \text{CM} = 120.66667 \text{ and}$$

$$\text{SSE} = \text{Total SS} - \text{SST} - \text{SSB} = 2.6667$$

Calculate $MS = SS/df$ and consolidate the information in an ANOVA table.

Source	df	SS	MS	F
Treatments	3	25.5833	8.5278	19.19
Blocks	2	120.6667	60.3333	135.75
Error	6	2.6667	0.4444	
Total	11	148.9167		

a To test the difference among treatment means, the test statistic is
$$F = \frac{MST}{MSE} = \frac{8.528}{0.4444} = 19.19$$
and the rejection region with $\alpha = 0.05$ and 3 and 6 *df* is $F > 4.76$. There is a significant difference among the treatment means.

b To test the difference among block means, the test statistic is
$$F = \frac{MSB}{MSE} = \frac{60.3333}{0.4444} = 135.75$$
and the rejection region with $\alpha = 0.05$ and 2 and 6 *df* is $F > 5.14$. There is a significant difference among the block means.

c With $k = 4$, $df = 6$, $n_t = 3$,
$$\omega = q_{0.01}(4, 6)\sqrt{\frac{MSE}{n_t}} = 7.03\sqrt{\frac{0.4444}{3}} = 2.71$$

The ranked means are shown below.

7.33	9.00	10.00	11.33
$\overline{x}_1$	$\overline{x}_3$	$\overline{x}_4$	$\overline{x}_2$

d The 95% confidence interval is
$$\left(\overline{x}_A - \overline{x}_B\right) \pm t_{0.025}\sqrt{MSE\left(\frac{2}{b}\right)}$$
$$\left(7.333 - 11.333\right) \pm 2.447\sqrt{0.4444\left(\frac{2}{3}\right)}$$
$$-4 \pm 1.332 \quad \text{or} \quad -5.332 < \mu_A - \mu_B < -2.668$$

e Since there is a significant difference among the block means, blocking has been effective. The variation due to block differences can be isolated using the randomized block design.

11.35 **a** By subtraction, the degrees of freedom for blocks is $b - 1 = 34 - 28 = 6$. Hence, there are $b = 7$ blocks.

b There are always $b = 7$ observations in a treatment total.

c There are $k = 4 + 1 = 5$ observations in a block total.

d

Source	df	SS	MS	F
Treatments	4	14.2	3.55	9.68
Blocks	6	18.9	3.15	8.59
Error	24	8.8	0.3667	
Total	34	41.9		

e To test the difference among treatment means, the test statistic is
$$F = \frac{MST}{MSE} = \frac{3.55}{0.3667} = 9.68$$
and the rejection region with $\alpha = 0.05$ and 4 and 24 *df* is $F > 2.78$. There is a significant difference among the treatment means.

f   To test the difference among block means, the test statistic is

$$F = \frac{\text{MSB}}{\text{MSE}} = \frac{3.15}{0.3667} = 8.59$$

and the rejection region with $\alpha = 0.05$ and 6 and 24 *df* is $F > 2.51$. There is a significant difference among the block means.

11.37   Similar to previous exercises. The *MINITAB* printout for this randomized block experiment is shown below.

```
Two-way ANOVA: Measurements versus Blocks, Chemicals
Source       DF       SS        MS       F       P
Blocks        2   7.1717   3.58583   40.21   0.000
Chemicals     3   5.2000   1.73333   19.44   0.002
Error         6   0.5350   0.08917
Total        11  12.9067
S = 0.2986    R-Sq = 95.85%    R-Sq(adj) = 92.40%
                    Individual 95% CIs For Mean Based on Pooled
                    StDev
Blocks     Mean     +---------+---------+---------+---------
1        10.875     (----*-----)
2        12.700                             (----*-----)
3        12.225                       (-----*----)
                    +---------+---------+---------+---------
                    10.50     11.20     11.90     12.60

                    Individual 95% CIs For Mean Based on
                    Pooled StDev
Chemicals     Mean  ------+---------+---------+---------+---
1          11.4000      (-----*-----)
2          12.3333                  (-----*-----)
3          11.2000  (-----*-----)
4          12.8000                          (-----*-----)
                    ------+---------+---------+---------+---
                    11.20     11.90     12.60     13.30
```

Both the treatment and block means are significantly different. Since the four chemicals represent the treatments in this experiment, Tukey's test can be used to determine where the differences lie:

$$\omega = q_{0.05}\left(4,6\right)\frac{\sqrt{\text{MSE}}}{\sqrt{n_t}} = 4.90\sqrt{\frac{0.08917}{3}} = 0.845$$

The ranked means are shown below.

$$
\begin{array}{cccc}
11.20 & 11.40 & 12.33 & 12.80 \\
\overline{x}_3 & \overline{x}_1 & \overline{x}_2 & \overline{x}_4
\end{array}
$$

The chemical falls into two significantly different groups: A and C versus B and D.

11.39   The factor of interest is "soil preparation," and the blocking factor is "locations." A randomized block design is used and the analysis of variance table can be obtained using the computer printout.
a   The *F* statistic to detect a difference due to soil preparations is

$$F = \frac{\text{MST}}{\text{MSE}} = 10.06$$

with *p*-value $= 0.012$. The null hypothesis can be rejected at the 5% level of significance; there is a significant difference among the treatment means.
b   The *F* statistic to detect a difference due to locations is

$$F = \frac{\text{MSB}}{\text{MSE}} = 10.88$$

with *p*-value $= 0.008$. The null hypothesis can be rejected at the 1% level of significance; there is a highly significant difference among the block means.

c Tukey's test can be used to determine where the differences lie:

$$\omega = q_{0.01}(3,6)\frac{\sqrt{MSE}}{\sqrt{n_t}} = 6.33\sqrt{\frac{1.8889}{4}} = 4.35$$

The ranked means are shown below.

$$\begin{array}{ccc} 12.0 & 12.5 & 16.0 \\ \overline{x}_3 & \overline{x}_1 & \overline{x}_2 \end{array}$$

Preparations 2 and 3 are the only two treatments that can be declared significantly different.

d The 95% confidence interval is

$$(\overline{x}_B - \overline{x}_A) \pm t_{0.025}\sqrt{MSE\left(\frac{2}{b}\right)}$$

$$(16.5 - 12.5) \pm 2.447\sqrt{1.89\left(\frac{2}{4}\right)}$$

$$3.5 \pm 2.38 \quad \text{or} \quad 1.12 < \mu_B - \mu_A < 5.88$$

11.41 A randomized block design has been used with "estimators" as treatments and "construction job" as the block factor. The analysis of variance table is found in the *MINITAB* printout below.

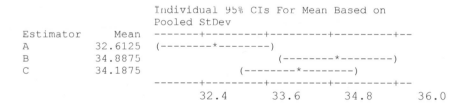

```
Two-way ANOVA: Cost versus Estimator, Job
         Source    DF      SS        MS       F       P
Estimator    2   10.8617    5.4308    7.20    0.025
Job          3   37.6073   12.5358   16.61    0.003
Error        6    4.5283    0.7547
Total       11   52.9973
S = 0.8687   R-Sq = 91.46%    R-Sq(adj) = 84.34%


                     Individual 95% CIs For Mean Based on
                     Pooled StDev
Estimator     Mean   -------+---------+---------+---------+--
A           32.6125   (--------*--------)
B           34.8875                      (--------*--------)
C           34.1875                  (--------*--------)
                     -------+---------+---------+---------+--
                         32.4      33.6      34.8      36.0
```

Both treatments and blocks are significant. The treatment means can be further compared using Tukey's test with

$$\omega = q_{0.05}(3,6)\frac{\sqrt{MSE}}{\sqrt{n_t}} = 4.34\sqrt{\frac{0.7547}{4}} = 1.885$$

The ranked means are shown below.

$$\begin{array}{ccc} 32.6125 & 34.1875 & 34.8875 \\ \overline{x}_A & \overline{x}_C & \overline{x}_B \end{array}$$

Estimators A and B show a significant difference in average costs.

11.43 **a** The complete ANOVA table is shown on the next page. Since factor A is run at 3 levels, it must have 2 *df*. Other entries are found by similar reasoning.

Source	df	SS	MS	F
A	2	5.3	2.6500	1.30
B	3	9.1	3.0333	1.49
$A \times B$	6	4.8	0.8000	0.39
Error	12	24.5	2.0417	
Total	23	43.7		

b The test statistic is $F = MS(AB)/MSE = 0.39$ and the rejection region is $F > 3.00$. Hence, H_0 is not rejected. There is insufficient evidence to indicate interaction between A and B.

c The test statistic for testing factor A is $F = 1.30$ with $F_{0.05} = 3.89$. The test statistic for factor B is $F = 1.49$ with $F_{0.05} = 3.49$. Neither A nor B are significant.

11.45 **a** The nine treatment (cell) totals needed for calculation are shown in the table.

	Factor A			
Factor B	*1*	*2*	*3*	*Total*
1	12	16	10	38
2	15	25	17	57
3	25	17	27	69
Total	52	58	54	164

$$CM = \frac{164^2}{18} = 1492.2222$$

Total SS $= 1662 - CM = 167.7778$

$$SSA = \frac{52^2 + 58^2 + 54^2}{6} - CM = 3.1111$$

$$SSB = \frac{38^2 + 57^2 + 69^2}{6} - CM = 81.4444$$

$$SS(AB) = \frac{12^2 + 16^2 + \cdots + 27^2}{2} - SSA - SSB - CM = 62.2222$$

Source	df	SS	MS	F
A	2	3.1111	1.5556	0.67
B	2	81.4444	40.7222	2.02
$A \times B$	4	62.2222	15.5556	6.67
Error	9	21.0000	2.3333	
Total	17	167.7778		

b–c The test statistic is $F = MS(AB)/MSE = 6.67$ and the rejection region is $F > 3.63$. There is evidence of a significant interaction. That is, the effect of factor A depends upon the level of factor B at which A is measured.

d Since $F = 6.67$ lies between $F_{0.01}$ and $F_{0.005}$, $0.005 < p\text{-value} < 0.01$.

e Since the interaction is significant, the differences in the four factor-level combinations should be explored individually, using an interaction plot such as the one generated by *MINITAB* shown on the next page.

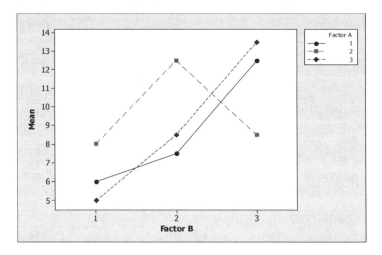

Look at the differences between the three levels of factor A when factor B changes from level 1 to level 2. Levels 2 and 3 behave very similarly, while level 1 behaves quite differently. When factor B changes from level 2 to level 3, levels 1 and 3 of factor A behave similarly, and level 2 behaves differently.

11.47 Use the computing formulas given in this section or a computer software package to generate the ANOVA table for this 2×3 factorial experiment. The following printout was generated using *MINITAB*

Two-way ANOVA: Percent Gain versus Markup, Location

Source	DF	SS	MS	F	P
Markup	2	835.17	417.583	11.87	0.008
Location	1	280.33	280.333	7.97	0.030
Interaction	2	85.17	42.583	1.21	0.362
Error	6	211.00	35.167		
Total	11	1411.67			

S = 5.930   R-Sq = 85.05%   R-Sq(adj) = 72.60%

a From the printout, $F = 1.21$ with p-value $= 0.362$. Hence, at the $\alpha = 0.05$ level, H_0 is not rejected. There is insufficient evidence to indicate interaction.

b Since no interaction is found, the effects of A and B can be tested individually. Both A and B are significant.

c The interaction plot generated by *MINITAB* is shown below. Notice that the lines, although not exactly parallel, do not indicate a significant difference in the behaviour of the mean responses for the two different locations.

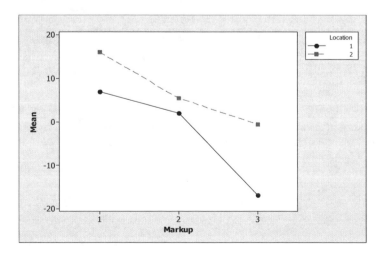

d The 95% confidence interval is

$$\left(\bar{x}_{31} - \bar{x}_{32} \right) \pm t_{0.025} \sqrt{\text{MSE} \left(\frac{2}{r} \right)}$$

$$\left(-17 + 0.5 \right) \pm 2.447 \sqrt{35.167 \left(\frac{2}{2} \right)}$$

$$-16.5 \pm 14.51 \quad \text{or} \quad -31.01 < \mu_{31} - \mu_{32} < -1.99$$

11.49 Answers will vary from student to student. There is no significant interaction, nor is the main effect for cities significant. There is a significant difference in the average cost per kilometre based on the distance travelled, with the cost per kilometre decreasing as the distance increases. Perhaps a straight line may model the costs as a function of time.

11.51 **a** The design is a 2×4 factorial experiment with $r = 5$ replications. There are two factors, Gender and School, one at two levels and one at four levels.

b The analysis of variance table can be found using a computer printout or the following calculations:

	Schools				
Gender	*1*	*2*	*3*	*4*	*Total*
Male	2919	3257	3330	2461	11967
Female	3082	3629	3344	2410	12465
Total	6001	6886	6674	4871	24432

$$CM = \frac{24432^2}{40} = 14923065.6$$

Total SS $= 15281392 - CM = 358326.4$

$$SSG = \frac{11967^2 + 12465^2}{20} - CM = 6200.1$$

$$SS(Sc) = \frac{6001^2 + 6886^2 + 6674^2 + 4871^2}{10} - CM = 246725.8$$

$$SS(G \times Sc) = \frac{2919^2 + 3257^2 + \cdots + 2410^2}{5} - SSG - SS(Sc) - CM = 10574.9$$

Source	*df*	SS	MS	*F*
G	1	6200.1	6200.100	2.09
Sc	3	246725.8	82241.933	27.75
G $\times$ Sc	3	10574.9	3524.967	1.19
Error	32	94825.6	2963.300	
Total	39	358326.4		

c The test statistic is $F = MS(GSc)/MSE = 1.19$ and the rejection region is $F > 2.92$ (with $\alpha = 0.05$). Alternately, you can bound the p-value > 0.10. Hence, H_0 is not rejected. There is insufficient evidence to indicate interaction between gender and schools.

d You can see in the interaction plot on the next page that there is a small difference between the average scores for male and female students at schools 1 and 2, but no difference to speak of at the other two schools. The interaction is not significant.

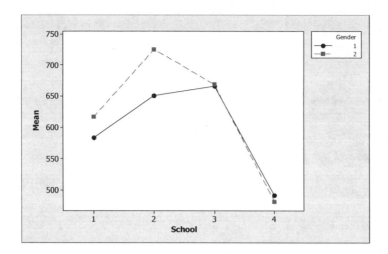

e The test statistic for testing gender is $F = 2.09$ with $F_{0.05} = 4.17$ (or p-value > 0.10). The test statistic for schools is $F = 27.75$ with $F_{0.05} = 2.92$ (or p-value < 0.005). There is a significant effect due to schools.

Using Tukey's method of paired comparisons with $\alpha = 0.01$, calculate

$$\omega = q_{0.01}\left(4, 32\right)\frac{\sqrt{\text{MSE}}}{\sqrt{n_t}} = 4.80\sqrt{\frac{2963.3}{10}} - 82.63$$

The ranked means are shown below.

487.1	600.1	667.4	688.6
$\overline{x}_4$	$\overline{x}_1$	$\overline{x}_3$	$\overline{x}_2$

11.53 **a** The analysis of variance table can be found using a computer printout or the following calculations:

	Training (A)		
Situation (B)	*Trained*	*Not Trained*	*Total*
Standard	334	185	185
Emergency	296	177	473
Total	630	362	992

$$CM = \frac{992^2}{16} = 61504$$

$$\text{Total SS} = 66640 - CM = 5136$$

$$SSA = \frac{630^2 + 362^2}{8} - CM = 65993 - 61504 = 4489$$

$$SSB = \frac{519^2 + 473^2}{8} - CM = 132.25$$

$$SS(A \times B) = \frac{334^2 + 296^2 + \cdots + 117^2}{4} - SSA - SSB - CM = 56.25$$

Source	*df*	SS	MS	*F*
A	1	4489	4489	117.49
B	1	132.25	132.25	3.46
A × B	1	56.25	56.25	1.47
Error	12	458.5	38.2083	
Total	15	5136		

b The test statistic is $F = \text{MS}(A \times B)/\text{MSE} = 1.47$ and the rejection region is $F > 4.75$ (with $\alpha = 0.05$). Alternately, you can bound the *p*-value > 0.10. Hence, H_0 is not rejected. The interaction term is not significant.

c The test statistic is $F = \text{MSB}/\text{MSE} = 3.46$ and the rejection region is $F > 4.75$ (with $\alpha = 0.05$). Alternately, you can bound the $0.05 < p\text{-value} < 0.10$. Hence, H_0 is not rejected. Factor B (Situation) is not significant.

d The test statistic is $F = \text{MSA}/\text{MSE} = 117.49$ and the rejection region is $F > 4.75$ (with $\alpha = 0.05$). Alternately, you can bound the *p*-value < 0.005. Hence, H_0 is rejected. Factor A (Training) is highly significant.

e The interaction plot is shown below. The response is much higher for the supervisors who have been trained. You can see very little change in the response for the two different situations (standard or emergency). The parallel lines indicate that there is no interaction between the two factors.

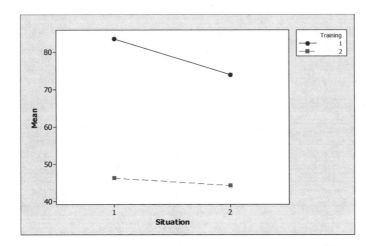

11.55 The intervals provided in the *MINITAB* printout allow you to declare a difference between a pair of means only when both endpoints have the same sign. Significant differences are observed between treatments A and C, B and C, C and E, and D and E. The ranked means are shown below.

E	A	B	D	C
0.48	0.62	0.67	0.92	1.07

11.57 The objective is to determine whether or not mean reaction time differs for the five stimuli. The four people used in the experiment act as blocks, in an attempt to isolate the variation from person to person. A randomized block design is used, and the analysis of variance table is given in the printout.

a The *F* statistic to detect a difference due to stimuli is

$$F = \frac{\text{MST}}{\text{MSE}} = 27.78$$

with *p*-value $= 0.000$. There is a significant difference in the effect of the five stimuli.

b The treatment means can be further compared using Tukey's test with

$$\omega = q_{0.05}(5,12)\frac{\sqrt{\text{MSE}}}{\sqrt{n_t}} = 4.51\sqrt{\frac{0.00708}{4}} = 0.190$$

The ranked means are shown below.

E	A	B	D	C
0.525	0.7	0.8	1.025	1.05

c The *F* test for blocks produces $F = 6.59$ with p-value $= 0.007$. The block differences are significant; blocking has been effective.

11.59 Answers will vary from student to student. A completely randomized design has been used. The analysis of variance table is shown in the printout.

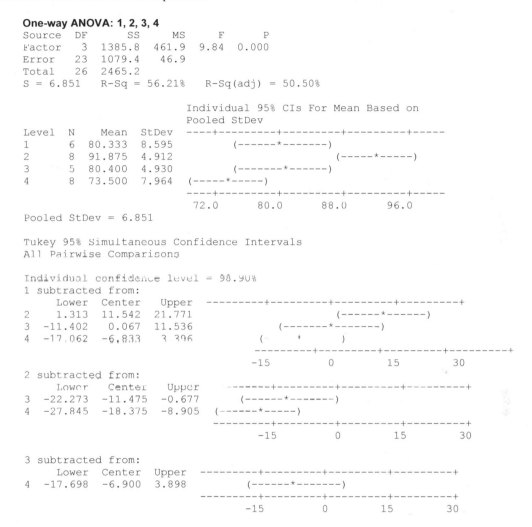

```
One-way ANOVA: 1, 2, 3, 4
Source   DF     SS      MS      F      P
Factor    3   1385.8   461.9   9.84  0.000
Error    23   1079.4    46.9
Total    26   2465.2
S = 6.851    R-Sq = 56.21%    R-Sq(adj) = 50.50%

                               Individual 95% CIs For Mean Based on
                               Pooled StDev
Level  N    Mean   StDev   ----+---------+---------+---------+-----
1      6  80.333   8.595           (------*-------)
2      8  91.875   4.912                        (-----*-----)
3      5  80.400   4.930         (-------*------)
4      8  73.500   7.964   (-----*-----)
                               ----+---------+---------+---------+-----
                               72.0      80.0      88.0      96.0
Pooled StDev = 6.851

Tukey 95% Simultaneous Confidence Intervals
All Pairwise Comparisons

Individual confidence level = 98.90%
1 subtracted from:
     Lower   Center   Upper   ---------+---------+---------+---------+
2    1.313   11.542  21.771                      (------*------)
3  -11.402    0.067  11.536            (-------*-------)
4  -17.062   -6.833   3.396        (       *      )
                               ---------+---------+---------+---------+
                               -15        0        15        30

2 subtracted from:
     Lower   Center   Upper   ------+---------+---------+---------+
3  -22.273  -11.475  -0.677      (------*-------)
4  -27.845  -18.375  -8.905  (------*-----)
                               ---------+---------+---------+---------+
                               -15        0        15        30

3 subtracted from:
     Lower   Center   Upper   ---------+---------+---------+---------+
4  -17.698   -6.900   3.898         (------*-------)
                               ---------+---------+---------+---------+
                               -15        0        15        30
```

Students should recognize the significant difference in the mean responses for the four training programs, and should further investigate these differences using Tukey's test with ranked means shown below:

4	1	3	2
73.5	80.33	80.4	91.875

11.61 This is similar to previous exercises. The complete ANOVA table is shown below.

Source	*df*	SS	MS	*F*
A	1	1.14	1.14	6.51
B	2	2.58	1.29	7.37
A × B	2	0.49	0.245	1.40
Error	24	4.20	0.175	
Total	29	8.41		

a The test statistic is $F = \text{MS}(\text{AB})/\text{MSE} = 1.40$ and the rejection region is $F > 3.40$. There is insufficient evidence to indicate an interaction.

b Using Table 6 with $df_1 = 2$ and $df_2 = 24$, the following critical values are obtained.

α	0.10	0.05	0.025	0.01	0.005
F_α	2.54	3.40	4.32	5.61	6.66

The observed value of F is less than $F_{0.10}$, so that p-value > 0.10.

c The test statistic for testing factor A is $F = 6.51$ with $F_{0.05} = 4.26$. There is evidence that factor A affects the response.

d The test statistic for factor B is $F = 7.37$ with $F_{0.05} = 3.40$. Factor B also affects the response.

11.63   **a** The experiment is an 2×3 factorial and a two-way analysis of variance is generated.

b Using the *MINITAB* printout given in the exercise, the F test for interaction is $F = 0.45$ with p-value $= 0.642$. There is insufficient evidence to suggest that the effect of temperature is different depending on the type of plant.

c The plot of treatment means for cotton and cucumber as a function of temperature is shown below. The temperature appears to have a quadratic effect on the number of eggs laid in both cotton and cucumber. However, the treatment means are higher overall for the cucumber plants.

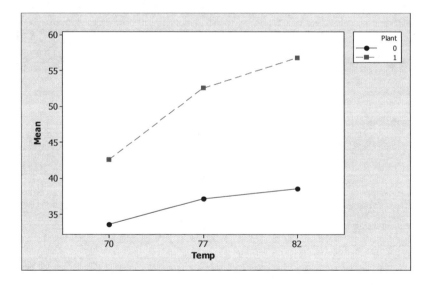

d The 95% confidence interval for $\mu_{Cotton} - \mu_{Cucumber}$ is

$$\left(\overline{x}_{Cotton} - \overline{x}_{Cucumber} \right) \pm t_{0.025} \sqrt{\text{MSE}\left(\frac{1}{n_{Cotton}} + \frac{1}{n_{Cucumber}} \right)}$$

$$\left(\frac{547}{15} - \frac{760}{15} \right) \pm 2.064 \sqrt{123.02\left(\frac{2}{15} \right)}$$

$$-14.2 \pm 8.36 \quad \text{or} \quad -22.56 < \mu_{Cotton} - \mu_{Cucumber} < -5.84$$

11.65 **a** The design is a randomized block design, with weeks representing blocks and stores as treatments.

b The *MINITAB* computer printout is shown below.

```
Two-way ANOVA: Total versus Week, Store
Source   DF        SS         MS      F      P
Week      3     571.71    190.570   8.27  0.003
Store     4     684.64    171.159   7.43  0.003
Error    12     276.38     23.032
Total    19    1532.73
S = 4.799   R-Sq - 81.97%   R-Sq(adj) = 71.45%
```

c The F test for treatments is $F = 7.43$ with p-value $= 0.003$. The p-value is small enough to allow rejection of H_0. There is a significant difference in the average weekly totals for the five supermarkets.

d With $k = 5$, $df = 12$, $n_t = 4$,

$$\omega = q_{0.05}(5,12)\frac{\sqrt{MSE}}{\sqrt{n_t}} = 4.51\sqrt{\frac{23.032}{4}} = 10.82$$

The ranked means are shown below.

1	5	4	3	2
240.23	249.19	252.18	254.87	256.99

11.67 **a** This is a randomized block design. We assume that there will be a lot of variability due to the type of crash (block) and are interested in how bumpers on different cars (treatments) prevent costly damage. The *MINITAB* analysis of variance is shown below.

```
Two-way ANOVA: Cost versus Auto, Crash Type
Source      DF        SS         MS      F      P
Auto         7    11866757   1695251   5.72  0.001
Crash Type   3     1876861    625620   2.11  0.129
Error       21     6221201    296248
Total       31    19964820
S = 544.3   R-Sq = 68.84%   R-Sq(adj) = 54.00%

                 Individual 95% CIs For Mean Based on
                 Pooled StDev
Auto    Mean   ----+---------+---------+---------+-----
1      209.75  (------*------)
2      653.50         (------*------)
3      370.25    (------*------)
4      637.75       (------*------)
5      690.25        (------*------)
6     1030.50             (------*----)
7     1294.25               (------*------)
8     2265.25                          (------*------)
               ----+---------+---------+---------+-----
                   0        800      1600      2400
```

b The F test for treatments is $F = 5.72$ with a p-value of 0.001. There is evidence of significant difference in the average cost due to the type of automobile.

c The F test for blocks is $F = 2.11$ with a p-value of 0.129. There is insufficient evidence to indicate a difference in the average cost due to the type of crash.

d Since the treatment means were significantly different, Tukey's test is used to explore the differences with

$$\omega = q_{0.05}(8,21)\frac{\sqrt{MSE}}{\sqrt{n_t}} \approx 4.77\sqrt{\frac{296248}{4}} = 1298.12$$

The ranked means are shown below.

1	3	4	2	5	6	7	8
209.75	370.25	637.75	653.5	690.25	1030.5	1294.25	2265.25

The Dodge Grand Caravan, Isuzu Rodeo, and Mitsubishi Montero are the most expensive to repair, and the Mitsubishi is significantly more expensive than at least five of the other types of autos.

11.69 **a** This is a 2×3 factorial design with $r = 5$ replications.

     b The *MINITAB* analysis of variance is shown below.

```
Two-way ANOVA: Salary versus Gender, School Type
Source         DF        SS       MS      F       P
Gender          1     69.92   69.921   1.35   0.256
School Type     2    694.41  347.206   6.72   0.005
Interaction     2    274.63  137.314   2.66   0.091
Error          24   1240.12   51.672
Total          29   2279.09
S = 7.188    R-Sq = 45.59%    R-Sq(adj) = 34.25%

                      Individual 95% CIs For Mean Based on
                      Pooled StDev
Gender     Mean    --+---------+---------+---------+-------
1        60.2933                (------------*------------)
2        57.2400    (------------*------------)
                    --+---------+---------+---------+-------
                    54.0      57.0      60.0      63.0

                      Individual 95% CIs For Mean Based on
School                Pooled StDev
Type       Mean    -------+---------+---------+---------+--
1         56.18    (-------*------)
2         65.51                    (-------*-------)
3         54.61    (-------*-------)
                   -------+---------+---------+---------+--
                   54.0      60.0      66.0      72.0
```

The F test for interaction is $F = 2.66$ with a p-value of 0.091. There is no evidence of significant interaction. The F test for gender is $F = 1.35$ with a p-value of 0.256 and the F test for school type is $F = 6.72$ with a p-value of 0.005. There is sufficient evidence to indicate a difference in the average salaries due faculty type, but not due to gender.

     c The 95% confidence interval for $\mu_M - \mu_F$ is

$$\left(\bar{x}_M - \bar{x}_F\right) \pm t_{0.025}\sqrt{\text{MSE}\left(\frac{1}{n_F} + \frac{1}{n_M}\right)}$$

$$\left(60.2933 - 57.24\right) \pm 2.064\sqrt{51.672\left(\frac{2}{15}\right)}$$

$$3.053 \pm 5.418 \quad \text{or} \quad -2.365 < \mu_M - \mu_F < 8.471$$

Since the value $\mu_M - \mu_F = 0$ falls in the interval, there is not enough evidence to indicate a difference in the average salaries for males and females.

     d Tukey's test is used to explore the differences due to school type with

$$\omega = q_{0.01}\left(3, 24\right)\frac{\sqrt{\text{MSE}}}{\sqrt{n_t}} \approx 4.55\sqrt{\frac{51.672}{10}} = 10.34$$

The ranked means are shown below.

Nursing	Arts	Science
54.61	56.18	65.51

There is a difference in average salary between Nursing and Science faculties, but not between the other two pairs.

11.71 **a** The experiment is run in a randomized block design, with telephone companies as treatments and cities as blocks.

b Use the computing formulas in Section 11.8 or the *MINITAB* printout below.

```
Two-way ANOVA: Score versus City, Carrier
Source    DF      SS       MS       F      P
City       3    55.688   18.5625   3.88   0.049
Carrier    3   285.688   95.2292  19.90   0.000
Error      9    43.063    4.7847
Total     15   384.438
S = 2.187    R-Sq = 88.80%    R-Sq(adj) = 81.33%
```

c The F test for treatments (carriers) has a test statistic $F = 19.90$ with p-value $= 0.000$. The null hypothesis is rejected and we conclude that there is a significant difference in the average satisfaction scores for the four carriers.

d The F test for blocks (cities) has a test statistic $F = 3.88$ with p-value $= 0.049$. The null hypothesis is rejected and we conclude that there is a significant difference in the average satisfaction scores for the four cities.

11.73 **a** This is a 2×4 factorial experiment, with cost at $a = 2$ levels and suppliers at $b = 4$ levels.

b Use the computing formulas or the *MINITAB* computer printout below.

```
Two-way ANOVA: Ratings versus Cost, Supplier
Source         DF      SS       MS       F       P
Cost            1    92.042   92.042   13.89   0.002
Supplier        3    81.125   27.042    4.08   0.025
Interaction     3    33.458   11.153    1.68   0.211
Error          16   106.000    6.625
Total          23   312.625

S = 2.574    R-Sq = 66.09%    R-Sq(adj) = 51.26%
```

c The F test for the interaction is $F = 1.68$ with p-value $= 0.211$. The p-value is large enough and H_0 is not rejected and we cannot conclude that there is significant interaction effect between cost and suppliers.

d The F test for the supplier is $F = 4.08$ with p-value $= 0.025$. Since P-value is small, we can reject the null hypothesis and conclude that there is significant difference in ratings for the four suppliers.

e The F test for the cost is $F = 13.89$ with p-value $= 0.002$. Since P-value is small, we can reject the null hypothesis and conclude that there is significant difference in ratings for the two cost levels.

f Answers will vary from student to student.

11.75 **a** The experiment is a 2×3 factorial experiment, with two factors (rank and gender). There are $r = 10$ replications per factor-level combination.

     b Use the computing formulas in Section 11.10 or the *MINITAB* printout below.

```
Two-way ANOVA: Salary versus Gender, Rank
Source        DF         SS          MS        F       P
Gender         1  1.18409E+08  1.18409E+08   17.25   0.000
Rank           2  7.29444E+10  3.64722E+10 5314.50   0.000
Interaction    2  3.39075E+07  1.69537E+07    2.47   0.094
Error         54  3.70589E+08  6.86277E+06
Total         59  7.34673E+10
S = 2620    R-Sq = 99.50%   R-Sq(adj) = 99.45%

     Individual 95% CIs For Mean Based on
          Pooled StDev
Rank      Mean  ------+---------+---------+---------+---
1       12313.6  (*
2       93564.3                                    *)
3       75733.0                            *)
          ------+---------+---------+---------+---
          25000     50000     75000    100000
```

     c The F test for Interaction has a test statistic $F = 2.47$ with p-value $= 0.094$. The null hypothesis is not rejected and we conclude that there is no significant interaction between rank and gender.

     d The F test for rank has a test statistic $F = 5314.50$ with p-value $= 0.000$, and the F test for gender has a test statistic $F = 17.25$ with p-value $= 0.000$. Both factors are highly significant. We conclude that there is a difference in average salary due to both gender and rank.

     e The interaction plot is shown below. Notice the differences in salary due to both rank and gender.

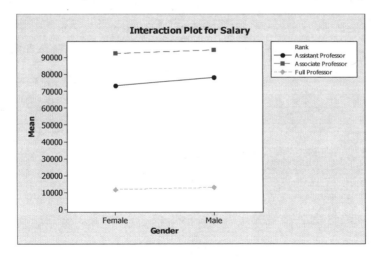

Using Tukey's test is used to explore the differences with

$$\omega = q_{0.05}(3, 54) \frac{\sqrt{\text{MSE}}}{\sqrt{n_t}} \approx 3.44 \sqrt{\frac{6{,}862{,}770}{20}} = 2015.084$$

The ranked means are shown below. All three of the ranks have significantly different average salaries.

Assistant Professor	Associate Professor	Full Professor
75733.0	93564.3	12313.6

Case Study: "A Fine Mess"

1   The design is a two-way classification, with type of ticket as the treatment and cities as blocks.

2   The *MINITAB* printout for the randomized block design is shown below.

```
Two-way ANOVA: Fine versus City, Type
Source  DF      SS       MS      F      P
City    10   3255.5   325.55   1.77  0.134
Type     2  10321.3  5160.64  27.99  0.000
Error   20   3687.4   184.37
Total   32  17264.2

S = 13.58    R-Sq = 78.64%   R-Sq(adj) = 65.83%

                   Individual 95% CIs For Mean Based on
                   Pooled StDev
Type     Mean    ----+---------+---------+---------+-----
1      17.3636   (-----*----)
2      57.2727                             (-----*-----)
3      22.7273       (-----*-----)
                   ----+---------+---------+---------+-----
                     15        30        45        60
```

Students should notice the significant difference in average ticket prices for the three types of tickets, but not from city to city. It does not appear that blocking has been effective. To explore the differences between the three types of tickets, use Tukey's procedure with

$$\omega = q_{0.05}(3,24)\frac{\sqrt{MSE}}{\sqrt{n_t}} = 3.53\sqrt{\frac{184.37}{11}} = 14.45$$

The ranked means are shown below.

Expired Meter	Fire Route	No Parking Zone
17.36	57.27	22.73

The expired meter and no parking zone ticket amounts are not significantly different, but the amount for Fire route parking appears to be significantly higher than the other two types.

3   Answers will vary, but should summarize the above results.

Project 11: Hard to Shake: *Globe and Mail* Series Exposes the Pervasive Health Risks Associated with Canada's Excessive Salt Consumption

Part a

i   The experimental design is called a Completely Randomized Design. There are four treatments (Provinces), each with five observations.

ii To complete the ANOVA table, we need to determine several quantities (provided in the table below).

	PQ	ON	AB	BC	
	2.50	2.90	2.80	2.60	
	3.10	2.70	3.20	2.70	
	2.60	3.20	3.20	2.90	
	2.80	3.00	2.90	2.90	
	2.40	2.20	3.30	3.10	
$T_i = \sum x_i$	13.40	14.00	15.40	14.20	57.00
$\sum x_i^2$	36.22	39.78	47.62	40.48	164.10
mean	2.68	2.80	3.08	2.84	2.85

Our ANOVA table will have $k - 1 = 4 - 1 = 3$ degrees of freedom for treatment, $N - 1 = 20 - 1 = 19$ degrees of freedom total, and thus $19 - 3 = 16$ degrees of freedom for error.

The total sums of squares (Total SS) is

$$\text{Total SS} = \sum_{i=1}^{k} \sum_{j=1}^{n_i} x_{ij}^2 - \frac{1}{n}\left(\sum_{i=1}^{k} \sum_{j=1}^{n_i} x_{ij}\right)^2$$

$$= 1.64.10 - \frac{1}{20}(57)^2$$

$$= 1.65$$

The sums of squares treatment (SST) is

$$\text{SST} = \sum_{i=1}^{k} \frac{T_i^2}{n_i} - \frac{1}{n}\left(\sum_{i=1}^{k} \sum_{j=1}^{n_i} x_{ij}\right)^2$$

$$= \frac{1}{5}\left(13.4^2 + 14.0^2 + 15.4^2 + 14.2^2\right) - \frac{1}{20}(57)^2$$

$$= 0.422$$

The sums of squares error (SSE) can be calculated using the formula

$$\text{SSE} = \text{Total SS} - \text{SST} = 1.65 - 0.422 = 1.2880$$

Our ANOVA table is thus

Source	df	SS	MS	F
Treatment	3	0.422	0.422/3 = 0.14067	0.14067/0.07675 = 1.83
Error	16	1.288	1.288/16 = 0.07675	
Total	19	1.650		

iii To test the null hypothesis of no differences in the true mean amount of sodium for the four provinces with $\alpha = 0.05$, we compare the F test value for treatment (1.83) to the critical value on 3 and 16 degrees of freedom. The critical value is obtained from Table 6 in Appendix I. The F critical value with $\alpha = 0.05$ on 3 and 16 degrees of freedom is 3.24. Since the F test statistic is smaller than our critical value, we do not reject the null hypothesis. There is insufficient evidence to suggest that the mean amount of sodium for the four provinces is different.

The approximate p-value can be obtained from Table 6 in Appendix I. With 3 and 16 degrees of freedom, we have p-value $= p\,(F > 1.83) > 0.10$.

iv A 90% confidence interval to compare Quebec and Alberta is

$$\bar{x}_Q - \bar{x}_A \pm t_{\frac{\alpha}{2}, n-k} \sqrt{MSE} \sqrt{\frac{1}{n_Q} + \frac{1}{n_A}}$$

$$2.68 - 3.08 \pm 1.746 \sqrt{0.07675 \sqrt{\frac{1}{5} + \frac{1}{5}}}$$

which gives $(-0.706, -0.094)$. We use the root of the mean square error as an estimate for σ. Since the interval does not cover zero, there is sufficient evidence to suggest that the means are different at the 90% level.

v If we perform a two-sample independent t test on the Quebec and Alberta data, we obtain

$$t_{test} = \frac{\bar{x}_A - \bar{x}_Q}{\sqrt{MSE}\sqrt{\frac{1}{n_Q} + \frac{1}{n_A}}}$$

$$= \frac{2.68 \quad 3.08}{\sqrt{0.07675}\sqrt{\frac{2}{5}}}$$

$$= 2.282921$$

Our null hypothesis is that there is no difference between the two means. The alternative is two-sided, suggesting there is a difference between the two means. We again use the root of the mean square error (MSE) as an estimate for σ as it represents a pooled estimate of the standard deviation. We compare this value to a critical t value with $\alpha/2 = 0.025$ and degrees of freedom (associated with MSE) of 16. The critical value is 2.120. Since our test statistic is greater than the critical value, we reject the null hypothesis. There is sufficient evidence to suggest that the two means are different.

vi A 90% confidence interval for the mean salt intake in Ontario is

$$\bar{x}_O \pm t_{\frac{\alpha}{2}, n-k} \sqrt{MSE} \sqrt{\frac{1}{n_O}}$$

$$2.80 \pm 1.746 \sqrt{0.07675} \sqrt{\frac{1}{5}}$$

which gives $(2.584, 3.016)$.

vii If we were to rank the means simply on magnitude, they would be ordered from smallest to largest as
$$PQ < ON < BC < AB$$
If we perform ordered pairwise comparisons for each of the means (as we did in part **v**), we obtain the following t test statistics (see table on next page). These are compared to a critical t value with 16 degrees of freedom. Assuming $\alpha = 0.05$, our critical t value is 2.120. Hence, we reject the null hypothesis (of equivalence between means) in favour of the two-sided alternative, if our test statistic is greater than 2.120, or less than -2.120. We can also compare the differences with

$$t_{crit} \times s \times \sqrt{\frac{1}{n_1} + \frac{1}{n_2}} = 0.3714.$$ Differences found to be larger than 0.3714 would be considered

significant (i.e., would result in rejecting the null hypothesis).

Comparison	Difference	t test	Comment
ON-PQ	0.12	0.6848762	Do not reject the null
BC-ON	0.04	0.2282921	Do not reject the null
AB-BC	0.24	1.369752	Do not reject the null

Thus, we find no differences between the ordered pairwise comparison of means.

viii To use Tukey's method, we require the yardstick. In our particular example, we have $k = 4$ treatments each with $n = 5$ observations, and an MSE $= 0.07675$ with 16 degrees of freedom. We also find our critical q value of 4.05 with $\alpha = 0.05$ from Tables 11a in Appendix I. Thus, our yardstick is

$$\omega = q_\alpha(k, df)\left(\frac{s}{\sqrt{n_t}}\right)$$

$$= q_{0.05}(4,16)\left(\frac{s}{\sqrt{n_t}}\right)$$

$$= 4.05\sqrt{\frac{0.07675}{5}}$$

$$= 0.5017752$$

ix Our pairwise comparisons are

Comparison	|Difference|	Comment
PQ-ON	0.12	Not significantly different
PQ-AB	0.40	Not significantly different
PQ-BC	0.16	Not significantly different
ON-AB	0.28	Not significantly different
ON-BC	0.04	Not significantly different
AB-BC	0.24	Not significantly different

Thus, none of the means are significantly different than the others.

Part b

i The experimental design is called a Randomized Complete Block Design. There are six treatments (Strategies), each with four observations over four blocks (Provinces).

ii The blocks are the provinces.

iii The treatments are the strategies for lowering salt intake.

iv Blocking is necessary in this particular problem since the experimental units (i.e., the provinces) are not necessarily homogenous. As a result, the provinces may represent a source of variation that needs to be accounted for.

v The ANOVA for the RCBD is (obtained using the R statistical package)

Source	df	SS	MS	F	p-value
Treatment	5	0.60708	0.12142	5.4981	0.004516
Block	3	0.48125	0.16042	7.2642	0.003099
Error	15	0.33125	0.02208		
Total	23	1.41958			

vi It is necessary to treat provinces as block in order to account for the variability observed within each of the provinces.

vii The p-value for treatment effects (i.e., the strategies) is $0.004516 < \alpha = 0.05$. This suggests that there is sufficient evidence to reject the null hypothesis (that the treatment means are equivalent) in favour of the alternative (at least one of the treatment means differs from the rest). There is a significant different among the five strategies in reducing added unnecessary salt.

viii The p-value for block effects (i.e., the provinces) is $0.003099 < \alpha = 0.05$. This suggests that there is sufficient evidence to reject the null hypothesis (that the block effects are equivalent) in favour of the alternative (at least one of the block effects differs from the rest). Thus, there is a significant different among the provinces' salt intake at the 0.05 level.

ix To calculate a 95% confidence interval for strategies 1 and 6, we have

$$\overline{T}_1 - \overline{T}_6 \pm t_{\frac{\alpha}{2}} \sqrt{s^2 \left(\frac{1}{b} + \frac{1}{b} \right)}$$

$$2.625 - 2.200 \pm 2.131 \sqrt{0.02208 \left(\frac{2}{4} \right)}$$

which gives $(0.2011, 0.6489)$. This interval indicates a significant difference between strategies 1 and 6.

x It does appear that the RCBD was justified. That is, the RCBD ANOVA has indicated that both strategies and blocks (i.e., provinces) are significant. In this particular case, the blocks explain a significant portion of the total variability in the observed data. By including blocks, we have improved the power of the experiment.

Part c

i The experimental design is called a Factorial Design. There are six levels of the first treatment (Strategies) and four levels of the second treatment (Education Level). Further, three observations are recorded for each of the strategy and education level combinations.

ii The ANOVA for the Factorial Design (using the R statistical package)

Source	df	SS	MS	F	p-value
A (Education)	3	3.6450	1.2150	24.7819	7.839×10^{-10}
B (Strategy)	5	0.9583	0.1917	3.9093	0.004714
AB	15	1.7783	0.1186	2.4181	0.010530
Error	48	2.3533	0.0490		
Total	71	1.41958			

The p-value associated with strategy is 0.004714. Given $\alpha = 0.05$, we will reject the null hypothesis of equivalence between the means for each of the strategies. That is, there is sufficient evidence to suggest that at least one of the strategy means is different than the others.

iii The F test for interaction between education level and strategy is 2.4649. On 15 and 48 degrees of freedom, this F test has a p-value of 0.010530. At the $\alpha = 0.05$ level, there is sufficient evidence to suggest that the interaction is significant. The data provides sufficient evidence to suggest the existence of an interaction between education level and strategy.

iv Since interactions are significant, the simple effects of strategy and education level should be discussed. The means for each of the education level and strategy combinations are summarized below.

	Less than High School	High School	University/ College	Postgraduate
Strategy 1	2.80	2.80	2.50	2.40
Strategy 2	2.40	2.53	2.60	2.30
Strategy 3	3.00	2.67	2.43	2.27
Strategy 4	2.77	2.53	2.53	2.20
Strategy 5	2.83	2.53	2.37	2.37
Strategy 6	3.03	2.27	2.10	1.67

Practically speaking, to obtain the largest drop in salt intake, researchers should consider the education level of individuals before implementing a particular strategy. For individuals with an education level less than high school, strategy 6 had the highest impact. The strategies with the highest impact (i.e., the largest mean reduction in salt intake) for the remaining education levels (high school, university, and postgraduate respectively) are strategies 1, 2, and 1 respectively. Of course, the significant differences among treatment combinations have not been considered here.

v   At the 10% level of significance, we can reject the null hypothesis that there are no differences among the means of the education levels of the subjects. Our F test statistic on 3 and 48 degrees of freedom is 7.839×10^{-10} which is less than 0.10. Hence, there is sufficient evidence to suggest that at least one of the education levels differs from the rest.

vi   A 95% confidence interval for the difference in mean between high school and postgraduate education levels for Strategy 6 is

$$\bar{x}_h - \bar{x}_p \pm t_{\frac{\alpha}{2}ab(r-1)} \sqrt{\text{MSE}\left(\frac{1}{n_h} + \frac{1}{n_p}\right)}$$

$$2.27 - 1.67 \pm 2.011 \sqrt{0.0490\left(\frac{1}{3} + \frac{1}{3}\right)}$$

which is equivalent to (0.2365, 0.9635).

Chapter 12: Linear Regression and Correlation

12.1 The line corresponding to the equation $y = 2x + 1$ can be graphed by locating the y values corresponding to $x = 0$, 1, and 2.

When $x = 0$, $y = 2(0) + 1 = 1$

When $x = 1$, $y = 2(1) + 1 = 3$

When $x = 2$, $y = 2(2) + 1 = 5$

The graph is shown below.

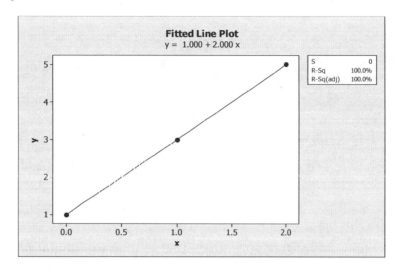

Note that the equation is in the form $y = \alpha + \beta x$.

Thus, the slope of the line is $\beta = 2$ and the y-intercept is $\alpha = 1$.

12.3 If $\alpha = 3$ and $\beta = -1$, the straight line is $y = 3 - x$.

12.5 A deterministic mathematical model is a model in which the value of a response y is exactly predicted from values of the variables that affect the response. On the other hand, a probabilistic mathematical model is one that contains random elements with specific probability distributions. The value of the response y in this model is not exactly determined.

12.7 **a** The equations for calculating the quantities a and b are found in Section 12.2 of the text and involve the preliminary calculations:

$$\sum x_i = 21 \qquad \sum y_i = 24.3 \qquad \sum x_i y_i = 75.3$$

$$\sum x_i^2 = 91 \qquad \sum y_i^2 = 103.99 \qquad n = 6$$

Then $S_{xy} = \sum x_i y_i - \dfrac{(\sum x_i)(\sum y_i)}{n} = 75.3 - \dfrac{21(24.3)}{6} = 75.3 - 85.05 = -9.75$

$S_{xx} = \sum x_i^2 - \dfrac{(\sum x_i)^2}{n} = 91 - \dfrac{21^2}{6} = 17.5$

$b = \dfrac{S_{xy}}{S_{xx}} = \dfrac{-9.75}{17.5} = -0.55714$ and $a = \bar{y} - b\bar{x} = \dfrac{24.3}{6} - (-0.557)\left(\dfrac{21}{6}\right) = 6$

and the least squares line is $\hat{y} = a + bx = 6 - 0.557x$.

b   The graph of the least squares line and the six data points are shown below.

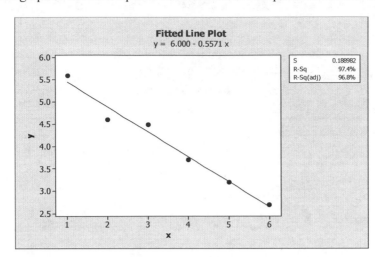

c   When $x = 3.5$, the value for y can be predicted using the least squares line as
$$\hat{y} = 6.00 - 0.55714(3.5) = 4.05$$

d   Using the additivity properties for the sums of sums of squares and degrees of freedom for an analysis of variance, and the fact that $MS = SS/df$, the completed ANOVA table is shown below.

```
Analysis of Variance
Source      DF      SS       MS
Regression  1    5.4321   5.4321
Error       4    0.1429   0.0357
Total       5    5.5750
```

12.9   **a**   The equations for calculating the quantities a and b are found using the preliminary calculations:

$$\sum x_i = 1,490 \qquad \sum y_i = 1,978 \qquad \sum x_i y_i = 653,830$$
$$\sum x_i^2 = 540,100 \qquad \sum y_i^2 = 827,504 \qquad n = 5$$

Then $S_{xy} = \sum x_i y_i - \dfrac{(\sum x_i)(\sum y_i)}{n} = 653,830 - \dfrac{1,490(1,978)}{5} = 64,386$

$S_{xx} = \sum x_i^2 - \dfrac{(\sum x_i)^2}{n} = 540,100 - \dfrac{1,490^2}{5} = 96,080$

$b = \dfrac{S_{xy}}{S_{xx}} = \dfrac{64,386}{96,080} = 0.670129$ and $a = \bar{y} - b\bar{x} = 395.6 - 0.670129(298) = 195.902$

and the least squares line is $\hat{y} = a + bx = 195.90 + 0.67x$.

b   The graph of the least squares line and the six data points is shown on the next page. There seems to be a curvilinear trend.

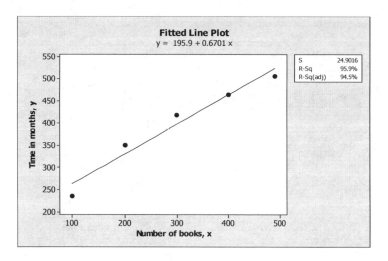

c Calculate Total $SS = S_{yy} = \sum y_i^2 - \frac{\left(\sum y_i\right)^2}{n} = 827,504 - \frac{(1978)^2}{5} = 45007.2$. Then

$$SSR = \frac{\left(S_{xy}\right)^2}{S_{rr}} = \frac{64386^2}{96080} = 43146.9296 \text{ and } SSE = \text{Total } SS - SSR = S_{yy} - \frac{\left(S_{xy}\right)^2}{S_{xx}} = 1860.2704$$

The ANOVA table with 1 *df* for regression and $n-2$ *df* for error is shown below. Remember that the mean squares are calculated as $MS = SS/df$.

Source	*df*	SS	MS
Regression	1	43146.9296	43146.9296
Error	3	1860.2704	620.0901
Total	4	45007.2000	

12.11 **a–b** There are $n = 2(5) = 10$ pairs of observations in the experiment, so that the total number of degrees of freedom are $n-1 = 9$.

c Using the additivity properties for the sums of sums of squares and degrees of freedom for an analysis of variance, and the fact that $MS = SS/df$, the completed ANOVA table is shown below.

```
Regression Analysis: y versus x
The regression equation is
y = 3.00 + 0.475 x

Predictor    Coef   SE Coef     T      P
Constant    3.000     2.127  1.41  0.196
x          0.4750    0.1253  3.79  0.005

S = 2.24165    R-Sq = 64.2%    R-Sq(adj) = 59.8%

Analysis of Variance

Source           DF       SS      MS      F      P
Regression        1   72.200  72.200  14.37  0.005
Residual Error    8   40.200   5.025
Total             9  112.400
```

d From the computer printout the least squares line is $\hat{y} = a + bx = 3.00 + 0.475x$.

e When $x = 10$, the value for y can be predicted using the least squares line as
$$\hat{y} = a + bx = 3.00 + 0.475(10) = 7.75$$

12.13 **a** The Temperature Anomaly is the dependent or response variable, y, and Year is the independent or explanatory variable, x.

 b The scatterplot is shown below. Notice the linear pattern in the points.

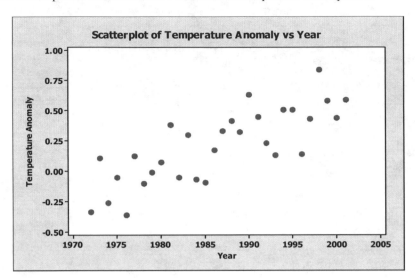

 c Calculate

$$\sum x_i = 59{,}595.0 \qquad \sum y_i = 6.513 \qquad \sum x_i y_i = 12{,}999$$

$$\sum x_i^2 = 118{,}387{,}715.0 \qquad \sum y_i^2 = 4.0928 \qquad n = 30$$

Then $S_{xy} = \sum x_i y_i - \dfrac{(\sum x_i)(\sum y_i)}{n} = 60.9255$

$$S_{xx} = \sum x_i^2 - \dfrac{(\sum x_i)^2}{n} = 2247.5$$

$$S_{yy} = \sum y_i^2 - \dfrac{(\sum y_i)^2}{n} = 2.6788277$$

Then $b = \dfrac{S_{xy}}{S_{xx}} = \dfrac{60.9255}{2247.5} = 0.027$ and $a = \bar{y} - b\bar{x} = 0.2171 - (0.027)(1986.5) = -53.42$

and the least squares line is $\hat{y} = a + bx = -53.42 - .027x$.

 d The fitted line and the plotted points are shown below.

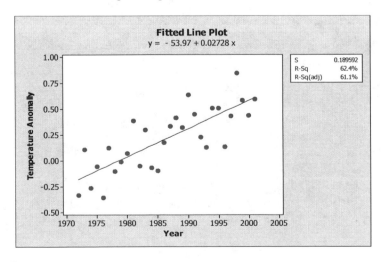

12.15 **a** The scatterplot generated by *MINITAB* is shown below. The assumption of linearity is reasonable.

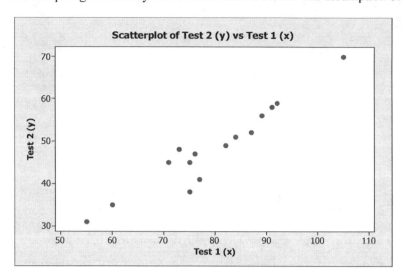

b Calculate

$$\sum x_i = 1,192 \qquad \sum y_i = 725 \qquad \sum x_i y_i = 59,324$$

$$\sum x_i^2 = 96,990 \qquad \sum y_i^2 = 36,461 \qquad n = 15$$

Then $S_{xy} = \sum x_i y_i - \dfrac{(\sum x_i)(\sum y_i)}{n} = 1710.6667$

$$S_{xx} = \sum x_i^2 - \frac{(\sum x_i)^2}{n} = 2265.7333$$

$$S_{yy} = \sum y_i^2 - \frac{(\sum y_i)^2}{n} = 1419.3333$$

$$b = \frac{S_{xy}}{S_{xx}} = \frac{1710.6667}{2265.7333} = 0.75502 \quad \text{and} \quad a = y - b\overline{x} = 48.3333 - (0.75502)(79.4667) = -11.665$$

(using full accuracy) and the least squares line is $\hat{y} = a + bx = -11.665 + 0.755x$.

c When $x = 85$, the value for y can be predicted using the least squares line as

$$\hat{y} = a + bx = -11.665 + .755(85) = 52.51$$

12.17 **a** The scatterplot is shown below. There is a positive linear relationship between armspan and height.

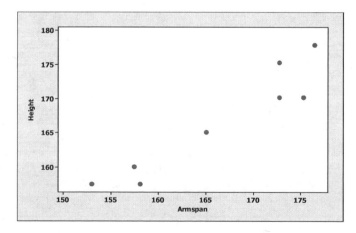

b   If armspan and height are roughly equal, the slope of the regression line should be approximately equal to 1.

c   Calculate

$$n = 8; \ \sum x_i = 1{,}330.9; \ \sum y_i = 1{,}333.6; \ \sum x_i^2 = 222{,}001.79; \ \sum y_i^2 = 222{,}749.52; \ \sum x_i y_i = 222{,}341.87$$

Then $S_{xy} = \sum x_i y_i - \dfrac{(\sum x_i)(\sum y_i)}{n} = 480.84$

$$S_{xx} = \sum x_i^2 - \frac{(\sum x_i)^2}{n} = 589.93875$$

$$S_{yy} = \sum y_i^2 - \frac{(\sum y_i)^2}{n} = 438.4$$

$$b = \frac{S_{xy}}{S_{xx}} = \frac{480.84}{589.93875} = 0.815068 \quad \text{and} \quad a = \bar{y} - b\bar{x} = 166.70 - (0.815068)(166.3625) = 31.103$$

and the least squares line is $\hat{y} = a + bx = 31.103 + 0.815x$.

The slope is quite close to the expected value of slope parameter $\beta = 1$.

d   When $x = 157.5$, the value for y can be predicted using the least squares line as

$$\hat{y} = a + bx = 31.103 + .815(157.5) = 159.4655$$

12.19   **a**   The hypothesis to be tested is H_0: $\beta = 0$ versus H_a: $\beta \neq 0$ and the test statistic is a Student's t, calculated as

$$t = \frac{b - \beta_0}{\sqrt{\text{MSE}/S_{xx}}} = \frac{1.2 - 0}{\sqrt{0.533/10}} = 5.20$$

The critical value of t is based on $n - 2 = 3$ degrees of freedom and the rejection region for $\alpha = 0.05$ is $|t| > t_{0.025} = 3.182$. Since the observed value of t falls in the rejection region, we reject H_0 and conclude that $\beta \neq 0$. That is, x is useful in the prediction of y.

b   From the ANOVA table in Exercise 12.6, calculate

$$F = \frac{\text{MSR}}{\text{MSE}} = \frac{14.4}{0.5333} = 27.00$$

which is the square of the t statistic from part **a**: $t^2 = (5.20)^2 = 27.0$.

c   The critical value of t from part **a** was $t_{0.025} = 3.182$, while the critical value of F from part **b** with $df_1 = 1$ and $df_2 = 3$ is $F_{0.05} = 10.13$. Notice that the relationship between the two critical values is

$$F = 10.13 = (3.182)^2 = t^2$$

12.21   **a**   The hypothesis to be tested is H_0: $\beta = 0$ versus H_a: $\beta \neq 0$ and the test statistic is

$$F = \frac{\text{MSR}}{\text{MSE}} = \frac{5.4321}{0.0357} = 152.10$$

with p-value $= 0.000$. Since the p-value is less than $\alpha = 0.01$, the null hypothesis is rejected. There is evidence to indicate that y and x are linearly related.

b   Use the formula for r^2 given in this section:

$$r^2 = \frac{\text{SSR}}{\text{Total SS}} = \frac{5.4321}{5.5750} = 0.974$$

The coefficient of determination measures the proportion of the total variation in y that is accounted for using the independent variable x. That is, the total variation in y is reduced by 97.4% by using $\hat{y} = a + bx$ rather than $\bar{y}$ to predict the response y.

12.23 **a** The equations for calculating the quantities a and b involve the following preliminary calculations:

$$\sum x_i = 11.6 \qquad\qquad \sum y_i = 45.68 \qquad\qquad \sum x_i y_i = 103.278$$

$$\sum x_i^2 = 25.76 \qquad\qquad \sum y_i^2 = 415.521 \qquad\qquad n = 6$$

Then $S_{xy} = \sum x_i y_i - \dfrac{(\sum x_i)(\sum y_i)}{n} = 103.278 - \dfrac{11.6(45.68)}{6} = 14.963333$

$S_{xx} = \sum x_i^2 - \dfrac{(\sum x_i)^2}{n} = 25.76 - \dfrac{11.6^2}{6} = 3.33333$

$b = \dfrac{S_{xy}}{S_{xx}} = 4.49$ and $a = \bar{y} - b\bar{x} = 7.6133 - 4.49(1.9333) = -1.07$

and the least squares line is $\hat{y} = a + bx = -1.07 + 4.49x$.

b Calculate Total SS $= S_{yy} = \sum y_i^2 - \dfrac{(\sum y_i)^2}{n} = 415.521 - \dfrac{(45.68)^2}{6} = 67.74393$. Then

$$\text{SSE} = S_{yy} - \dfrac{(S_{xy})^2}{S_{xx}} = 67.74393 - \dfrac{(14.963333)^2}{3.33333} = 0.5735 \text{ and } \text{MSE} = \dfrac{\text{SSE}}{n-2} = \dfrac{0.5735}{4} = 0.14338$$

The hypothesis to be tested is $H_0: \beta = 0$ versus $H_a: \beta \neq 0$ and the test statistic is

$$t = \dfrac{b - \beta_0}{\sqrt{\text{MSE}/S_{xx}}} = \dfrac{4.49 - 0}{\sqrt{0.14338/3.3333}} = 21.64$$

The critical value of t is based on $n - 2 = 4$ degrees of freedom and the rejection region for $\alpha = 0.05$ is $|t| > t_{0.025} = 2.776$, and H_0 is rejected. There is evidence at the 5% level to indicate that x and y are linearly related.

c Calculate $r^2 = \dfrac{(S_{xy})^2}{S_{xx} S_{yy}} = \dfrac{(14.96333)^2}{(3.3333)(67.74393)} = 0.992$

Then 99.2% of the total variation in y is accounted for by the independent variable x. That is, the total variation in y is reduced by 99.2% by using $\hat{y} = a + bx$ rather than $\bar{y}$ to predict the response y.

12.25 **a** The dependent variable (to be predicted) is $y =$ average longevity, and the independent variable is $x =$ gestation time.

b Preliminary calculations:

$$\sum x_i = 2,401 \qquad\qquad \sum y_i = 192 \qquad\qquad \sum x_i y_i = 36,711$$

$$\sum x_i^2 = 507,919 \qquad\qquad \sum y_i^2 = 2,878 \qquad\qquad n = 15$$

Then $S_{xy} = \sum x_i y_i - \dfrac{(\sum x_i)(\sum y_i)}{n} = 5,978.2$

$S_{xx} = \sum x_i^2 - \dfrac{(\sum x_i)^2}{n} = 123,598.933333$

$b = \dfrac{S_{xy}}{S_{xx}} = 0.0483677$ and $a = \bar{y} - b\bar{x} = 12.8 - 0.0483677(160.066667) = 5.0579$

and the least squares line is $\hat{y} = a + bx = 5.0579 + 0.0484x$.

c The plot is shown on the next page. The line appears to fit well through the 15 data points.

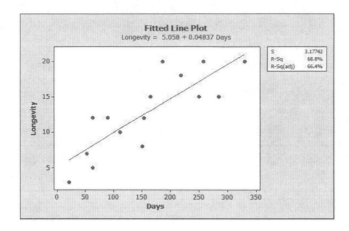

d Calculate

$$\text{Total SS} = S_{yy} = \sum y_i^2 - \frac{\left(\sum y_i\right)^2}{n} = 2878 - \frac{(192)^2}{15} = 420.4$$

$$\text{Then } \text{SSE} = S_{yy} - \frac{\left(S_{xy}\right)^2}{S_{xx}} = 420.4 - \frac{(5978.2)^2}{123,598.9333} = 131.24803 \text{ and}$$

$$\text{MSE} = \frac{\text{SSE}}{n-2} = \frac{131.24803}{13} = 10.096002$$

The hypothesis to be tested is H_0: $\beta = 0$ versus H_a: $\beta \neq 0$ and the test statistic is

$$t = \frac{b - \beta_0}{\sqrt{\text{MSE}/S_{xx}}} = \frac{0.0483677 - 0}{\sqrt{10.096/123,598.9333}} = 5.35$$

The critical value of t is based on $n - 2 = 13$ degrees of freedom and the rejection region for $\alpha = 0.05$ is $|t| > t_{0.025} = 2.160$, and H_0 is rejected. There is evidence at the 5% level to indicate that x and y are linearly related. That is, the regression model $y = \alpha + \beta x + \varepsilon$ is useful in predicting average

longevity y. You can also calculate $r^2 = \dfrac{S_{xy}^2}{S_{xx}S_{yy}} = \dfrac{(5978.2)^2}{123,598.9333(420.4)} = 0.688.$

That is, 68.8% of the total variation in y is accounted for by the independent variable x. The total variation in y is reduced by 68.8% by using $\hat{y} = a + bx$ rather than $\bar{y}$ to predict the response y.

12.27 **a** From the *MINITAB* printout, the test of H_0: $\beta = 0$ versus H_a: $\beta \neq 0$ is performed using one of two test statistics:

$t = 3.79$ or $F = 14.37$ with p-value $= 0.005$

Since the p-value is smaller than $\alpha = 0.01$, H_0 is rejected, and the results are declared highly significant. There is evidence to indicate that x and y are linearly related.

b If a person is deprived of sleep for as much as 48 hours, their number of errors will probably become extremely high. The relationship will not remain linear, but will become curvilinear.

c From the printout, R-Sq = 64.2%. That is, 64.2% of the total variation in the experiment can be explained by the independent variable x. The total variation in y is reduced by 64.2% by using $\hat{y} = a + bx$ rather than $\bar{y}$ to predict the response y. This is a relatively strong relationship.

d The population variance σ^2 is estimated using $s^2 = \text{MSE} = 5.025$.

e The 95% confidence interval for the slope β is

$$b \pm t_{\alpha/2}\sqrt{\text{MSE}/S_{xx}} \Rightarrow 0.475 \pm 2.306(0.1253) \Rightarrow 0.475 \pm 0.289$$

or $0.186 < \beta < 0.764$

12.29 **a** The scatterplot generated by *MINITAB* is shown below. The assumption of linearity is reasonable.

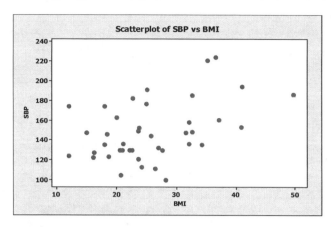

b Using the *MINITAB* printout, the equation of the regression line is $y = 109 + 1.55x$.

c The hypothesis to be tested is $H_0: \beta = 0$ versus $H_a: \beta \neq 0$ and the test statistic is a Student's t, calculated as

$$t = \frac{b - \beta_0}{\sqrt{\text{MSE}/S_{xx}}} = 3.01$$

with p-value $= 0.005$. Since the p-value is less than $\alpha = 0.01$, we reject H_0 and conclude that $\beta \neq 0$. That is, SBP measurement and BMI are linearly related.

d The 99% confidence interval for the slope β is

$$b \pm t_{\alpha/2}\sqrt{\text{MSE}/S_{xx}} \rightarrow 1.55 \pm 2.576(0.5128) \rightarrow 1.55 \pm 1.3210$$
or $0.229 < \beta < 2.871$

12.31 Refer to Exercise 12.17.

a The hypothesis to be tested is $H_0: \beta = 0$ versus $H_a: \beta \neq 0$ and the test statistic is a Student's t, calculated as

$$t = \frac{b - \beta_0}{\sqrt{\text{MSE}/S_{xx}}} = \frac{.815}{\sqrt{\dfrac{7.7472}{589.93875}}} = 7.11$$

The rejection region, with $\alpha = 0.05$, is $|t| > t_{0.025,6} = 2.447$ and we reject H_0. That is, there is a linear relationship between armspan and height.

b The 95% confidence interval for the slope β is

$$b \pm t_{\alpha/2}\sqrt{\text{MSE}/S_{xx}} \Rightarrow 0.815 \pm 2.447\sqrt{\frac{7.7472}{589.93875}} \Rightarrow 0.815 \pm 0.2804$$

or $0.5346 < \beta < 1.0954$

c Since the value $\beta = 1$ is in the confidence interval, da Vinci's supposition is confirmed by the confidence interval in part **b**.

12.33 Use a plot of residuals versus fits. The plot should appear as a random scatter of points, free of any patterns.

12.35 Although there is one data point in each graph that appears somewhat unusual, there is no reason to doubt the validity of the regression assumptions.

12.37 The two plots behave as expected if the regression assumptions have been satisfied.

12.39 **a**   The random error ε must have a normal distribution with mean 0 and a common variance σ^2, independent of x.

      b   The best estimate of σ^2 is MSE $= 722.0$.

      c   The normal probability plot does not show much deviation from normality and the residual plot does not seem to have unusual observations. There does not appear to be any extreme violations of the regression assumptions.

12.41 **a**   In order to obtain an estimate for the expected value of y for a given value of x (or for a particular value of y), it would seem reasonable to use the prediction equation, $\hat{y} = a + bx$. Notice that x_p represents the given value of x for which we are estimating $E(y)$. The point estimator for $E(y)$ when $x = 1$ is $\hat{y} = 3 + 1.2(1) = 4.2$ and the 90% confidence interval is

$$\hat{y} \pm t_{0.05}\sqrt{\text{MSE}\left(\frac{1}{n} + \frac{(x_0 - \bar{x})^2}{S_{xx}}\right)}$$

$$4.2 \pm 2.353\sqrt{(0.5333)\left(\frac{1}{5} + \frac{(1-0)^2}{10}\right)}$$

$$4.2 \pm 0.941$$

or $3.259 < E(y) < 5.141$

      b   It is necessary to find a 90% prediction interval for y when $x = 1$. The interval used in predicting a particular value of y is

$$\hat{y} \pm t_{0.05}\sqrt{\text{MSE}\left(1 + \frac{1}{n} + \frac{(x_0 - \bar{x})^2}{S_{xx}}\right)}$$

$$4.2 \pm 2.353\sqrt{(0.5333)\left(1 + \frac{1}{5} + \frac{(1-0)^2}{10}\right)}$$

$$4.2 \pm 1.96$$

or $2.24 < y < 6.16$

We are 90% confident that the true value of y when $x = 1$ is in the above interval. Note that the above interval is much wider than the interval calculated for the expected value of y. The variability of predicting a particular value of y is greater than the variability of predicting the population mean for a particular value of x.

12.43 **a**   Use a computer program or the hand calculations shown below.

$$\sum x_i = 45 \qquad\qquad \sum y_i = 132 \qquad\qquad \sum x_i y_i = 411$$
$$\sum x_i^2 = 145 \qquad\qquad \sum y_i^2 = 1204 \qquad\qquad n = 15$$

Then $S_{xy} = \sum x_i y_i - \dfrac{(\sum x_i)(\sum y_i)}{n} = 411 - \dfrac{45(132)}{15} = 15$

$S_{xx} = \sum x_i^2 - \dfrac{(\sum x_i)^2}{n} = 145 - \dfrac{45^2}{15} = 10$

$S_{yy} = \sum y_i^2 - \dfrac{(\sum y_i)^2}{n} = 1204 - \dfrac{132^2}{15} = 42.4$

$b = \dfrac{S_{xy}}{S_{xx}} = \dfrac{15}{10} = 1.5$ and $a = \bar{y} - b\bar{x} = 8.8 - 1.5(3) = 4.3$

and the least squares line is $\hat{y} = a + bx = 4.3 + 1.5x$.

b   The graph of the least squares line and the 15 data points are shown below.

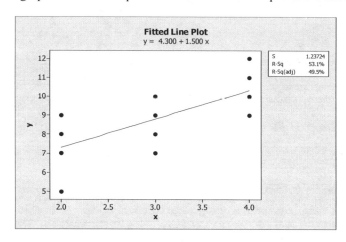

c   Calculate

$$SSE = S_{yy} - \frac{\left(S_{xy}\right)^2}{S_{xx}} = 42.4 - \frac{15^2}{10} = 19.9 \text{ and } s^2 = \frac{SSE}{n-2} = 1.53$$

d   To test $H_0: \beta = 0$ versus $H_a: \beta \neq 0$, the test statistic is

$$t = \frac{b - \beta_0}{s/\sqrt{S_{xx}}} = \frac{1.5}{\sqrt{1.53/10}} = 3.83$$

The rejection region for $\alpha = 0.05$ is $|t| > t_{0.025} = 2.160$ and we reject H_0. There is sufficient evidence to indicate that the independent variable x does help in predicting values of the dependent variable y.

e   From Table 4, notice that $t = 3.834$ is larger than the largest tabulated value with $n - 2 = 13$ degrees of freedom ($t_{0.005} = 3.012$). Hence, the p-value for this two-tailed test is

$$2P(t > 3.834) < 2(0.005) = 0.01$$

f   The diagnostic plots are shown below. There is no reason to doubt the validity of the regression assumptions.

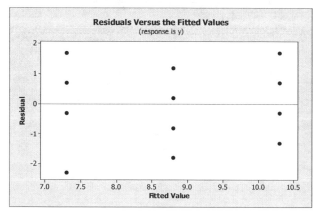

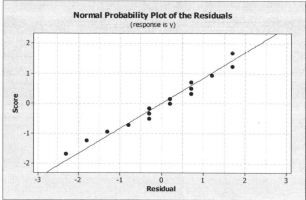

g   When $x = 3$, $\hat{y} = 4.3 + 1.5(3) = 8.8$ and the 95% confidence interval is

$$\hat{y} \pm t_{0.025} \sqrt{MSE\left(\frac{1}{n} + \frac{(x_p - \bar{x})^2}{S_{xx}}\right)}$$

$$8.8 \pm 2.160 \sqrt{1.53\left(\frac{1}{15} + \frac{(3-3)^2}{10}\right)}$$

$$8.8 \pm 0.69$$
or $8.11 < E(y) < 9.49$

12.45 **a**   From the computer printout, the least squares line is $\hat{y} = a + bx = 151,206 + 295x$. The 99% confidence interval for β is

$$b \pm t_{0.005} \times (\text{std error of } b) \Rightarrow 295 \pm 3.169(19.68) \Rightarrow 295 \pm 62.366$$
or $232.634 < \beta < 357.366$

b   When $x = 185.8$, $\hat{y} = 151,206 + 295(185.8) = 206,017$ and the 95% confidence interval is given on the printout as $204,676 < E(y) < 207,360$.

c   For each house in the sample, the price per square metre is calculated as $z_i = y_i/x_i$, and the results are shown below.

$$\begin{array}{cccccc}
1391.59 & 1068.40 & 1243.98 & 1371.86 & 1168.59 & 967.58 \\
1118.13 & 1316.84 & 1353.02 & 1212.97 & 1207.45 & 1028.17
\end{array}$$

Then the average cost per square metre is

$$\bar{z} = \frac{\sum z_i}{n} = 1204.00$$

This is not the same as $b = 295$ and should not be, since they are calculated in totally different ways.

d   When $x = 165.4$, $\hat{y} = 199,999$ and the 95% prediction interval is given on the printout as

$$195,826 < y < 204,151$$

12.47 **a**   Use a computer program or the hand calculations shown below.

$$\sum x_i = 40.24 \qquad \sum y_i = 22.96 \qquad \sum x_i y_i = 132.758$$
$$\sum x_i^2 = 234.255 \qquad \sum y_i^2 = 75.512 \qquad n = 7$$

Then $S_{xy} = \sum x_i y_i - \frac{(\sum x_i)(\sum y_i)}{n} = 0.7708$

$$S_{xx} = \sum x_i^2 - \frac{(\sum x_i)^2}{n} = 2.9325$$

$$S_{yy} = \sum y_i^2 - \frac{(\sum y_i)^2}{n} = 0.2032$$

$$b = \frac{S_{xy}}{S_{xx}} = 0.263 \quad \text{and} \quad a = \bar{y} - b\bar{x} = 3.28 - 0.263(5.749) = 1.769$$

and the least squares line is $\hat{y} = 1.769 + .263x$.

b   The proportion of the total variation explained by regression is

$$r^2 = \frac{S_{xy}^2}{S_{xx}S_{yy}} = \frac{0.7708^2}{(2.9325)(.2032)} = 0.998$$

c   The diagnostic plots, generated by *MINITAB* are shown on the next page. The plots do not show any strong violation of assumptions.

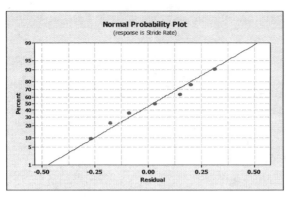

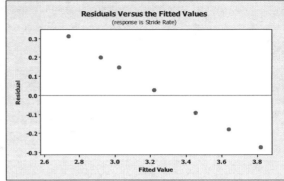

12.49　**a**　Preliminary calculations:

$$\sum x_i = 438 \qquad\qquad \sum y_i = 4620 \qquad\qquad \sum x_i y_i = 127,944$$
$$\sum x_i^2 = 12,294 \qquad \sum y_i^2 = 1,377,862 \qquad n = 16$$

Then $S_{xy} = \sum x_i y_i - \dfrac{(\sum x_i)(\sum y_i)}{n} = 1471.5$

$$S_{xx} = \sum x_i^2 - \frac{(\sum x_i)^2}{n} = 303.75 \qquad\qquad S_{yy} = \sum y_i^2 - \frac{(\sum y_i)^2}{n} = 43,837$$

$$b = \frac{S_{xy}}{S_{xx}} = \frac{1471.5}{303.75} = 4.8444 \quad \text{and} \quad a = \bar{y} - b\bar{x} = 288.75 - 4.8444(27.375) = 156.135$$

and the least squares line is $\hat{y} = a + bx = 156.135 + 4.844x$.

b　The proportion of the total variation explained by the regression is about 16.3% as explained below

$$r^2 = \frac{S_{xy}^2}{S_{xx}S_{yy}} = \frac{(1471.5)^2}{303.75(43,837)} = 0.163$$

c　The diagnostic plots are shown below. The plots do not show any strong violation of the assumptions.

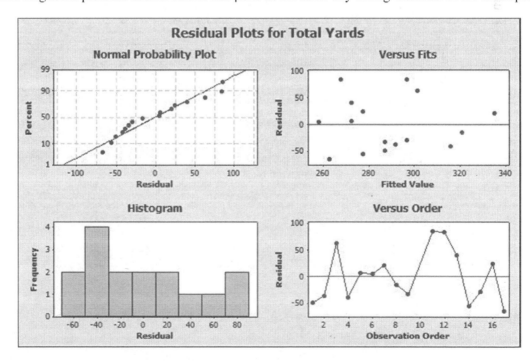

12.51   The significance of the algebraic sign and the magnitude of r, the coefficient of correlation, will be discussed in Exercise 12.52. Note, however, that r^2 provides a meaningful measure of the strength of the linear relationship between two variables, y and x. It is the ratio of the reduction in the sum of squares of deviations obtained using the model, $y = \alpha + \beta x + \varepsilon$, to the sum of squares of deviations that would be obtained if the variable x were ignored. That is, r^2 measures the amount of variation that can be attributed to the variable x.

12.53   Refer to Exercise 12.52. In the first instance, $r = +1$; in the second, $r = -1$.

12.55   **a**   Refer to the figure below. The sample correlation coefficient will be negative.

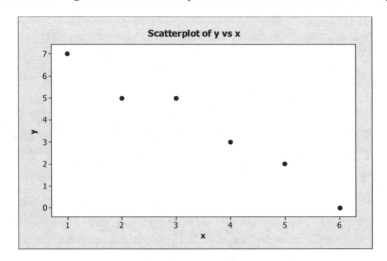

b   Calculate $S_{xy} = \sum x_i y_i - \dfrac{\left(\sum x_i\right)\left(\sum y_i\right)}{n} = 54 - \dfrac{21(22)}{6} = -23$

$S_{xx} = \sum x_i^2 - \dfrac{\left(\sum x_i\right)^2}{n} = 91 - \dfrac{21^2}{6} = 17.5$

$S_{yy} = \sum y_i^2 - \dfrac{\left(\sum y_i\right)^2}{n} = 112 - \dfrac{22^2}{6} = 31.33333$

Then $r = \dfrac{S_{xy}}{\sqrt{S_{xx} S_{yy}}} = \dfrac{-23}{\sqrt{17.5(31.3333)}} = -0.982$

c   We first calculate the coefficient of determination:

$r^2 = (-0.982)^2 = 0.9647$

This value implies that the sum of squares of deviations is reduced by 96.47% using the linear model $\hat{y} = a + bx$ instead of $\bar{y}$ to predict values of y.

12.57   **a**   When x is large, y should be small if the barnacles compete for space on the lobster's surface. Hence, we would expect to find negative correlation.

b–c   The test of hypothesis is $H_0: \rho = 0$ versus $H_a: \rho < 0$

Calculate $S_{xy} = \sum x_i y_i - \dfrac{\left(\sum x_i\right)\left(\sum y_i\right)}{n} = 42,556 - \dfrac{2,379(652)}{10} = -112,554.8$

$S_{xx} = \sum x_i^2 - \dfrac{\left(\sum x_i\right)^2}{n} = 973,255 - \dfrac{2,379^2}{10} = 407,290.9$

$S_{yy} = \sum y_i^2 - \dfrac{\left(\sum y_i\right)^2}{n} = 114,624 - \dfrac{652^2}{10} = 102,113.4$

Then $r = \dfrac{S_{xy}}{\sqrt{S_{xx}S_{yy}}} = \dfrac{-112,544.8}{\sqrt{407,290.9(102,113.6)}} = -0.5519$

and the test statistic is

$$t = \dfrac{r\sqrt{n-2}}{\sqrt{1-r^2}} = \dfrac{-0.5519\sqrt{8}}{\sqrt{1-(-0.5519)^2}} = -1.872$$

The rejection region for $\alpha = 0.05$ is $t < -t_{0.05} = -1.860$ and H_0 is rejected. There is evidence of negative correlation.

12.59 **a** The hypothesis of interest is $H_0: \rho = 0$ versus $H_a: \rho \neq 0$ and the test statistic is

$$t = \dfrac{r\sqrt{n-2}}{\sqrt{1-r^2}} = \dfrac{-0.37\sqrt{67}}{\sqrt{1-(-0.37)^2}} = -3.260$$

The rejection region is $|t| > t_{0.025} \approx 1.96$ and H_0 is rejected. There is evidence of correlation between x and y.

b The p-value can be bounded using Table 4 as
p-value $= 2P(t > 3.26) < 2(0.005) = 0.01$

c The negative correlation observed above implies that, if the skater's stride is large, his time to completion will be small.

12.61 Using a computer program, your scientific calculator or the computing formulas given in the text to calculate the correlation coefficient r.

$$S_{xy} = \sum x_i y_i - \dfrac{(\sum x_i)(\sum y_i)}{n} = 1,901,500 - \dfrac{8,050(2,100)}{9} = 23,166.667$$

$$S_{xx} = \sum x_i^2 - \dfrac{(\sum x_i)^2}{n} = 7,802,500 - \dfrac{8,050^2}{9} = 602,222.22$$

$$S_{yy} = \sum y_i^2 - \dfrac{(\sum y_i)^2}{n} = 498,200 - \dfrac{2,100^2}{9} = 8,200$$

Then $r = \dfrac{S_{xy}}{\sqrt{S_{xx}S_{yy}}} = \dfrac{23,166.667}{\sqrt{602,222.22(8200)}} = 0.3297$

The test of hypothesis is $H_0: \rho = 0$ versus $H_a: \rho > 0$ and the test statistic is

$$t = \dfrac{r\sqrt{n-2}}{\sqrt{1-r^2}} = \dfrac{0.3297\sqrt{7}}{\sqrt{1-(0.3297)^2}} = 0.92$$

with p-value bounded as p-value $= P(t > 0.92) > 0.10$. The results are not significant; H_0 is not rejected. There is insufficient evidence to indicate a positive correlation between average maximum drill hole depth and average maximum temperature.

12.63 **a** Use a computer program, your scientific calculator, or the computing formulas given in the text to calculate the correlation coefficient r.

$$S_{xy} = \sum x_i y_i - \dfrac{(\sum x_i)(\sum y_i)}{n} = 33,032.1 - \dfrac{442.3(896)}{12} = 7.033333$$

$$S_{xx} = \sum x_i^2 - \dfrac{(\sum x_i)^2}{n} = 16,305.79 - \dfrac{442.3^2}{12} = 3.34917$$

$$S_{yy} = \sum y_i^2 - \dfrac{(\sum y_i)^2}{n} = 67,312 - \dfrac{896^2}{12} = 410.6667$$

Then $r = \dfrac{S_{xy}}{\sqrt{S_{xx}S_{yy}}} = \dfrac{7.03333}{\sqrt{3.34917(410.6667)}} = 0.1896$

b The test of hypothesis is $H_0: \rho = 0$ versus $H_a: \rho \neq 0$ and the test statistic is

$$t = \dfrac{r\sqrt{n-2}}{\sqrt{1-r^2}} = \dfrac{0.1896\sqrt{10}}{\sqrt{1-(0.1896)^2}} = 0.6106$$

The rejection region with $\alpha = 0.05$ is $|t| > t_{0.025} = 2.228$ and H_0 is not rejected. There is insufficient evidence to indicate a correlation between body temperature and heart rate.

12.65 a The scatterplot is given below. There appears to be some relationship between total home runs and the team batting average, but it may be curvilinear rather than linear.

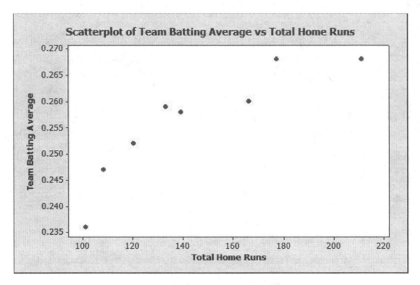

b Assuming that the relationship between x and y is linear, calculate

$$S_{xy} = \sum x_i y_i - \dfrac{(\sum x_i)(\sum y_i)}{n} = 298.205 - \dfrac{1155(2.048)}{8} = 2.525$$

$$S_{xx} = \sum x_i^2 - \dfrac{(\sum x_i)^2}{n} = 176,681 - \dfrac{1155^2}{8} = 9927.875$$

$$S_{yy} = \sum y_i^2 - \dfrac{(\sum y_i)^2}{n} = 0.525102 - \dfrac{2.048^2}{8} = 0.000814$$

Then $r = \dfrac{S_{xy}}{\sqrt{S_{xx}S_{yy}}} = \dfrac{2.525}{\sqrt{9927.875(0.000814)}} = 0.8882$

The test of hypothesis is $H_0: \rho = 0$ versus $H_a: \rho > 0$ and the test statistic is

$$t = \dfrac{r\sqrt{n-2}}{\sqrt{1-r^2}} = \dfrac{0.8882\sqrt{6}}{\sqrt{1-(0.8882)^2}} = 4.735$$

The rejection region with $\alpha = 0.05$ is $t > t_{0.05} = 1.943$ and H_0 is rejected. There is sufficient evidence to indicate a positive correlation between the two variables.

c Answers will vary.

12.67   **a**   The data are plotted with the least squares line below. There appears to be a linear relationship.

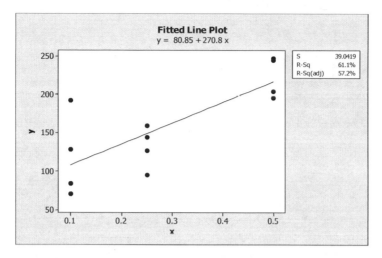

b   Using the printout, the least squares line is $\hat{y} = a + bx = 80.85 + 270.82x$.

c   To test H_0: $\beta = 0$ versus H_a: $\beta \neq 0$, the test statistic is $t = 3.96$ with p-value $= 0.003$. Since this p-value is less than 0.01, we reject H_0. There is sufficient evidence to indicate that the independent variable x does help in predicting values of the dependent variable y.

d   When $x = 0.20$, $\hat{y} = 80.85 + 270.82(0.20) = 135.0$. The 90% confidence interval is shown at the bottom of the printout as $(112.1, 157.9)$ or $112.1 < E(y) < 157.9$.

12.69   Answers will vary. The *MINITAB* output for this linear regression problem is shown below.

```
Regression Analysis: y versus x
The regression equation is
y = 21.9 + 15.0 x

Predictor      Coef    SE Coef       T       P
Constant     21.867      3.502    6.24   0.000
x           14.9667     0.9530   15.70   0.000

S = 3.69098    R-Sq = 96.1%    R-Sq(adj) = 95.7%


Analysis of Variance
Source            DF       SS      MS       F       P
Regression         1   3360.0  3360.0  246.64   0.000
Residual Error    10    136.2    13.6
Total             11   3496.2

Correlations: x, y
Pearson correlation of x and y = 0.980
P-Value = 0.000
```

a   The correlation coefficient is $r = 0.980$.

b   The coefficient of determination is $r^2 = 0.961$ (or 96.1%).

c   The least squares line is $\hat{y} = 21.867 + 14.9667x$.

d   We wish to estimate the mean percentage of kill for an application of 1.82 kilograms of nematicide per hectare. Since the percent kill y is actually a binomial percentage, the variance of y will change depending on the value of p, the proportion of nematodes killed for a particular application rate. The residual plot versus the fitted values shows this phenomenon as a "football-shaped" pattern. The normal probability plot also shows some deviation from normality in the tails of the plot. A transformation may be needed to assure that the regression assumptions are satisfied.

12.71 **a–b** Answers will vary. The *MINITAB* output is shown below, along with two diagnostic plots. These plots give no indications of any violation of assumptions. The printout indicates a significant linear regression $(t = 6.82; p\text{-value} \approx 0)$ with the regression line given as $\hat{y} = -54.0 + 0.0273x$.

Regression Analysis: Temperature Anomaly versus Year

```
The regression equation is
Temperature Anomaly = - 54.0 + 0.0273 Year

Predictor        Coef    SE Coef       T      P
Constant      -53.972      7.944   -6.79  0.000
Year         0.027279   0.003999    6.82  0.000

S = 0.189592    R-Sq = 62.4%    R-Sq(adj) = 61.1%

Analysis of Variance

Source          DF       SS       MS       F      P
Regression       1   1.6724   1.6724   46.53  0.000
Residual Error  28   1.0065   0.0359
Total           29   2.6789
```

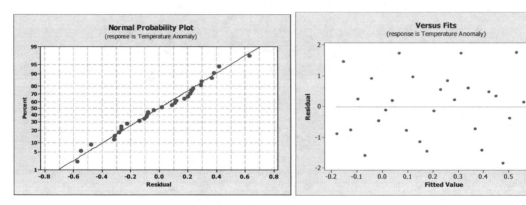

12.73 **a** Stiffness is inherent material quality, hence the two kinds of stiffness should be positively correlated. Use a computer program, your scientific calculator or the computing formulas given in the text to calculate the correlation coefficient r.

$$S_{xy} = \sum x_i y_i - \frac{(\sum x_i)(\sum y_i)}{n} = 1{,}233{,}987 - \frac{5{,}028(2856)}{12} = 37{,}323$$

$$S_{xx} = \sum x_i^2 - \frac{(\sum x_i)^2}{n} = 2{,}212{,}178 - \frac{5{,}028^2}{12} = 105{,}446$$

$$S_{yy} = \sum y_i^2 - \frac{(\sum y_i)^2}{n} = 723{,}882 - \frac{2{,}856^2}{12} = 44{,}154$$

Then $r = \dfrac{S_{xy}}{\sqrt{S_{xx}S_{yy}}} = \dfrac{37{,}323}{\sqrt{105{,}446(44{,}154)}} = 0.5470$

The test of hypothesis is H_0: $\rho = 0$ versus H_a: $\rho > 0$ and the test statistic is

$$t = \frac{r\sqrt{n-2}}{\sqrt{1-r^2}} = \frac{0.5470\sqrt{10}}{\sqrt{1-(0.5470)^2}} = 2.066$$

with $p\text{-value} = P(t > 2.066)$ bounded as $0.05 < p\text{-value} < 0.10$

If the experimenter is willing to tolerate a p-value this large, then H_0 can be rejected. Otherwise, you would declare the results not significant; there is insufficient evidence to indicate that bending stiffness and twisting stiffness are positively correlated.

b $r^2 = (0.5470)^2 = 0.2992$ so that 29.9% of the total variation in y can be explained by the independent variable x.

12.75 The relationship between y = penetrability and x = number of days is apparently non-linear, as seen by the strong curvilinear pattern in the residual plot. The regression analysis discussed in this chapter is not appropriate; we discuss the appropriate model in Chapter 13.

12.77 **a** The plot is shown below. Notice that there is a strong positive relationship between x and y: either linear or possibly curvilinear.

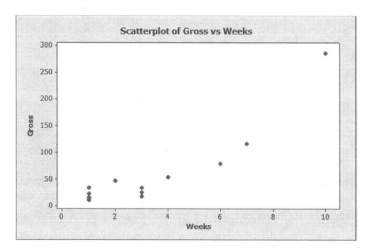

b Assuming that the relationship between x and y is linear, calculate

$$S_{xy} = \sum x_i y_i - \frac{(\sum x_i)(\sum y_i)}{n} = 4756.4 \quad \frac{42(737.5)}{12} = 2175.15$$

$$S_{xx} = \sum x_i^2 - \frac{(\sum x_i)^2}{n} = 236 - \frac{42^2}{12} = 89$$

$$S_{yy} = \sum y_i^2 - \frac{(\sum y_i)^2}{n} = 110,319.09 - \frac{737.5^2}{12} = 64,993.56917$$

Then $r^2 = \dfrac{S_{xy}^2}{S_{xx}S_{yy}} = \dfrac{(2175.15)^2}{89(64993.56917)} = 0.8179$. That is, 81.79% of the total variation is explained by using $\hat{y} = a + bx$ rather than $\bar{y}$ to predict the response y.

c Calculate

$$b = \frac{S_{xy}}{S_{xx}} = \frac{2175.15}{89} = 24.439887 \quad \text{and} \quad a = \bar{y} - b\bar{x} = 61.45833 - (24.439887)(3.5) = -24.0813$$

and the least squares line is $\hat{y} = a + bx = -24.0813 + 24.440x$.

The hypothesis to be tested is H_0: $\beta = 0$ versus H_a: $\beta \neq 0$.

Calculate $\text{SSE} = S_{yy} - \dfrac{(S_{xy})^2}{S_{xx}} = 64,993.56917 - \dfrac{2,175.15^2}{89} = 11,833.14757$

and $\text{MSE} = \dfrac{\text{SSE}}{n-2} = \dfrac{11,833.14757}{10} = 11,83.314757$

Then the test statistic is a Student's t, calculated as

$$t = \frac{b - \beta_0}{\sqrt{\text{MSE}/S_{xx}}} = \frac{24,440 - 0}{\sqrt{1,183.314757/89}} = 6.70$$

The critical value of t is based on $n - 2 = 10$ degrees of freedom and the rejection region for $\alpha = 0.05$ is $|t| > t_{0.025} = 2.228$. Since the observed value of t falls in the rejection region, we reject H_0 and conclude that $\beta \neq 0$. That is, x is useful in the prediction of y.

    d   Since the regression is significant, it is appropriate to use the regression line in the estimation or prediction. However, because of the possibility that a curvilinear model might be better, it would be not advisable to estimate or predict y outside of the experimental region.

12.79   The error will be a maximum for the values of x at the extremes of the experimental region.

12.81   **a**   The calculations shown below are done using the computing formulas. An appropriate computer program will provide identical results to within rounding error.

$$\sum x_i = 150 \qquad \sum y_i = 91 \qquad \sum x_i y_i = 986$$
$$\sum x_i^2 = 2750 \qquad \sum y_i^2 = 1120.04 \qquad n = 10$$

Then $S_{xy} = \sum x_i y_i - \dfrac{(\sum x_i)(\sum y_i)}{n} = 986 - \dfrac{150(91)}{10} = -379$

$$S_{xx} = \sum x_i^2 - \dfrac{(\sum x_i)^2}{n} = 2750 - \dfrac{150^2}{10} = 500$$

$$S_{yy} = \sum y_i^2 - \dfrac{(\sum y_i)^2}{n} = 1120.04 - \dfrac{91^2}{10} = 291.94$$

    a $b = \dfrac{S_{xy}}{S_{xx}} = \dfrac{-379}{500} = -0.758$ and $a = \bar{y} - b\bar{x} = 9.1 - (-.758)(15) = 20.47$

and the least squares line is $\hat{y} = a + bx = 20.47 - 0.758x$.

    b   Since Total SS $= S_{yy} = 291.94$ and SSR $= \dfrac{(S_{xy})^2}{S_{xx}} = \dfrac{(-379)^2}{500} = 287.282$

Then SSE = Total SS − SSR $= S_{yy} - \dfrac{(S_{xy})^2}{S_{xx}} = 4.658$

The ANOVA table with 1 *df* for regression and $n - 2$ *df* for error is shown below. Remember that the mean squares are calculated as $MS = SS/df$.

Source	df	SS	MS
Regression	1	287.282	287.282
Error	8	4.658	0.58225
Total	9	291.940	

    c   To test H_0: $\beta = 0$ versus H_a: $\beta \neq 0$, the test statistic is

$$t = \dfrac{b - \beta_0}{s/\sqrt{S_{xx}}} = \dfrac{-0.758}{\sqrt{0.58225/500}} = -22.21$$

The rejection region for $\alpha = 0.05$ is $|t| > t_{0.025} = 2.306$ and we reject H_0. There is sufficient evidence to indicate that x and y are linearly related.

    d   The 95% confidence interval for the slope β is

$$b \pm t_{\alpha/2}\sqrt{MSE/S_{xx}} \Rightarrow -0.758 \pm 2.896\sqrt{0.58225/500} \Rightarrow -0.758 \pm 0.099$$

or $-0.857 < \beta < -0.659$

e   When $x = 14$, the estimate of expected freshness $E(y)$ is $\hat{y} = 20.47 - 0.758(14) = 9.858$ and the 95% confidence interval is

$$\hat{y} \pm t_{0.025} \sqrt{MSE\left(\frac{1}{n} + \frac{\left(x_p - \bar{x}\right)^2}{S_{xx}}\right)}$$

$$9.858 \pm 2.306 \sqrt{0.58225\left(\frac{1}{10} + \frac{\left(14 - 15\right)^2}{500}\right)}$$

9.858 ± 0.562

or $9.296 < E(y) < 10.420$

f   Calculate $r^2 = \dfrac{SSR}{\text{Total SS}} = \dfrac{287.282}{291.94} = 0.984$

The total variation has been reduced by 98.4%% by using the linear model.

12.83   Answers will vary from student to student.

Case Study: Are Foreign Companies "Buying Up the Canadian Economy"?

1   A plot of the data using the years 1975 to 1985 is shown below. The relationship appears to be linear.

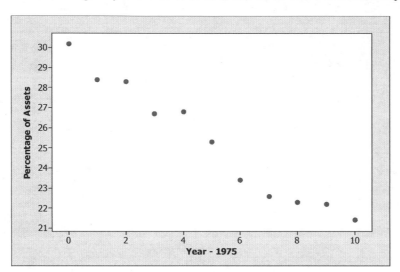

2   A *MINITAB* program was run to provide a simple regression analysis for the years 1975 to 1985. The printout is shown below.

```
Regression Analysis: y versus x
The regression equation is
y = 29.7 - 0.895 x

Predictor      Coef   SE Coef        T      P
Constant    29.7091    0.3509    84.67  0.000
x           -0.89455   0.05931  -15.08  0.000

S = 0.622020   R-Sq = 96.2%   R-Sq(adj) = 95.8%
Analysis of Variance

Source          DF       SS       MS       F      P
Regression       1   88.023   88.023  227.50  0.000
Residual Error   9    3.482    0.387
Total           10   91.505

Predicted Values for New Observations
New
Obs    Fit  SE Fit      95% CI            95% PI
  1  5.556   1.318  (2.574, 8.538)  (2.259, 8.854)XX
  2  4.662   1.377  (1.547, 7.777)  (1.244, 8.080)XX
  3  3.767   1.436  (0.520, 7.015)  (0.228, 7.307)XX

XX denotes a point that is an extreme outlier in the predictors.
Values of Predictors for New Observations

New
Obs     x
  1 27.0
  2  28.0
  3  29.0
```

3   From the printout, the test statistic for testing H_0: $\beta = 0$, H_a: $\beta \neq 0$ is $t = -15.08$. Since the observed significance level is p-value $= 0.000$, there is a strong linear relationship between x and y.

4–5 The prediction intervals for the three years of interest are shown on the printout. Notice that the predictions are not accurate, illustrating the dangers of *extrapolation*—predicting outside of the experimental region.

6 When the data for 1986–2004 are added to the database, the following computer output results.

Regression Analysis: y versus x
```
The regression equation is
y = 24.5 + 0.0478 x

Predictor      Coef   SE Coef      T      P
Constant    24.5034    0.8941  27.40  0.000
x            0.04781   0.05295   0.90  0.374

S = 2.51021   R-Sq = 2.8%   R-Sq(adj) = 0.0%
Analysis of Variance
Source           DF       SS     MS     F      P
Regression        1    5.137  5.137  0.82  0.374
Residual Error   28  176.433  6.301
Total            29  181.570
```

Notice that the slope of the line has changed from negative to positive and that error measured by SSE = 176.433 has increased.

7 A quadratic or a cubic model, which is discussed in Chapter 13, might be more appropriate. There is a cubic pattern in the plot of the data points from 1975 2004 and in the residual plot for the analysis in part **6**, shown below.

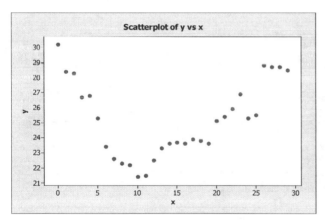

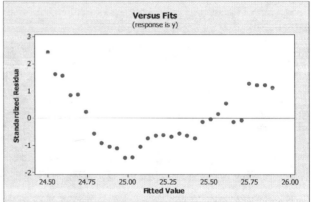

Project 12: Aspen Mixedwood Forests in Alberta

a   A scatterplot for the forest data is below.

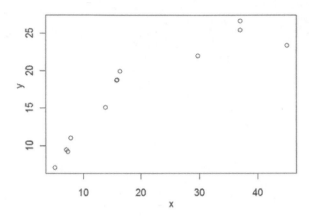

b   From the scatterplot, there is evidence of a positive relationship between DBH and canopy height. The relationship is somewhat curvilinear, but a linear fit would probably be adequate.

c   The appropriate hypothesis test can be found from the text, where it describes the test statistic as

$$t = r\sqrt{\frac{n-2}{1-r^2}}$$

Now, $r = \dfrac{s_{xy}}{\sqrt{s_{xx}s_{yy}}} = \dfrac{920.5808}{\sqrt{(2077.009)(500.8492)}} = 0.902587$

and $t = 0.902587\sqrt{\dfrac{12-2}{1-0.902587^2}} = 6.63$

Clearly, since this test statistic is so large, at any reasonable level of significance α, the null hypothesis that $\rho = 0$ would be strongly rejected. Therefore yes, there is a significant positive correlation between x and y.

d   Instead of *MINITAB*, we will use *R* to perform the analysis. The results are as follows:

```
Coefficients:
               Estimate      Std. Error      t value      Pr(>|t|)
(Intercept)    8.43997       1.59248         5.30         0.000348
   x           0.44322       0.06685         6.63         5.85e-05
Residual standard error: 3.047 on 10 degrees of freedom
Multiple R-squared: 0.8147,     Adjusted R-squared: 0.7961
F-statistic: 43.96 on 1 and 10 DF, p-value: 5.854e-05

Analysis of Variance Table

Response: y
            Df  Sum Sq  Mean Sq  F value    Pr(>F)
   x         1  408.02   408.02   43.956  5.854e-05
   Residuals 10   92.83     9.28
```

e   The equation of the regression line is $\hat{y} = 8.43997 + 0.44322x$.

f   This is represented by the slope of the line, which is 0.44322.

g Since the r^2 value is fairly high at 0.8147, we can conclude that the strength of the linear relationship between x and y is strong.

h The coefficient of determination is the same thing as r^2, which equals 0.8147. It can be found in the R output above. It can also be interpreted as found in part **i** below.

i The percentage of total variation in y that can be explained by the regression is $0.8147 = r^2$. This is the classical interpretation of r^2.

j The text interprets the phrase, "a linear regression model is useful" when the slope is significantly different from 0. Mimicking Example 12.2, the null hypothesis is that $\beta = 0$ versus $\beta \neq 0$. The test statistic is

$$t = \frac{b-0}{\sqrt{\text{MSE}/s_{xx}}} = \frac{0.44322}{\sqrt{(3.047)^2/2077.009}} = 6.629$$

At this value, the p-value is essentially 0, and so, since the p-value is less than the 5% significance level, we can reject the null hypothesis, and conclude that the regression is "useful," as the text puts it.

k From the computer output found in part **d** above, the value of the F-statistic is 43.956. This can also be calculated by hand using

$$F = \frac{\text{MSR}}{\text{MSE}}, \text{ where MSR} = \frac{(s_{xy})^2}{s_{xx}} = \frac{(920.5808)^2}{2077.009} = 408.023754$$

$$\text{and MSE} = \frac{\left(s_{yy} - \frac{(s_{xy})^2}{s_{xx}}\right)}{(n-2)} = \frac{\left(500.8492 - \frac{(902.5808)^2}{2077.009}\right)}{(12-2)} = 9.2854$$

implying that $F = \frac{408.023754}{9.28254} = 43.956$

The p-value is also given in the output (5.854×10^{-5}), which is clearly less than $\alpha = 5\%$. Thus, by the F test we can again reject the null hypothesis that $\beta = 0$.

l The critical value at $\alpha = 2.5\%$ for the t test is 2.228139 (based on 10 degrees of freedom). The critical value for the F test at $\alpha = 5\%$ is 4.964603 (based on 1 and 10 degrees of freedom). The relationship between them is as follows: $2.228139^2 = 4.964603$.

m Plugging $x = 42$ into the regression equation yields, $\hat{y} = 8.43997 + 0.44322(42) = 27.05521$ as the predicted tree canopy height.

n As a general rule, the linear regression should not be used to make predictions outside of the range of values used to make the line, since we have no evidence that the linear relationship will persist in these areas. In this case, a DBH of 52 is very close to the largest observed value of 45, and so it might be okay in this instance, although technically not allowed.

o A 95% confidence interval for β is $b \pm t_{\alpha/2}\sqrt{\frac{s^2}{s_{xx}}}$, where the notation is from the text. The value of s is given in the computer output above ($s = 3.047$) and S_{xx} was computed in part **c** as $S_{xx} = 2077.009$. We have $(12-2)$ degrees of freedom for this question. And so, we obtain

$$0.44322 \pm 2.228\sqrt{\frac{3.047^2}{2077.009}} = (0.29426, 0.59218)$$

p   The estimate is simply b, or 0.44322. A 99% confidence interval is the same procedure as in the previous question, but $t_{\alpha/2} = 3.169$ instead. Thus, the 99% interval is

$$0.44322 \pm 3.169\sqrt{\frac{3.047^2}{2077.009}} = (0.23135,\ 0.565509)$$

This interval is wider than the one in part **o**, as it should since it is a 99% interval.

q   The best estimate for σ^2 is s^2, which from the output (part **d** above) is $s^2 = (3.047)^2 = 9.284$.

r   The residuals are equal to the difference between y and $\hat{y}$ as can be seen below:

y	$\hat{y}$	residual
7.10	10.70	−3.60
11.00	11.94	−0.94
9.50	11.59	−2.09
9.20	11.72	−2.52
18.70	15.44	3.26
19.90	15.71	4.19
18.80	15.49	3.31
15.10	14.60	0.50
25.50	24.84	0.66
22.00	21.65	0.35
23.40	28.38	−4.98
26.70	24.84	1.86

s   A plot of the residuals versus the fitted values is shown below. It does not really appear that the constant variance assumption has been violated, as there is no increasing or decreasing pattern in the size of the residuals to be found in the plot. It is hard to make strong conclusions for such a small number of points, but everything looks okay, other than the fact that lower fitted values tend to have negative residuals, which may be a slight cause for concern.

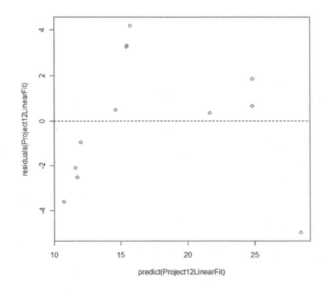

t   The following plot is a frequency histogram of the residuals. No, it does not appear that the errors are normally distributed, as the histogram is not mound-shaped.

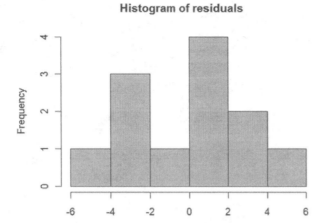

Histogram of residuals

u   The method needed to do this is not covered in Chapter 12.

v   As none of the standardized residuals are greater than 2 in absolute value, we can safely say that there are no major outliers, although point 11 is somewhat suspect.

w   A normal probability plot of the residuals is below.

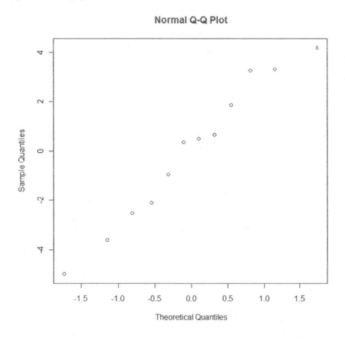

Normal Q-Q Plot

The pattern is linear, indicating that the residuals follow a normal distribution, as they should.

x   A 95% confidence interval for the mean of y when DBH $= x_0 = 10$ can be found using formula given in the text as:

$$\hat{y} \pm t_{\alpha/2}\sqrt{\text{MSE}\left[\frac{1}{n} + \frac{(x_0 - \bar{x})^2}{S_{xx}}\right]} = 12.87217 \pm 2.228\sqrt{(3.047)^2\left[\frac{1}{12} + \frac{(10 - 19.85833)^2}{2077.009}\right]}$$

$$= 12.87217 \pm 0.42392$$

$$= (12.448, 13.296)$$

y   A 95% prediction interval for the mean of y when DBH $= x_0 = 10$ can be found using the formula from the text as:

$$\hat{y} \pm t_{\alpha/2}\sqrt{\text{MSE}\left[1 + \frac{1}{n} + \frac{(x_0 - \bar{x})^2}{S_{xx}}\right]} = 12.87217 \pm 2.228\sqrt{(3.047)^2\left[1 + \frac{1}{12} + \frac{(10 - 19.85833)^2}{2077.009}\right]}$$

$$= 12.87217 \pm 7.21690$$

$$= (5.655, 20.089)$$

z   The confidence interval is narrower. As stated in the text, "the prediction interval is wider because of the extra variability in predicting the actual value of the response y."

Chapter 13: Multiple Regression Analysis

13.1 **a** When $x_2 = 2$, $E(y) = 3 + x_1 - 2(2) = x_1 - 1$.

When $x_2 = 1$, $E(y) = 3 + x_1 - 2(1) = x_1 + 1$.

When $x_2 = 0$, $E(y) = 3 + x_1 - 2(0) = x_1 + 3$.

These three straight lines are graphed below.

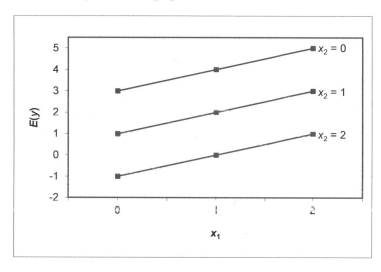

b Notice that the lines are parallel (they have the same slope).

13.3 **a** The hypothesis to be tested is $H_0: \beta_1 = \beta_2 = \beta_3 = 0$ versus H_a: at least one β_i differs from zero and the test statistic is

$$F = \frac{\text{MSR}}{\text{MSE}} = 57.44$$

which has an F distribution with $df_1 = k = 3$ and $df_2 = n - k - 1 = 15 - 3 - 1 = 11$. The rejection region for $\alpha = 0.05$, which is found in the upper tail of the F distribution, is $F > 3.59$ and H_0 is rejected. There is evidence that the model contributes information for the prediction of y.

b Use the fact that

$$F = \frac{R^2/k}{\left(1 - R^2\right)/\left[n - (k+1)\right]} = 57.44$$

Solving for R^2 you find

$$\frac{R^2/3}{\left(1 - R^2\right)/11} = 57.44$$

$$0.33R^2 = 5.2218 - 5.2218R^2$$

$$R^2 = \frac{5.2218}{5.5551} = 0.94$$

If $R^2 = 0.94$, the total sum of squares of deviations of the y-values about their mean has been reduced by 94% by using the linear model to predict y.

13.5 **a** The model is quadratic.

      b Since $R^2 = 0.815$, the sum of squares of deviations is reduced by 81.5% using the quadratic model rather than $\bar{y}$ to predict y.

      c The hypothesis to be tested is H_0: $\beta_1 = \beta_2 = 0$ versus H_a: at least one β_i differs from zero and the test statistic is

$$F = \frac{\text{MSR}}{\text{MSE}} = 37.37$$

      which has an F distribution with $df_1 = k = 2$ and $df_2 = n - k - 1 = 20 - 2 - 1 = 17$. The p-value given in the printout is P = 0.000 and H_0 is rejected. There is evidence that the model contributes information for the prediction of y.

13.7 **a** Refer to Exercise 13.5. When $x = 0$, the estimate of $E(Y)$ is

$$\hat{y} = 10.5638 + 4.4366(0) - 0.64754(0)^2 = 10.5638$$

      b Since $E(Y) = \beta_0 + \beta_1 x + \beta_2 x^2$, when $x = 0$, $E(Y) = \beta_0$. A test of $E(Y$ given $x = 0) = 0$ is equivalent to a test of H_0: $\beta_0 = 0$ versus H_a: $\beta_0 \neq 0$

      The individual t test is

$$t = \frac{b_0}{SE(b_0)} = \frac{10.5638}{0.6951} = 15.20$$

      with p-value = 0.000 and H_0 is rejected. The mean value of y differs from zero when $x = 0$.

13.9 **a** Rate of increase is measured by the slope of a line tangent to the curve; this line is given by an equation obtained as dy/dx, the derivative of y with respect to x. In particular,

$$\frac{dy}{dx} = \frac{d}{dx}\left(\beta_0 + \beta_1 x + \beta_2 x^2\right) = \beta_1 + 2\beta_2 x$$

      which has slope $2\beta_2$. If β_2 is negative, then the rate of increase is decreasing. Hence, the hypothesis of interest is H_0: $\beta_2 = 0$ versus H_a: $\beta_2 < 0$.

      b The individual t test is $t = -8.11$ as in Exercise 13.8b. However, the test is one-tailed, which means that the p-value is half of the amount given in the printout. That is, $p\text{-value} = \frac{1}{2}(0.000) = 0.000$.

      Hence, H_0 is again rejected. There is evidence to indicate a decreasing rate of increase.

13.11 Refer to Exercise 13.10.

      a From the printout, SSR = 234.96 and Total SS = S_{yy} = 236.02. Then

$$R^2 = \frac{\text{SSR}}{\text{Total SS}} = \frac{234.96}{236.02} = 0.9955, \text{ which agrees with the printout.}$$

      b–c Calculate $R^2(\text{adj}) = \left(1 - \dfrac{\text{MSE}}{\text{Total SS}/(n-1)}\right)100\% = \left(1 - \dfrac{0.35}{236.02/5}\right)100\% = 99.3\%$

      The value of $R^2(\text{adj})$ can be used to compare two or more regression models using different numbers of independent predictor variables. Since the value of $R^2(\text{adj}) = 99.3\%$ is just slightly larger than the value of $R^2(\text{adj}) = 95.7\%$ for the linear model, the quadratic model fits just slightly better.

13.13 **a** The values of $R^2(\text{adj})$ should be used to compare several different regression models. For the seven possible models given in the printout, the largest value of $R^2(\text{adj})$ is 29.7%, which occurs when x_2, x_3, and x_4 are included in the model. This agrees with the decision made in Exercise 13.12b.

      b Even using the best of all possible subsets of these four predictor variables, the model does not fit well. The experimenter may want to look for some other possible predictor variables for the taste score.

13.15 **a** The *MINITAB* printout fitting the model to the data is shown below. The least squares line is
$$\hat{y} = -8.177 + 0.292x_1 + 4.434x_2$$

Regression Analysis: y versus x1, x2
```
The regression equation is
y = - 8.18 + 0.292 x1 + 4.43 x2

Predictor    Coef   SE Coef      T       P
Constant   -8.177     4.206   -1.94   0.093
x1          0.2921    0.1357   2.15   0.068
x2          4.4343    0.8002   5.54   0.001
S = 3.30335   R-Sq = 82.3%   R-Sq(adj) = 77.2%

Analysis of Variance
Source           DF      SS      MS       F      P
Regression        2   355.22  177.61   16.28  0.002
Residual Error    7    76.38   10.91
Total             9   431.60

Source   DF   Seq SS
x1        1    20.16
x2        1   335.05
```

b The *F* test for the overall utility of the model is $F = 16.28$ with P = 0.002. The results are highly significant; the model contributes significant information for the prediction of *y*.

c To test the effect of advertising expenditure, the hypothesis of interest is
H_0: $\beta_2 = 0$ versus H_a: $\beta_2 \neq 0$ and the test statistic is $t = 5.54$ with *p*-value = 0.001. Since $\alpha = 0.01$, H_0 is rejected. We conclude that advertising expenditure contributes significant information for the prediction of *y*, given that capital investment is already in the model.

d From the *MINITAB* printout, R-Sq = 82.3%, which means that 82.3% of the total variation can be explained by the quadratic model. The model is very effective.

13.17 **a** Quantitative
    b Quantitative
    c Qualitative ($x_1 = 1$ if B; 0 otherwise $x_2 = 1$ if C; 0 otherwise)
    d Quantitative
    e Qualitative ($x_1 = 1$ if night shift; 0 otherwise)

13.19 **a** The variable x_2 must be the quantitative variable, since it appears as a quadratic term in the model. Qualitative variables appear only with exponent 1, although they may appear as the coefficient of another quantitative variable with exponent 2 or greater.

    b When $x_1 = 0$, $\hat{y} = 12.6 + 3.9x_2^2$ while when $x_1 = 1$,
$$\hat{y} = 12.6 + .54(1) - 1.2x_2 + 3.9x_2^2$$
$$= 13.14 - 1.2x_2 + 3.9x_2^2$$

c   The following graph shows the two parabolas.

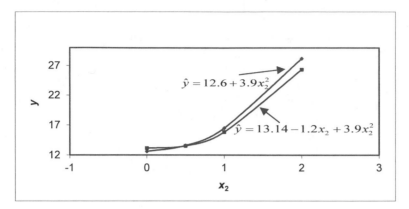

13.21 **a**   The model involves two variables and an interaction between the two:
$$E(Y) = \beta_0 + \beta_1 x_1 + \beta_2 x_2 + \beta_3 x_1 x_2$$
where $x_1 = 0$ if cotton; 1 if cucumber and $x_2 =$ temperature.

b   The *MINITAB* regression printout is shown below.

```
Regression Analysis: y versus x1, x2, x1x2
The regression equation is
y = 10.9 - 12.0 x1 + 1.13 x2 + 0.97 x1x2

Predictor     Coef   SE Coef      T      P
Constant     10.93     27.11   0.40  0.691
x1          -12.03     37.32  -0.32  0.750
x2           1.128     1.119   1.01  0.324
x1x2         0.969     1.531   0.63  0.533

S = 10.5737   R-Sq = 37.8%   R-Sq(adj) = 29.3%

Analysis of Variance

Source           DF       SS      MS      F      P
Regression        3   1492.8   497.6   4.45  0.014
Residual Error   22   2459.7   111.8
Total            25   3952.5

Source   DF   Seq SS
x1        1    928.6
x2        1    519.4
x1x2      1     44.8
```

c   Look first at the interaction effect. The interaction term is not significant ($t = 0.63$ with $P = 0.533$). That is, there is insufficient evidence to indicate that the effect of temperature on the number of eggs is different depending on the type of plant.

d   Since the interaction term is not significant, it could be removed and the data refit using the model
$$E(Y) = \beta_0 + \beta_1 x_1 + \beta_2 x_2$$
The *MINITAB* printout for the regression analysis with interaction removed is shown below.

```
Regression Analysis: y versus x1, x2
The regression equation is
y = - 1.5 + 11.4 x1 + 1.65 x2

Predictor     Coef   SE Coef      T      P
Constant     -1.54     18.39  -0.08  0.934
x1          11.442     4.113   2.78  0.011
x2          1.6456    0.7535   2.18  0.039

S = 10.4350   R-Sq = 36.6%   R-Sq(adj) = 31.1%
```

```
Analysis of Variance

Source             DF      SS      MS      F      P
Regression          2   1448.0   724.0   6.65   0.005
Residual Error     23   2504.5   108.9
Total              25   3952.5
```

Notice that both variables are significant, and that the overall model contributes significant information for the prediction of y. However, since $R^2 = 36.6\%$, there is still much variation that has not been accounted for. The model without interaction is better, but still does not fit as well as it might. There are perhaps other variables that the experimenter should explore.

e   Answers will vary.

13.23   The basic response equation for a specific type of bonding compound would be

$$E(Y) = \beta_0 + \beta_1 x_1 + \beta_2 x_1^2$$

Since the qualitative variable "bonding compound" is at two levels, one dummy variable is needed to incorporate this variable into the model. Define the dummy variable x_2 as follows:

$$x_2 = 1 \text{ if bonding compound 2}$$

$$= 0 \text{ otherwise}$$

The expanded model is now written as

$$E(Y) = \beta_0 + \beta_1 x_1 + \beta_2 x_1^2 + \beta_3 x_2 + \beta_4 x_1 x_2 + \beta_5 x_1^2 x_2$$

13.25   **a**   From the printout, the prediction equation is $\hat{y} = 8.585 + 3.8208x - 0.21663x^2$.

b R^2 is labelled "R-sq" or $R^2 = 0.944$. Hence, 94.4% of the total variation is accounted for by using x and x^2 in the model.

c   The hypothesis of interest is $H_0: \beta_1 = \beta_2 = 0$ versus H_a: at least one β_i differs from zero and the test statistic is $F = 33.44$ with p-value $= 0.003$. Hence, H_0 is rejected, and we conclude that the model contributes significant information for the prediction of y.

d   The hypothesis of interest is $H_0: \beta_2 = 0$ versus $H_a: \beta_2 \neq 0$ and the test statistic is $t = -4.93$ with p-value $= 0.008$. Hence, H_0 is rejected, and we conclude that the quadratic model provides a better fit to the data than a simple linear model.

e   The pattern of the diagnostic plots does not indicate any obvious violation of the regression assumptions.

13.27   The *MINITAB* printout for the data is shown below.

```
Regression Analysis: y versus x1, x2, x3, x1x2, x1x3
The regression equation is
y = 4.10 + 1.04 x1 + 3.53 x2 + 4.76 x3 - 0.00430 x1x2 - 0.00080 x1x3

Predictor        Coef    SE Coef       T       P
Constant       4.1000     0.3860   10.62   0.000
x1             1.0400     0.1164    8.94   0.000
x2             3.5300     0.5459    6.47   0.000
x3             4.7600     0.5459    8.72   0.000
x1x2        -0.004300    0.001646   -2.61   0.028
x1x3        -0.000800    0.001646   -0.49   0.639
S = 0.368028   R-Sq = 98.4%   R-Sq(adj) = 97.5%

Analysis of Variance
Source             DF      SS       MS        F       P
Regression          5   74.830   14.966   110.50   0.000
Residual Error      9    1.219    0.135
Total              14   76.049
```

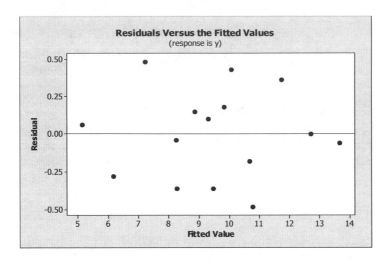

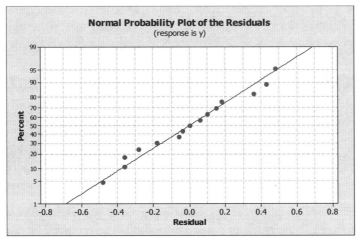

a   The model fits very well, with an overall $F = 110.50$ (P = 0.000) and $R^2 = 0.984$. The diagnostic plots indicate no violations of the regression assumptions.

b   The parameter estimates are found in the column marked "Coef" and the prediction equation is

$$\hat{y} = 4.10 + 1.04x_1 + 3.53x_2 + 4.76x_3 - 0.43x_1x_2 - 0.08x_1x_3$$

Using the dummy variables defined in Exercise 13.26, the coefficients can be combined to give the three lines that are graphed in the figure on the next page.

Men: $\hat{y} = 4.10 + 1.04x_1$
Children: $\hat{y} = 7.63 + 0.61x_1$
Women: $\hat{y} = 8.86 + 0.96x_1$

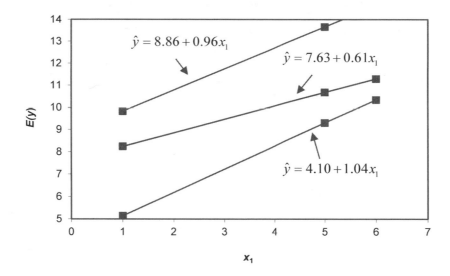

c The hypothesis of interest is $H_0: \beta_4 = 0$ versus $H_a: \beta_4 \neq 0$ and the test statistic is $t = -2.61$ with $P = 0.028$. Since this value is less than 0.05, the results are significant at the 5% level of significance and H_0 is rejected. There is a difference in the slopes.

d The hypothesis of interest is $H_0: \beta_4 = \beta_5 = 0$ H_a: at least one β_i differs from zero for $i = 4, 5$. Using the methods of Section 13.5 and the *MINITAB* printout above, $\text{SSE}_2 = 1.219$ with 9 degrees of freedom, while the printout below fit using the reduced model gives $\text{SSE}_1 = 2.265$ with 11 degrees of freedom.

Regression Analysis (reduced model): y versus x1, x2, x3
```
The regression equation is
y = 4.61 + 0.870 x1 + 2.24 x2 + 4.52 x3

Predictor      Coef   SE Coef       T       P
Constant     4.6100    0.3209   14.37   0.000
x1           0.87000   0.08285  10.50   0.000
x2           2.2400    0.2870    7.81   0.000
x3           4.5200    0.2870   15.75   0.000

S = 0.453772    R-Sq = 97.0%    R-Sq(adj) = 96.2%

Analysis of Variance
Source            DF       SS       MS        F       P
Regression         3   73.784   24.595   119.44   0.000
Residual Error    11    2.265    0.206
Total             14   76.049
```

Hence, the degrees of freedom associated with $\text{SSE}_1 - \text{SSE}_2 = 1.046$ is $11 - 9 = 2$. The test statistic is

$$F = \frac{(\text{SSE}_1 - \text{SSE}_2)/2}{\text{SSE}_2/9} = \frac{1.046/2}{0.1354} = 3.86$$

The rejection region with $\alpha = 0.05$ is $F > F_{0.05} = 4.26$ (with 2 and 9 *df*) and H_0 is not rejected. The interaction terms in the model are not significant. The experimenter should consider eliminating these terms from the model.

e Answers will vary.

13.29 **a** The model is $Y = \beta_0 + \beta_1 x_1 + \beta_2 x_2 + \beta_3 x_1^2 + \beta_4 x_1 x_2 + \beta_5 x_1^2 x_2 + \varepsilon$ and the *MINITAB* printout is shown below.

```
Regression Analysis: y versus x1, x2, x1sq, x1x2, x1sqx2
The regression equation is
y = 4.5 + 6.39 x1 - 50.9 x2 + 0.132 x1sq + 17.1 x1x2 - 0.502 x1sqx2

Predictor      Coef   SE Coef       T       P
Constant       4.51     42.24    0.11   0.916
x1            6.394     5.777    1.11   0.275
x2           -50.85     56.21   -0.90   0.371
x1sq         0.1318    0.1687    0.78   0.439
x1x2         17.064     7.101    2.40   0.021
x1sqx2      -0.5025    0.1992   -2.52   0.016
S = 71.6891   R-Sq = 76.8%   R-Sq(adj) = 73.8%

Analysis of Variance
Source            DF       SS      MS       F       P
Regression         5   664164  132833   25.85   0.000
Residual Error    39   200434    5139
Total             44   864598
```

b The fitted prediction model uses the coefficients given in the column marked "Coef" in the printout:
$$\hat{y} = 4.51 + 6.394 x_1 - 50.85 x_2 + 17.064 x_1 x_2 + .1318 x_1^2 - .5025 x_1^2 x_2$$

The F test for the model's utility is $F = 25.85$ with P = 0.000 and $R^2 = 0.768$. The model fits quite well.

c If the dolphin is female, $x_2 = 0$ and the prediction equation becomes $\hat{y} = 4.51 + 6.394 x_1 + 0.1318 x_1^2$.

d If the dolphin is male, $x_2 = 1$ and the prediction equation becomes $\hat{y} = -46.34 + 23.458 x_1 - 0.3707 x_1^2$.

e The hypothesis of interest is $H_0: \beta_4 = 0$ versus $H_a: \beta_4 \neq 0$ and the test statistic is $t = 0.78$ with p-value $= 0.439$. H_0 is not rejected and we conclude that the quadratic term is not important in predicting mercury concentration for female dolphins.

f Answers will vary from student to student.

13.31 **a–b** The data is plotted below. It appears to be a curvilinear relationship, which could be described using the quadratic model $Y = \beta_0 + \beta_1 x + \beta_2 x^2 + \varepsilon$.

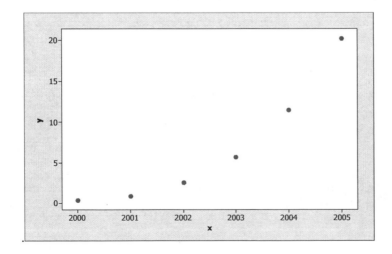

c   The *MINITAB* printout is shown below.

```
Regression Analysis: y versus x, x_sq
The regression equation is
y = 4114749 - 4113 x + 1.03 x_sq

Predictor      Coef    SE Coef       T       P
Constant    4114749     343582   11.98   0.001
x           -4113.4      343.2  -11.99   0.001
x_sq        1.02804    0.08568   12.00   0.001
S = 0.523521   R-Sq = 99.7%    R-Sq(adj) = 99.5%

Analysis of Variance
Source          DF       SS      MS       F       P
Regression       2   297.16  148.58  542.11   0.000
Residual Error   3     0.82    0.27
Total            5   297.98
```

d   The hypothesis of interest is H_0: $\beta_1 = \beta_2 = 0$ and the test statistic is $F = 542.11$ with p-value $= 0.000$. H_0 is rejected and we conclude that the model provides valuable information for the prediction of y.

e $R^2 = 0.997$. Hence, 99.7% of the total variation is accounted for by using x and x^2 in the model.

f   The residual plots are shown below. There is no reason to doubt the validity of the regression assumptions.

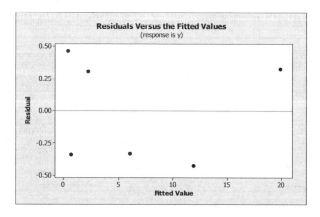

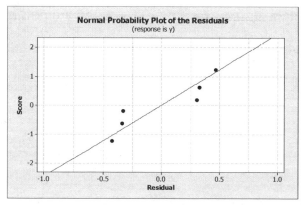

13.33   **a–b**   The data from the table are the values of y, entered into one column of the spreadsheet. The values of x_1 and x_2 are entered using the coding in the exercise, and the values of x_1x_2 are found by multiplying the appropriate values of x_1 and x_2 together. From the printout, the least squares prediction equation is
$$\hat{y} = 1.1473 - 0.2508x_1 + 0.0777x_2 + 0.3058x_1x_2$$

    c   The interaction is not significant ($t = 0.92$ with p-value $= 0.365$).

d Neither main effect is significant ($t = -1.37$ and $t = 0.29$ with p-values of 0.180 and 0.771, respectively.)

e The model does not fit well ($F = 1.49$ with p-value $= 0.235$; $R^2 = 0.119$).

13.35 **a** $R^2 = 0.998$. Hence, 99.8% of the total variation is accounted for by using x and x^2 in the model.

b The hypothesis of interest is H_0: $\beta_1 = \beta_2 = 0$ and the test statistic is $F = 1470.84$ with p-value $= 0.000$. H_0 is rejected and we conclude that the model provides valuable information for the prediction of y.

c When $x_2 = 4$,

$$\hat{y} = -28.3906 + 1.463x_1 + 3.8446(4)$$
$$\hat{y} = -13.0122 + 1.463x_1$$

d When $x_1 = 25, x_2 = 3$,

$$\hat{y} = -28.3906 + 1.46306(25) + 3.8446(3) = 19.7197$$

e The diagnostic plots do not show any violations of the regression assumptions.

13.37 **a** $R^2 = 0.922$. Hence, 92.2% of the total variation is accounted for by using $x_1, x_2,$ and x_3 in the model.

b The hypothesis of interest is H_0: $\beta_1 = \beta_2 = \beta_3 = 0$ and the test statistic is $F = 23.78$ with p-value $= 0.001$. H_0 is rejected and we conclude that the model provides valuable information for the prediction of y.

c–d The hypothesis of interest is H_0: $\beta_3 = 0$ and the test statistic is $t = -0.64$ with p-value $= 0.543$. H_0 is not rejected and we conclude that independent variable x_3 is not useful in predicting y.

Case Study: "Buying Up the Canadian Economy"— Another Look

1   The three figures shown below represent the data with a linear, quadratic, and cubic model fitted to them.

Linear Model

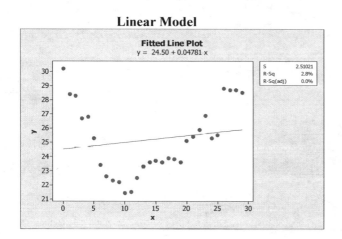

Quadratic Model

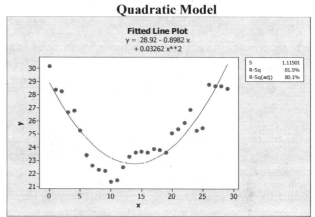

Cubic Model

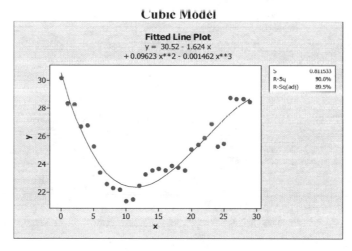

2   The residuals using the fitted linear regression model are found by calculating $y_i - \hat{y}_i$ for each of the 30 values of y. These values are plotted in the figure below. Notice the periodic trend to the residuals, indicating that a higher order, possibly quadratic or cubic model might be useful.

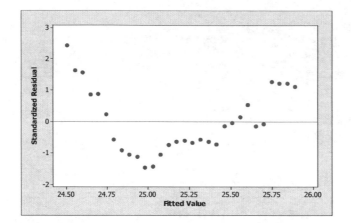

3   When the linear model is fit, $R^2 = 2.8\%$ while $R^2 = 81.5\%$ for the quadratic fit. The quadratic term is highly significant ($t = 7.45$ with p-value $= 0.000$) and the residuals from the quadratic fit are plotted in the figure below.

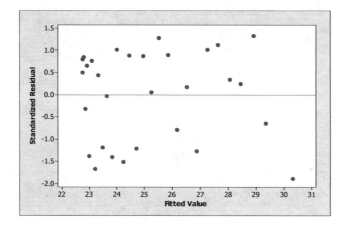

4   When the cubic model is fit, $R^2 = 90.6\%$ —higher than R^2 for the quadratic model. Also, for the cubic model, $R^2(\text{adj}) = 89.5\%$ compared to $R^2(\text{adj}) = 80.1\%$ for the quadratic model. The cubic term is significant ($t = -5$ with p-value $= 0$). The cubic model is the best of the three choices.

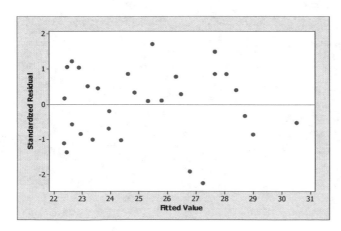

Project 13: Aspen Mixedwood Forests in Canada, Part 2

a   Scatterplots of all the variables are shown below.

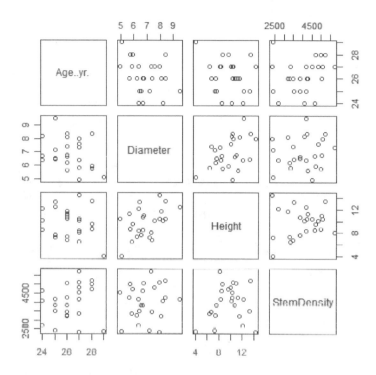

It is difficult to say whether linear regression would be useful in this case, based solely on these plots.

b   Next, we will model each variable separately.

Fit 1: Dependent: Age, Independent: Diameter

```
              Estimate Std. Error t value Pr(>|t|)
(Intercept)   28.5331     1.6368   17.432   9.44e-15
Diameter      -0.3311     0.2333   -1.419    0.169
Residual standard error: 1.304 on 23 degrees of freedom
Multiple R-squared: 0.08051,    Adjusted R-squared: 0.04054
F-statistic: 2.014 on 1 and 23 DF,  p-value: 0.1693
```

Fit 2: Dependent: Age, Independent: Height

```
              Estimate Std. Error t value Pr(>|t|)
(Intercept)   27.3704     1.0982   24.922   <2e-16
Height        -0.1160     0.1094   -1.061    0.3
Residual standard error: 1.328 on 23 degrees of freedom
Multiple R-squared: 0.04665,    Adjusted R-squared: 0.005196
F-statistic: 1.125 on 1 and 23 DF,  p-value: 0.2998
```

Fit 3: Dependent: Age, Independent: Stem Density

```
              Estimate   Std. Error t value  Pr(>|t|)
(Intercept)   2.508e+01  1.175e+00   21.347   <2e-16
StemDensity   2.893e-04  2.855e-04    1.013    0.322
Residual standard error: 1.331 on 23 degrees of freedom
Multiple R-squared: 0.04272,    Adjusted R-squared: 0.001102
F-statistic: 1.026 on 1 and 23 DF,  p-value: 0.3215
```

In all three cases, the slope of the regression is not significant, judging from the high *p*-values. The *p*-values for the overall *F* test are also all high. So, taking each variable separately, linear regression is not appropriate for modelling the dependent variable *y*.

c   A model with all possible interactions (including a 3-way interaction) is fit, and the results are below.

```
                          Estimate  Std. Error  t value  Pr(>|t|)
(Intercept)               6.059e+01  2.025e+01    2.992    0.0082
Diameter                 -5.064e+00  2.946e+00   -1.719    0.1038
Height                   -4.342e+00  2.288e+00   -1.898    0.0748
StemDensity              -4.010e-03  6.654e-03   -0.603    0.5547
Diameter:Height           5.880e-01  3.079e-01    1.910    0.0732
Diameter:StemDensity      5.755e-04  9.257e-04    0.622    0.5424
Height:StemDensity        6.794e-04  7.062e-04    0.962    0.3495
Diameter:Height:StemDensity -8.667e-05 9.359e-05  -0.926    0.3674
Residual standard error: 1.068 on 17 degrees of freedom
Multiple R-squared: 0.544,      Adjusted R-squared: 0.3562
F-statistic: 2.897 on 7 and 17 DF,  p-value: 0.03462
```

The question asks that we use the overall *F* test to assess the merits of the model. In this case, since the *p*-value for the *F*-statistic is 0.03462, and since the *p*-value is less than 5% significance, we can conclude that some of the parameters are relevant/significant.

d   We can conduct a separate *t* test for each independent variable to determine if they are significant. The *p*-values are given in the table of the preceding question. For all three independent variables, the *p*-value is greater than 5% significance, and so we would not reject the hypothesis that their regression parameters are equal to 0. The same conclusion can be drawn if we look at the *p*-values for each independent variable separately, as we did in question **b**.

e   In this case, we obtain:

```
                 Estimate  Std. Error  t value  Pr(>|t|)
(Intercept)      44.83589   5.96431     7.517    2.2e-07
Diameter         -2.74817   0.91615    -3.000    0.00683
Height           -1.61817   0.56865    -2.846    0.00968
Diameter:Height   0.23574   0.08436     2.794    0.01086
Residual standard error: 1.16 on 21 degrees of freedom
Multiple R-squared: 0.3364,      Adjusted R-squared: 0.2416
F-statistic: 3.549 on 3 and 21 DF,  p-value: 0.03199
```

This fit is better than the one from part **c**. The *p*-values for all terms are very low, and therefore significant. The residual standard error and the *p*-value for the *F*-Statistic are comparable to the fit in part **c**, but based on less independent variables. As a whole, the fit here is superior.

f   From part **e** above, $\beta_1 = -2.74817$, $\beta_2 = -1.61817$, and $\beta_3 = 0.23574$. In the absence of interaction terms, each individual parameter would represent the change in the response for a one unit increase in that independent variable, if all of the other variables were held constant. But with interaction terms, such an interpretation is not meaningful. Thus, we interpret them simply as parameters used for this particular model.

g   Yes, the quadratic term in part **e** seems to be very useful. The *p*-value for the *t* test for β_3 is 0.01086, which implies that it is significant (it is less than 5%). The R^2 value is somewhat low, but reasonable. The residual standard error and the *p*-value for the *F*-statistic are comparable to the regression from part **c**, and are decent.

h   The residual plots on the next page indicate no serious violation of the regression model assumptions.

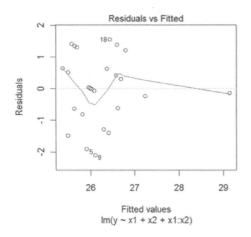

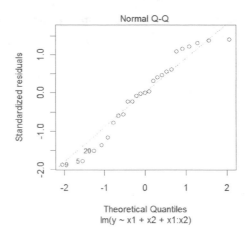

i	Diameter at Breast Height makes the most significant contribution, since it has the lowest *p*-value for its *t* test.

j	Yes, the interaction term is certainly significant, judging from its low *p*-value (0.01086).

k	The results from the regression are shown below.

```
                   Estimate Std. Error t value Pr(>|t|)
(Intercept)        46.46127    6.69899   6.936 9.82e-07
Diameter           -3.36046    1.42120  -2.365   0.0283
Height             -1.46794    0.63521  -2.311   0.0316
I(Height^2)        -0.02775    0.04865  -0.570   0.5748
Diameter:Height     0.29320    0.13229   2.216   0.0384
Residual standard error: 1.179 on 20 degrees of freedom
Multiple R-squared: 0.347,     Adjusted R-squared: 0.2164
F-statistic: 2.657 on 4 and 20 DF,  p-value: 0.063
```

The additional quadratic term is not significant, as the *p*-value is 0.5748. This term should not be added to the model.

l	The best model is the one from part **e**. Note that Stem Density is not an independent variable for this model, and so the value 4900 is ignored. Using statistical software, we find that a point prediction for *y* (Age) is 26.86701 when DBH is 8 and Canopy Height is 15. A 95% prediction interval is found to be (24.04376, 29.69027).

m	Adding Stem Density produces the following fit:

```
                   Estimate Std. Error t value Pr(>|t|)
(Intercept)       46.9099595  5.3251686   8.809 2.55e-08
Diameter          -3.4047892  0.8465425  -4.022 0.000668
Height            -2.0292136  0.5258319  -3.859 0.000978
StemDensity        0.0006109  0.0002320   2.633 0.015944
Diameter:Height    0.2943709  0.0777478   3.786 0.001159
Residual standard error: 1.024 on 20 degrees of freedom
Multiple R-squared: 0.5072,     Adjusted R-squared: 0.4087
F-statistic: 5.147 on 4 and 20 DF,  p-value: 0.005127

Analysis of Variance Table
Model 1: y ~ x1 + x2 + x1:x2
Model 2: y ~ x1 + x2 + x1:x2 + x3
  Res.Df    RSS Df Sum of Sq      F  Pr(>F)
1     21 28.243
2     20 20.973  1     7.270 6.9328 0.01594
With an F-value of 6.9328, the null hypothesis is rejected.
```

A partial F test on x_3 yields a p-value of 0.01594, exactly the same as the p-value for the t test for that variable (as it must when the reduced model is exactly one variable less). And so, at 5% significance, the reduced model is deemed to be inadequate.

Chapter 14: Analysis of Categorical Data

14.1 See Section 14.1 of the text.

14.3 For a test of specified cell probabilities, the degrees of freedom are $k - 1$. Use Table 5, Appendix I:

  a $df = 6$; $\chi^2_{0.05} = 12.59$; reject H_0 if $\chi^2 > 12.59$

  b $df = 9$; $\chi^2_{0.01} = 21.666$; reject H_0 if $\chi^2 > 21.666$

  c $df = 13$; $\chi^2_{0.005} = 29.8194$; reject H_0 if $\chi^2 > 29.8194$

  d $df = 2$; $\chi^2_{0.01} = 9.21$; reject H_0 if $\chi^2 > 9.21$

14.5 **a**   Three hundred responses were each classified into one of five categories. The objective is to determine whether or not one category is preferred over another. To see if the five categories are equally likely to occur, the hypothesis of interest is

$$H_0: \ p_1 = p_2 = p_3 = p_4 = p_5 - \frac{1}{5}$$

  versus the alternative that at least one of the cell probabilities is different from 1/5.

  b   The number of degrees of freedom is equal to the number of cells, k, less one degree of freedom for each linearly independent restriction placed on $p_1, p_2, \ldots, p_k$. For this exercise, $k = 5$ and one degree of freedom is lost because of the restriction that

$$\Sigma p_i = 1$$

  Hence, χ^2 has $k - 1 = 4$ degrees of freedom.

  c   The rejection region for this test is located in the upper tail of the chi-square distribution with $df = 4$. From Table 5, Appendix I, the appropriate upper-tailed rejection region is $\chi^2 > \chi^2_{0.05} = 9.4877$.

  d   The test statistic is

$$\chi^2 = \sum \frac{(O_i - E_i)^2}{E_i}$$

  which, when n is large, possesses an approximate chi-square distribution in repeated sampling. The values of O_i are the actual counts *observed* in the experiment, and

$$E_i = np_i = 300(1/5) = 60$$

  A table of observed and expected cell counts follows:

Category	1	2	3	4	5
O_i	47	63	74	51	65
E_i	60	60	60	60	60

  Then

$$\chi^2 = \frac{(47 - 60)^2}{60} + \frac{(63 - 60)^2}{60} + \frac{(74 - 60)^2}{60} + \frac{(51 - 60)^2}{60} + \frac{(65 - 60)^2}{60}$$

$$= \frac{480}{60} = 8.00$$

  e   Since the observed value of χ^2 does not fall in the rejection region, we cannot conclude that there is a difference in the preference for the five categories.

14.7 One thousand cars were each classified according to the lane which they occupied (one through four). If no lane is preferred over another, the probability that a car will be driven in lane i, $i = 1, 2, 3, 4$ is 1/4. The null hypothesis is then

$$H_0: \ p_1 = p_2 = p_3 = p_4 = \frac{1}{4}$$

and the test statistic is

$$\chi^2 = \sum \frac{(O_i - E_i)^2}{E_i}$$

with $E_i = np_i = 1000(1/4) = 250$ for $i = 1, 2, 3, 4$. A table of observed and expected cell counts follows:

Lane	1	2	3	4
O_i	294	276	238	192
E_i	250	250	250	250

Then

$$\chi^2 = \frac{(294-250)^2}{250} + \frac{(276-250)^2}{250} + \frac{(238-250)^2}{250} + \frac{(192-250)^2}{250}$$

$$= \frac{6120}{250} = 24.48$$

The rejection region with $k - 1 = 3$ *df* is $\chi^2 > \chi^2_{0.05} = 7.81$. Since the observed value of χ^2 falls in the rejection region, we reject H_0. There is a difference in preference for the four lanes.

14.9 If the frequency of occurrence of a heart attack is the same for each day of the week, then when a heart attack occurs, the probability that it falls in one cell (day) is the same as for any other cell (day). Hence,

$$H_0: \ p_1 = p_2 = \cdots = p_7 = \frac{1}{7} \quad \text{versus} \quad H_a: \text{at least one } p_i \text{ is different from the others}$$

or equivalently, H_a: $p_i \neq p_j$ for some pair $i \neq j$

Since $n = 200$, $E_i = np_i = 200(1/7) = 28.571429$ and the test statistic is

$$\chi^2 = \frac{(24 - 28.571429)^2}{28.571429} + \cdots + \frac{(29 - 28.571429)^2}{28.571429} = \frac{103.71429}{28.571429} = 3.63$$

The degrees of freedom for this test of specified cell probabilities is $k - 1 = 7 - 1 = 6$ and the upper tailed rejection region is

$$\chi^2 > \chi^2_{0.05} = 12.59$$

H_0 is not rejected. There is insufficient evidence to indicate a difference in frequency of occurrence from day to day.

14.11 Similar to previous exercises. The hypothesis to be tested is

$$H_0: \ p_1 = p_2 = \cdots = p_{12} = \frac{1}{12} \quad \text{versus} \quad H_a: \text{at least one } p_i \text{ is different from the others}$$

with $E_i = np_i = 400(1/12) = 33.333$

The test statistic is

$$\chi^2 = \frac{(38 - 33.33)^2}{33.33} + \cdots + \frac{(35 - 33.33)^2}{33.33} = 13.58$$

The upper tailed rejection region is with $\alpha = 0.05$ and $k - 1 = 11$ *df* is $\chi^2 > \chi^2_{0.05} = 19.675$. The null hypothesis is not rejected and we cannot conclude that the proportion of cases varies from month to month.

14.13 It is necessary to determine whether proportions given by Mars Inc. are correct. The null hypothesis to be tested is H_0: $p_1 = 0.13$; $p_2 = 0.14$; $p_3 = 0.13$; $p_4 = 0.24$; $p_5 = 0.20$; $p_6 = 0.16$ against the alternative that at least one of these probabilities is incorrect. A table of observed and expected cell counts follows:

Colour	Brown	Yellow	Red	Blue	Orange	Green
O_i	70	72	61	118	108	85
E_i	66.82	71.96	66.82	123.36	102.80	82.24

The test statistic is

$$\chi^2 = \frac{(70 - 66.82)^2}{66.82} + \frac{(72 - 71.96)^2}{71.96} + \cdots + \frac{(85 - 82.24)^2}{82.24} = 1.247$$

The number of degrees of freedom is $k - 1 = 5$ and, since the observed value of $\chi^2 = 1.247$ is less than $\chi^2_{0.10} = 9.24$, the p-value is greater than 0.10 and the results are not significant. We conclude that the proportions reported by Mars Inc. are substantiated by our sample.

14.15 It is necessary to determine whether admission rates differ from the previously reported rates. A table of observed and expected cell counts follows:

	Unconditional	Trial	Refused	Totals
O_i	329	43	128	500
E_i	300	25	175	500

The null hypothesis to be tested is H_0: $p_1 = 0.60$; $p_2 = 0.05$; $p_3 = 0.35$ against the alternative that at least one of these probabilities is incorrect. The test statistic is

$$\chi^2 = \frac{(329 - 300)^2}{300} + \frac{(43 - 25)^2}{25} + \frac{(128 - 175)^2}{175} = 28.386$$

The number of degrees of freedom is $k - 1 = 2$ and the rejection region $\chi^2 > \chi^2_{0.05} = 5.99$. The null hypothesis is rejected, and we conclude that there has been a departure from previous admission rates. Notice that the percentage of unconditional admissions has risen slightly, the number of conditional admissions has increased, and the percentage refused admission has decreased at the expense of the first two categories.

14.17 Refer to Section 14.4 of the text. For a 3×5 contingency table with $r = 3$ and $c = 5$, there are $(r - 1)(c - 1) = (2)(4) = 8$ degrees of freedom.

14.19 The hypotheses to be tested are

H_0: opinion groups are independent of gender

H_a: opinion groups are dependent on gender

and the test statistic is the chi-square statistic given in the printout as $\chi^2 = 18.352$ with p-value $= 0.000$. Because of the small p-value, the results are highly significant, and H_0 is rejected. There is evidence of a dependence between opinion group and gender. The conditional distributions of the three groups for males and females are shown in the following table.

	Group 1	Group 2	Group 3	Total
Males	$\frac{37}{158} = 0.23$	$\frac{49}{158} = 0.31$	$\frac{72}{158} = 0.46$	1.00
Females	$\frac{7}{88} = 0.08$	$\frac{50}{88} = 0.57$	$\frac{31}{88} = 0.35$	1.00

You can see that men tend to favour the group 3 opinion, while almost 60% of the women favour the group 2 opinion. The group 1 opinion contains a very small proportion of the women, but almost 25% of the men.

14.21 **a** The hypothesis of independence between attachment pattern and child care time is tested using the chi-square statistic. The contingency table, including column and row totals and the estimated expected cell counts, follows.

	Child Care			
Attachment	Low	Moderate	High	**Total**
Secure	24 (24.09)	35 (30.97)	5 (8.95)	64
Anxious	11 (10.91)	10 (14.03)	8 (4.05)	29
Total	111	51	297	459

The test statistic is

$$\chi^2 = \frac{(24-24.09)^2}{24.09} + \frac{(35-30.97)^2}{30.97} + \cdots + \frac{(8-4.05)^2}{4.05} = 7.267$$

and the rejection region is $\chi^2 > \chi^2_{0.05} = 5.99$ with 2 *df*. H_0 is rejected. There is evidence of a dependence between attachment pattern and child care time.

b The value $\chi^2 = 7.267$ is between $\chi^2_{0.05}$ and $\chi^2_{0.025}$ so that $0.025 < p$-value < 0.05. The results are significant.

14.23 **a** The hypothesis of independence between type of pharmacy and waiting time is tested using the chi-square statistic. The contingency table, including column and row totals and the estimated expected cell counts, follows.

	Waiting Time				
Pharmacy	15 minutes or less	16–20 minutes	More than 20 min	Other	**Total**
Supermarket	75 (83.14)	44 (27.86)	21 (24.86)	10 (14.14)	150
Drugstore	119 (110.86)	21 (37.14)	37 (33.14)	23 (18.86)	200
Total	194	65	58	33	350

The test statistic is

$$\chi^2 = \frac{(75-83.14)^2}{83.14} + \frac{(44-27.86)^2}{27.86} + \cdots + \frac{(23-18.86)^2}{18.86} = 20.937$$

and the rejection region is $\chi^2 > \chi^2_{0.01} = 11.3449$ with 3 *df*. H_0 is rejected. There is evidence of a difference in waiting times between pharmacies in supermarkets and drugstores.

b The contingency table is collapsed to include only "more than 20 minutes" and "not more than 20 minutes." The table is shown below, along with the estimated expected cell counts.

	Waiting Time		
Pharmacy	More than 20 min	Other	**Total**
Superstore	21 (24.86)	129 (125.14)	150
Drugstore	37 (33.14)	163 (166.86)	200
Total	58	292	350

The test statistic is

$$\chi^2 = \frac{(21-24.86)^2}{24.86} + \cdots + \frac{(163-166.86)^2}{166.86} = 1.255$$

and the rejection region is $\chi^2 > \chi^2_{0.01} = 6.63$ with 1 *df*. H_0 is not rejected. There is insufficient evidence to indicate a difference in waiting times between pharmacies in supermarkets and drugstores.

14.25 **a** The hypothesis of independence between salary and number of workdays at home is tested using the chi-square statistic. The contingency table, including column and row totals and the estimated expected cell counts, generated by *MINITAB*, follows.

Chi-Square Test: Less than one, At least one, not all, All at home
```
Expected counts are printed below observed counts
Chi-Square contributions are printed below expected counts

                      At
                   least
           Less     one,     All
           than      not      at
           one       all    home   Total
      1      38       16      14      68
           36.27    21.08   10.65
           0.083    1.224   1.051

      2      54       26      12      92
           49.07    28.52   14.41
           0.496    0.223   0.404

      3      35       22       9      66
           35.20    20.46   10.34
           0.001    0.116   0.174

      4      33       29      12      74
           39.47    22.94   11.59
           1.060    1.601   0.014

Total     160       93      47     300

Chi-Sq = 6.447, DF = 6, P-Value = 0.375
```

The test statistic is

$$\chi^2 = \frac{(38-36.27)^2}{36.27} + \frac{(16-21.08)^2}{21.08} + \cdots + \frac{(12-11.59)^2}{11.59} = 6.447$$

and the rejection region with $\alpha = 0.05$ and $df = 3(2) = 6$ is $\chi^2 > \chi^2_{0.05} = 12.59$ and the null hypothesis is not rejected. There is insufficient evidence to indicate that salary is dependent on the number of workdays spent at home.

b The observed value of the test statistic, $\chi^2 = 6.447$, is less than $\chi^2_{0.10} = 10.6446$ so that the *p*-value is more than 0.10. This would confirm the non-rejection of the null hypothesis from part **a**.

14.27 Similar to previous exercises, except that the number of observations per row was selected prior to the experiment. The test procedure is identical to that used for an $r \times c$ contingency table. The contingency table, including column and row totals and the estimated expected cell counts, is presented on the next page.

		Category		
Population	1	2	3	**Total**
1	108 (102.33)	52 (47.33)	40 (50.33)	200
2	87 (102.33)	51 (47.33)	62 (50.33)	200
3	112 (102.33)	39 (47.33)	49 (50.33)	200
Total	307	142	151	600

a   The test statistic is

$$\chi^2 = \frac{(108-102.33)^2}{102.33} + \frac{(52-47.33)^2}{47.33} + \cdots + \frac{(49-50.33)^2}{50.33} = 10.597$$

using calculator accuracy.

b   With $(r-1)(c-1) = 4$ *df* and $\alpha = 0.01,$ the rejection region is $\chi^2 > 13.2767.$

c   The null hypothesis is not rejected. There is insufficient evidence to indicate that the proportions depend upon the population from which they are drawn.

d   Since the observed value, $\chi^2 = 10.597,$ falls between $\chi^2_{0.05}$ and $\chi^2_{0.025},$ $0.025 < p$-value $< 0.05.$

14.29   Because a set number of Canadian children in each sub-population were each fixed at 1000, we have a contingency table with fixed rows. The table, with estimated expected cell counts appearing in parentheses, follows.

	Overweight/Obese	**Not Overweight/Obese**	**Total**
White	189 (200)	811 (800)	1000
Black	301 (200)	699 (800)	1000
Southeast/East Asian	117 (200)	883 (800)	1000
Off-reserves Aboriginal	231 (200)	769 (800)	1000
Other	162 (200)	838 (800)	1000
Total	1000	4000	5000

The test statistic is

$$\chi^2 = \frac{(189-200)^2}{200} + \frac{(301-200)^2}{200} + \cdots + \frac{(838-800)^2}{800} = 122.6$$

and the rejection region with 4 *df* is $\chi^2 > 13.2767.$ H_0 is rejected and we conclude that the incidence of overweight/obese children is dependent on the ethnic origin.

14.31   **a**   The number of people in each of the three income categories was chosen in advance; each of these populations represents a multinomial population in which we measure education levels.

      b   The 4×3 contingency table is analyzed as in previous exercises. The *MINITAB* printout on the next page shows the observed and estimated expected cell counts, the test statistic and its associated *p*-value.

Chi-Square Test: 70-99K, 100-249K, 250K or more
```
Expected counts are printed below observed counts
Chi-Square contributions are printed below expected counts

                          250K
                           or
         70-99K  100-249K  more   Total
    1      32       20      23      75
         25.00    25.00   25.00
          1.960    1.000   0.160

    2      13       16       1      30
         10.00    10.00   10.00
          0.900    3.600   8.100

    3      43       51      60     154
         51.33    51.33   51.33
          1.353    0.002   1.463

    4      12       13      16      41
         13.67    13.67   13.67
          0.203    0.033   0.398

Total    100      100     100     300

Chi-Sq = 19.172, DF = 6, P-Value = 0.004
```

The results are significant at the 1% level (p-value $= 0.004$) and we conclude that there is a difference in the level of wealth depending on educational attainment.

c Answers will vary from student to student.

14.33 The number of observations per column were selected prior to the experiment. The test procedure is identical to that used for an $r \times c$ contingency table. The contingency table, including column and row totals and the estimated expected cell counts, follows.

Family Members	Type			
	Apartment	Duplex	Single residence	Total
1	8 (9.67)	20 (9.67)	1 (9.67)	29
2	16 (11)	8 (11)	9 (11)	33
3	10 (11.33)	10 (11.33)	14 (11.33)	34
4 or more	6 (8)	2 (8)	16 (8)	24
Total	40	40	40	120

The test statistic is

$$\chi^2 = \frac{(8-9.67)^2}{9.67} + \frac{(20-9.67)^2}{9.67} + \cdots + \frac{(16-8)^2}{8} = 36.499$$

using computer accuracy. With $(r-1)(c-1) = 6$ df and $\alpha = 0.01$, the rejection region is $\chi^2 > 16.8119$.

The null hypothesis is rejected. There is sufficient evidence to indicate that family size is dependent on type of family residence. It appears that as the family size increases, it is more likely that people will live in single residences.

14.35 a The number of observations per column were selected prior to the experiment. The test procedure is identical to that used for an $r \times c$ contingency table. The contingency table generated by *MINITAB*, including column and row totals and the expected cell counts, is presented on the next page.

Chi-Square Test: Affiliated, Not Affiliated
```
Expected counts are printed below observed counts
Chi-Square contributions are printed below expected counts

                        Not
         Affiliated  Affiliated  Total
    1           47         152    199
             56.86      142.14
             1.709       0.684

    2           53          98    151
             43.14      107.86
             2.252       0.901

Total          100         250    350
Chi-Sq = 5.545, DF = 1, P-Value = 0.019
```

The observed value of the test statistic is $\chi^2 = 5.545$ with p-value $= 0.019$ and H_0 is rejected at the 5% level of significance. There is sufficient evidence to indicate that the proportion of young adults who believe that evolution is the best explanation for the development of human life differs depending on religious affiliation.

b The percentage who believe that evolution is the best explanation for the development of human life is higher for those who do not have a religious affiliation.

14.37 To test for homogeneity of the four binomial populations, we use chi-square statistic and the 2×4 contingency table shown below.

	British Columbia	Alberta	Ontario	Quebec	Total
Participate	46	63	108	121	338
	(63.32)	(78.63)	(97.88)	(97.88)	
Do not participate	149	178	192	179	698
	(131.38)	(162.37)	(202.12)	(202.12)	
Total	195	241	300	300	1036

The test statistic is

$$\chi^2 = \frac{(46 - 63.62)^2}{63.62} + \frac{(63 - 78.63)^2}{78.63} + \cdots + \frac{(179 - 202.12)^2}{202.12} = 21.51$$

With $df = 3$, the p-value is less than 0.005 and H_0 is rejected. There is a difference in the proportions for the four provinces. The difference can be seen by considering the proportion of people participating in each of the four provinces:

	British Columbia	Alberta	Ontario	Quebec
Participate	$\frac{46}{195} = 0.24$	$\frac{63}{241} = 0.26$	$\frac{108}{300} = 0.36$	$\frac{121}{300} = 0.40$

14.39 a To test for homogeneity of the five binomial populations, we use chi-square statistic. The contingency table generated by *MINITAB* is shown on the next page.

Chi-Square Test: Britain, France, Italy, Spain, Germany
```
Expected counts are printed below observed counts
Chi-Square contributions are printed below expected counts

       Britain  France   Italy   Spain  Germany   Total
  1        475     485     531     660      562    2713
         542.60  542.60  542.60  542.60   542.60
          8.422   6.115   0.248  25.401    0.694

  2        525     515     469     340      438    2287
         457.40  457.40  457.40  457.40   457.40
          9.991   7.254   0.294  30.133    0.823

Chi-Sq = 89.374, DF = 4, P-Value = 0.000
```

b   The observed value of the test statistic is $\chi^2 = 89.374$ with p-value $= 0$ and the null hypothesis is rejected. There is sufficient evidence to indicate that there is a difference in people's opinion from one country to another.

14.41   The flower fall into one of four classifications, with theoretical ratio 9:3:3:1. Converting these ratios to probabilities,

$$p_1 = 9/16 = 0.5625 \qquad p_2 = 3/16 = 0.1875$$
$$p_3 = 3/16 = 0.1875 \qquad p_4 = 1/16 = 0.0625$$

We will test the null hypothesis that the probabilities are as above against the alternative that they differ. The table of observed and expected cell counts follows:

	AB	Ab	aB	aa
O_i	95	30	28	7
E_i	90	30	30	10

The test statistic is

$$\chi^2 = \frac{(95-90)^2}{90} + \frac{(30-30)^2}{30} + \frac{(28-30)^2}{30} + \frac{(7-10)^2}{10} = 1.311$$

The number of degrees of freedom is $k - 1 = 3$ and the rejection region with $\alpha = 0.01$ is $\chi^2 > \chi^2_{0.01} = 11.3449$. Since the observed value of χ^2 does not fall in the rejection region, we do not reject H_0. We do not have enough information to contradict the theoretical model for the classification of flower colour and shape.

14.43   **a**   Similar to previous exercises. The contingency table, including column and row totals and the estimated expected cell counts, follows.

Condition	Treated	Untreated	Total
Improved	117	74	191
	(95.5)	(95.5)	
Not improved	83	126	209
	(104.5)	(104.5)	
Total	200	200	400

The test statistic is

$$\chi^2 = \frac{(117-95.5)^2}{95.5} + \frac{(74-95.5)^2}{95.5} + \cdots + \frac{(126-104.5)^2}{104.5} = 18.527$$

To test a one-tailed alternative of "effectiveness," first check to see that $\hat{p}_1 > \hat{p}_2$. Then the rejection region with 1 df has a right-tail area of $2(0.05) = 0.10$ or $\chi^2 > \chi^2_{2(0.05)} = 2.706$. H_0 is rejected and we conclude that the serum is effective.

b   Consider the treated and untreated patients as comprising random samples of 200 each, drawn from two populations (i.e., a sample of 200 treated patients and a sample of 200 untreated patients). Let p_1 be the probability that a treated patient improves, and let p_2 be the probability that an untreated patient improves. Then the hypothesis to be tested is H_0: $p_1 - p_2 = 0$ versus H_a: $p_1 - p_2 > 0$. Using the procedure described in Chapter 9 for testing an hypothesis about the difference between two binomial parameters, the following estimators are calculated:

$$\hat{p}_1 = \frac{x_1}{n_1} = \frac{117}{200} \qquad \hat{p}_2 = \frac{x_2}{n_2} = \frac{74}{200} \qquad \hat{p} = \frac{x_1 + x_2}{n_1 + n_2} = \frac{117 + 74}{400} = 0.4775$$

The test statistic is

$$z = \frac{\hat{p}_1 - \hat{p}_2 - 0}{\sqrt{\hat{p}\hat{q}\left(1/n_1 + 1/n_2\right)}} = \frac{0.215}{\sqrt{0.4775(0.5225)(0.01)}} = 4.304$$

And the rejection region for $\alpha = 0.05$ is $z > 1.645$. Again, the test statistic falls in the rejection region. We reject the null hypothesis of no difference and conclude that the serum is effective. Notice that

$$z^2 = \left(4.304\right)^2 = 18.52 = \chi^2 \text{ (to within rounding error)}$$

14.45   Refer to Section 9.6. The two-tailed z test was used to test the hypothesis

$$H_0:\ p_1 - p_2 = 0 \quad \text{versus} \quad H_a:\ p_1 - p_2 \neq 0$$

using the test statistic $z = \dfrac{\hat{p}_1 - \hat{p}_2}{\sqrt{\hat{p}\hat{q}\left(\dfrac{1}{n_1} + \dfrac{1}{n_2}\right)}} \ \Rightarrow\ z = \dfrac{\left(\hat{p}_1 - \hat{p}_2\right)^2}{\hat{p}\hat{q}\left(\dfrac{n_1 + n_2}{n_1 n_2}\right)} = \dfrac{n_1 n_2 \left(\hat{p}_1 - \hat{p}_2\right)^2}{\hat{p}\hat{q}\left(n_1 + n_2\right)}$

Note that $\hat{p} = \dfrac{x_1 + x_2}{n_1 + n_2} = \dfrac{n_1 \hat{p}_1 + n_2 \hat{p}_2}{n_1 + n_2}$

Now consider the chi-square test statistic used in Exercise 14.44. The hypothesis to be tested is

     H_0: independence of classification   versus H_a: dependence of classification

That is, the null hypothesis asserts that the percentage of patients who show improvement is independent of whether or not they have been treated with the serum. If the null hypothesis is true, then $p_1 = p_2$. Hence, the two tests are designed to test the same hypothesis. In order to show that z^2 is equivalent to χ^2, it is necessary to rewrite the chi-square test statistic in terms of the quantities, $\hat{p}_1$, $\hat{p}_2$, $\hat{p}$, n_1, and n_2.

1   Consider O_{11}, the observed number of treated patients who have improved. Since $\hat{p}_1 = O_{11}/n_1$, we have $O_{11} = n_1 \hat{p}_1$. Similarly,

     $O_{21} = n_1 \hat{q}_1 \qquad O_{12} = n_2 \hat{p}_2 \qquad O_{22} = n_2 \hat{q}_2$

2   The estimated expected cell counts are calculated under the assumption that the null hypothesis is true. Consider

$$E_{11} = \frac{r_1 c_1}{n} = \frac{\left(O_{11} + O_{12}\right)\left(O_{11} + O_{21}\right)}{n_1 + n_2} = \frac{\left(x_1 + x_2\right)\left(O_{11} + O_{21}\right)}{n_1 + n_2} = n_1 \hat{p}$$

Similarly,

     $\hat{E}_{21} = n_1 \hat{q} \qquad \hat{E}_{12} = n_2 \hat{p} \qquad \hat{E}_{22} = n_2 \hat{q}$

The table of observed and estimated expected cell counts follows.

	Treated	Untreated	Total
Improved	$n_1 \hat{p}_1$ $\left(n_1 \hat{p}\right)$	$n_2 \hat{p}_2$ $\left(n_2 \hat{p}\right)$	$x_1 + x_2$
Not improved	$n_1 \hat{q}_1$ $\left(n_1 \hat{q}\right)$	$n_2 \hat{q}_1$ $\left(n_2 \hat{q}\right)$	$n - \left(x_1 + x_2\right)$
Total	n_1	n_2	n

Then

$$\chi^2 = \sum \frac{\left(O_{ij} - E_{ij}\right)^2}{E_{ij}}$$

$$= \frac{n_1^2 \left(\hat{p}_1 - \hat{p}\right)^2}{n_1 \hat{p}} + \frac{n_1^2 \left(\hat{q}_1 - \hat{q}\right)^2}{n_1 \hat{q}} + \frac{n_2^2 \left(\hat{p}_2 - \hat{p}\right)^2}{n_2 \hat{p}} + \frac{n_2^2 \left(\hat{q}_2 - \hat{q}\right)^2}{n_2 \hat{q}}$$

$$= \frac{n_1 \left(\hat{p}_1 - \hat{p}\right)^2}{\hat{p}} + \frac{n_1 \left[\left(1 - \hat{p}_1\right) - \left(1 - \hat{p}\right)\right]^2}{\hat{q}} + \frac{n_2 \left(\hat{p}_2 - \hat{p}\right)^2}{\hat{p}} + \frac{n_2 \left[\left(1 - \hat{p}_2\right) - \left(1 - \hat{p}\right)\right]^2}{\hat{q}}$$

$$= \frac{\left(1 - \hat{p}_1\right) n_1 \left(\hat{p}_1 - \hat{p}\right)^2 + n_1 \hat{p} \left(\hat{p}_1 - \hat{p}\right)^2}{\hat{p}\hat{q}} + \frac{\left(1 - \hat{p}_2\right) n_2 \left(\hat{p}_2 - \hat{p}\right)^2 + n_2 \hat{p} \left(\hat{p}_2 - \hat{p}\right)^2}{\hat{p}\hat{q}}$$

$$= \frac{n_1 \left(\hat{p}_1 - \hat{p}\right)^2}{\hat{p}\hat{q}} + \frac{n_2 \left(\hat{p}_2 - \hat{p}\right)^2}{\hat{p}\hat{q}}$$

Substituting for $\hat{p}$, we obtain

$$\chi^2 = \frac{n_1}{\hat{p}\hat{q}} \left[\frac{n_1 \hat{p}_1 + n_2 \hat{p}_1 - n_1 \hat{p}_1 - n_2 \hat{p}_2}{n_1 + n_2}\right]^2 + \frac{n_2}{\hat{p}\hat{q}} \left[\frac{n_1 \hat{p}_2 + n_2 \hat{p}_2 - n_1 \hat{p}_1 - n_2 \hat{p}_2}{n_1 + n_2}\right]^2$$

$$= \frac{n_1 n_2^2 \left(\hat{p}_1 - \hat{p}_2\right)^2 + n_1^2 n_2 \left(\hat{p}_1 - \hat{p}_2\right)^2}{\hat{p}\hat{q}\left(n_1 + n_2\right)^2} = \frac{n_1 n_2 \left(\hat{p}_1 - \hat{p}_2\right)^2}{\hat{p}\hat{q}\left(n_1 + n_2\right)}$$

Note that χ^2 is identical to z^2, as defined at the beginning of the exercise.

14.47 The null hypothesis is that the two methods of classification are independent. The 2×2 contingency table with estimated expected cell counts in parentheses follows.

	Infection	No Infection	Total
Antibody	4 (8.91)	78 (73.09)	82
No antibody	11 (6.09)	45 (49.91)	56
Total	15	123	138

The test statistic is

$$\chi^2 = \frac{\left(4 - 8.91\right)^2}{8.91} + \frac{\left(78 - 73.09\right)^2}{73.09} + \cdots + \frac{\left(45 - 49.91\right)^2}{49.91} = 7.477$$

($\chi^2 = 7.488$ using computer accuracy). The rejection region with $\alpha = 0.05$ and 1 df is $\chi^2 > 3.84$ and H_0 is rejected. There is evidence that the injection of antibodies affects the likelihood of infections.

14.49 The null hypothesis to be tested is H_0: $p_1 = p_2 = p_3 = \frac{1}{3}$

and the test statistic is $\chi^2 = \sum \frac{\left(O_i - E_i\right)^2}{E_i}$

with $E_i = np_i = 200(1/3) = 66.67$ for $i = 1, 2, 3$. A table of observed and expected cell counts follows:

Entrance	1	2	3
O_i	83	61	56
E_i	66.67	66.67	66.67

Then $\chi^2 = \dfrac{(84-66.67)^2}{66.67} + \dfrac{(61-66.67)^2}{66.67} + \dfrac{(56-66.67)^2}{66.67} = 6.190$

With $df = k-1 = 2$, the *p*-value is between 0.025 and 0.05 and we can reject H_0 at the 5% level of significance. There is a difference in preference for the three doors. A 95% confidence interval for p_1 is given as

$$\frac{x_1}{n} \pm z_{.025}\sqrt{\frac{\hat{p}_1\hat{q}_1}{n}} \ \Rightarrow\ \frac{83}{200} \pm 1.96\sqrt{\frac{.415(.585)}{200}} \ \Rightarrow\ .415 \pm .068$$

or $0.347 < p_1 < 0.483$

14.51   **a–b**   The *MINITAB* printouts below are used to analyze the data for the two contingency tables. The observed values of the test statistics are $\chi^2 = 19.043$ and $\chi^2 = 60.139$, for faculty and student responses, respectively. The rejection region, with $(3)(2) = 6\ df$ is $\chi^2 > 16.81$ with $\alpha = 0.01$ and H_0 is rejected for both cases.

Chi-Square Test (a): High, Medium, Low
```
Expected counts are printed below observed counts
Chi-Square contributions are printed below expected counts
         High   Medium    Low   Total
   1        4        0      0       4
         1.53     1.47   1.00
         3.968    1.467  1.000

   2       15       12      3      30
        11.50    11.00   7.50
         1.065    0.091  2.700

   3        2        7      7      16
         6.13     5.87   4.00
         2.786    0.219  2.250

   4        2        3      5      10
         3.83     3.67   2.50
         0.877    0.121  2.500

Total      23       22     15      60

Chi-Sq = 19.043, DF = 6, P-Value = 0.004
7 cells with expected counts less than 5.
```

Chi-Square Test (b): High, Medium, Low
```
Expected counts are printed below observed counts
Chi-Square contributions are printed below expected counts
         High   Medium    Low   Total
   1       19        6      2      27
         6.88     9.56  10.57
        21.379    1.325  6.944

   2       19       41     27      87
        22.16    30.80  34.04
         0.449    3.377  1.457

   3        3        7     31      41
        10.44    14.52  16.04
         5.303    3.891 13.943

   4        0        3      3       6
         1.53     2.12   2.35
         1.528    0.361  0.181

Total      41       57     63     161

Chi-Sq = 60.139, DF = 6, P-Value = 0.000
3 cells with expected counts less than 5.
```

c   Answers will vary.

d   Notice that the computer printout in both tables warns that some cells have expected cell counts less than 5. This is a violation of the assumptions necessary for this test, and results should thus be viewed with caution.

14.53   **a**   Since the percentages do not add to 100%, there is a category missing. We call this category "Other" colour, with expected percentage $100-(19+17+\cdots+12)=8$. Since there were 250 compact and sports cars in the survey, the number falling in the "Other" category is $250-(52+43+\cdots+19)=15$.

    b   The null hypothesis to be tested is
$$H_0:\ p_1=0.19;\ p_2=0.17;\ p_3=0.17;\ p_4=0.15;\ p_5=0.12;\ p_6=0.12;\ p_7=0.08$$
A table of observed and expected cell counts follows:

Colour	Silver	Black	Grey	Blue	Red	White	Other
O_i	52	43	48	41	32	19	15
E_i	47.5	42.5	42.5	37.5	30	30	20

Then the test statistic is
$$\chi^2=\frac{(52-47.5)^2}{47.5}+\frac{(43-42.5)^2}{42.5}+\cdots+\frac{(15-20)^2}{20}=6.887$$
Since the observed value of χ^2 with $df=k-1=6$ is less than $\chi^2_{0.10}$, the p-value is greater than 0.10. We cannot reject H_0. There is insufficient evidence to suggest a difference from the given percentages.

14.55   The *MINITAB* printout for this 2×4 contingency table is shown below.

```
Chi-Square Test: Banna, Cherry, WildFruit, Straw_Ban
Expected counts are printed below observed counts
Chi-Square contributions are printed below expected counts

        Banna   Cherry  WildFruit  Straw_Ban  Total
    1      14       20          7          9     50
        12.86    24.29       5.00       7.86
        0.102    0.756      0.800      0.166

    2       4       14          0          2     20
         5.14     9.71       2.00       3.14
         0.254    1.891      2.000      0.416

Total      18       34          7         11     70

Chi-Sq = 6.384, DF = 3, P-Value = 0.094
2 cells with expected counts less than 5.
```

The test statistic for the test of independence of the two classifications is $\chi^2=6.384$ with p-value $=0.094$ and H_0 is not rejected. There is insufficient evidence to indicate a difference in perception of the best taste between adults and children. If the company intends to use a flavour as a marketing tool, the cherry flavour does not seem to provide an incentive to buy this product.

14.57   **a**   The *MINITAB* printout gives $\chi^2=3.660$ with p-value $=0.454$. The results are not significant; H_0 is not rejected, and there is insufficient evidence to indicate a difference in the distribution of injury types for rugby forwards and backs. However, *MINITAB* warns you that the assumption that E_i is greater than or equal to 5 for each cell has been violated. Since the effect of a small expected value is to inflate the value of χ^2, you need not be too concerned (χ^2 was not big enough to reject H_0 anyway).

b A difference in the proportion of MCL sprains for the two positions involves a 2×2 contingency table or a z-test for the difference in two binomial proportions. The *MINITAB* chi-square printout is shown below.

```
Chi-Square Test: Forwards, Backs
Expected counts are printed below observed counts
Chi-Square contributions are printed below expected counts
         Forwards Backs  Total
   1        14        9     23
            11.50    11.50
            0.543    0.543

   2        24       29     53
            26.50    26.50
            0.236    0.236

Total       38       38     76

Chi-Sq = 1.559, DF = 1, P-Value = 0.212
```

The p-value is greater than the 0.05 claimed by the researchers, and does not suggest a significant difference.

The test for the difference in the proportion of ACL tears is shown in the *MINITAB* printout with p-value $= 0.073$. Again, these results do not agree with the researchers' conclusions.

```
Chi-Square Test: Forwards, Backs
Expected counts are printed below observed counts
Chi-Square contributions are printed below expected counts
         Forwards Backs  Total
   1         7       14     21
            10.50    10.50
            1.167    1.167

   2        31       24     55
            27.50    27.50
            0.445    0.445

Total       38       38     76
Chi-Sq = 3.224, DF = 1, P-Value = 0.073
```

14.59 a The 2×3 contingency table is analyzed as in previous exercises. The *MINITAB* printout below shows the observed and estimated expected cell counts, the test statistic and its associated p-value.

```
Chi-Square Test: 3 or fewer, 4 or 5, 6 or more
Expected counts are printed below observed counts
Chi-Square contributions are printed below expected counts
          3 or
          fewer  4 or 5  6 or more   Total
   1        49       43         34     126
            37.89    42.63      45.47
            3.254    0.003      2.895

   2        31       47         62     140
            42.11    47.37      50.53
            2.929    0.003      2.605

Total       80       90         96     266
Chi-Sq = 11.690, DF = 2, P-Value = 0.003
```

The results are highly significant (p-value $= 0.003$) and we conclude that there is a difference in the susceptibility to colds depending on the number of relationships one has.

b The proportion of people with colds is calculated conditionally for each of the three groups, and is shown in the table below.

	Three or Fewer	**Four or Five**	**Six or More**
Cold	$\dfrac{49}{80} = 0.61$	$\dfrac{43}{90} = 0.48$	$\dfrac{34}{96} = 0.35$
No cold	$\dfrac{31}{80} = 0.39$	$\dfrac{47}{90} = 0.52$	$\dfrac{62}{96} = 0.65$
Total	1.00	100	1.00

As the researcher suspects, the susceptibility to a cold seems to decrease as the number of relationships increases!

14.61 The null hypothesis to be tested is H_0: $p_1 = \dfrac{1}{8}$; $p_2 = \dfrac{1}{8}$; $p_3 = \dfrac{1}{8}$; $p_4 = \dfrac{1}{8}$; $p_5 = \dfrac{2}{8}$; $p_6 = \dfrac{2}{8}$

against the alternative that at least one of these probabilities is incorrect. A table of observed and expected cell counts follows:

Day	Monday	Tuesday	Wednesday	Thursday	Friday	Saturday
O_i	95	110	125	75	181	214
E_i	100	100	100	100	200	200

The test statistic is

$$\chi^2 = \frac{(95-100)^2}{100} + \frac{(110-100)^2}{100} + \cdots + \frac{(214-200)^2}{200} = 16.535$$

The number of degrees of freedom is $k - 1 = 5$ and the rejection region with $\alpha = 0.05$ is $\chi^2 > \chi_{0.05}^2 = 11.07$ and H_0 is rejected. The manager's claim is refuted.

Case Study: Can a Marketing Approach Improve Library Services?

1 There are seven different 2×2 contingency tables to test the null hypothesis H_0: $p_1 = p_2$ for each of the seven questions. Using *MINITAB*, the test statistics for the seven tests are shown below.

$$\chi_1^2 = 10.342 \quad \chi_2^2 = 6.358 \quad \chi_3^2 = 0.661$$

$$\chi_4^2 = 3.213 \quad \chi_5^2 = 9.654 \quad \chi_6^2 = 1.948$$

$$\chi_7^2 = 0.040$$

Since each test statistic has an approximate χ^2 distribution with 1 degree of freedom, the 3rd, 6th, and 7th tests are not significant. The first test statistic has p-value < 0.005; the 2nd test statistic has $0.025 < p$-value < 0.01; the 4th has $0.05 < p$-value < 0.10; the 5th has p-value < 0.005. All of these values agree with the published results except for the 4th test statistic.

2 Notice that questions 11 and 13 (design) produce non-significant results, and that questions 5 and 6 (staff) produce one non-significant and one not too highly significant ($0.05 < p$-value < 0.10) result. Questions 3, 4, and 7 are highly significant; that is, for questions about atmosphere, there is a significant difference in the responses for students and non-students.

3 No. The questions were asked of the same two groups of people and hence are dependent. They do not fit the normal criteria for a contingency table approach. There are techniques available, but they are not given in this text.

Project 14-A: Child Safety Seat Survey, Part 3

a   A test of independence between age group and restraint type would best be tested using a contingency table and the χ^2 statistical test of significance. Our null hypothesis would assume independence between the categories of age group and restraint type.

b   The sampling distribution of the test statistic is approximately chi-square with $(r-1)(c-1)$ degrees of freedom. For this particular example, we have $r = 4$ and $c = 4$. Hence, our test statistic would be chi-square with 9 degrees of freedom.

c   **i**   The null and alternative hypotheses would be
H_0: classification by age group and classification by restraint type are independent
versus
H_a: the classification methods are dependent

     ii   The statistic used to test the hypotheses is a chi-square test on $(4-1)(4-1) = 9$ degrees of freedom (i.e., our test statistic is approximately chi-square with 9 degrees of freedom). Specifically,

$$\chi^2_{test} = \sum_{i=1}^{r}\sum_{j=1}^{c}\frac{\left(O_{ij} - \hat{E}_{ij}\right)^2}{\hat{E}_{ij}}$$

where

$$\hat{E}_{ij} = \frac{r_i c_j}{n}$$

and r_i and c_j are the row and column totals for row i and column j respectively.

    iii   The main difficulty in calculating the test statistic is the fact that we have several cells with 0 counts. This may be a situation where insufficient individuals have been surveyed. However, one may also expect 0 counts within some of the cells. For example, infant seats are not typically used for children over 9 years of age. In a similar manner, one would not expect infants to be secured by seat belt only.

    iv   One of the statistical issues associated with performing a formal test on the hypotheses described in part **i** is the presence of low observation counts. Specifically, we have several cells that have fewer than five observations. It is possible that these small counts do not adequately reflect the true number of observations that should fall within these particular cells. As such, the marginal values might be lower than they should be. This could lead to inflated estimates of proportions in the other cells within any row (or column). Ultimately, the expected counts and observed counts will not be close, leading to inflated test statistics and an increased probability of rejecting the null hypothesis when it should not be rejected.

    v   To alleviate the problems described above, one may wish to survey more individuals in order to potentially eliminate the zero counts. Another option would be to conduct the survey until k individuals are surveyed within each age group or within each restraint type. Of course, as previously mentioned, the counts may necessarily be zero based on the standard use for each type of restraint specific to age group.

d   **i**   The null and alternative hypotheses are
H_0: $p_A = p_B = p_C$. The type of restraint used is independent of the age group.
versus
H_a: at least two of the restraint types differ

    ii   Our particular study has been set up as a two-way classification with fixed column totals. In this case, our column totals are each 600. To test the null hypothesis, we use the χ^2 test for independence of row and column classifications. The test statistic is

$$\chi^2_{test} = \sum_{i=1}^{R}\sum_{j=1}^{C}\frac{\left(O_{ij} - \hat{E}_{ij}\right)^2}{\hat{E}_{ij}}$$

The bracketed quantities in the table below represent the expected cell counts:

Age Group	A	B	C	Total
Todler	483 (261)	250 (261)	50 (261)	783
School	117 (339)	350 (339)	550 (339)	1017
Total	**600**	**600**	**600**	**1800**

Where, for example, the expected count for the school-aged group who use a forward-facing infant seat (restraint type B) is

$$\hat{E}_{2,2} = \frac{1017 \times 600}{1800}$$
$$= 339$$

Hence, our test statistic is

$$\chi^2_{test} = \sum_{i=1}^{R} \sum_{j=1}^{C} \frac{\left(O_{ij} - \hat{E}_{ij}\right)^2}{\hat{E}_{ij}}$$
$$= \frac{\left(483 - 261\right)^2}{261} + \frac{\left(250 - 261\right)^2}{261} + \cdots + \frac{\left(550 - 339\right)^2}{261}$$
$$= 636.9376$$

iii   The p-value for this test can be approximated using Table 5 in Appendix I. With $(r-1)(c-1) = (2-1)(3-1) = 2$ degrees of freedom, we have $P(\chi^2 > 636.9376) < 0.005$. Since our p-value is smaller than $\alpha = 0.05$, we reject the null hypothesis in favour of the alternative. There is sufficient evidence to suggest that at least two of the proportions are different. The three binomial proportions are

$$\hat{p}_A = \frac{483}{600}$$
$$= 0.805$$

$$\hat{p}_B = \frac{250}{600}$$
$$= 0.417$$

$$\hat{p}_C = \frac{50}{600}$$
$$= 0.083$$

Note that these proportions are specific to the age group classified as toddler (1–4 years). For this age group there is a clear pattern of restraint use. That is, most toddlers use the forward-facing infant seat. Next in line are the booster seat, and finally seat belt only. This probably makes sense given the age and size of the children in question. If we calculate the proportions for the school-aged children (4–9 years), the pattern is reversed. The proportions using restraint type A, B, and C are 0.195, 0.583, 0.917, respectively. Few school children fall under the forward-facing infant seat. Most use seat belts only.

    We could also compare each of the three proportions listed above via pair-wise comparisons using a large sample z-test. Our null hypothesis would assume equality between the two proportions in question (i.e., $\hat{p}_A = \hat{p}_B$, or $\hat{p}_A = \hat{p}_C$, or $\hat{p}_B = \hat{p}_C$), while the alternative hypothesis would assume they were different.

    The z-tests comparing $\hat{p}_A - \hat{p}_B$, $\hat{p}_A - \hat{p}_C$, and $\hat{p}_B - \hat{p}_C$ would be 13.795, 25.157, and 13.333, respectively. At a 95% level of significance, we would reject each of the null hypotheses. There is sufficient evidence to suggest that each of the proportions of toddlers using forward-facing seats is significantly different than the proportion of toddlers using a booster seat or seat belt only. Further, there is sufficient evidence to suggest that the proportion of toddlers using a booster seat is significantly different that the proportion of toddlers using a seat belt only.

iv   If there are more than two row categories in a contingency table with fixed-total c columns, then the test of independence is equivalent to a test of the equality of c sets of multinomial proportions. Assume that there exist r row categories across each of the c columns. Note that within each column, we have a multinomial experiment. That is, we have a total of n trials (which is the same for each of the c columns) that are independently and identically assigned to each of the r rows. Specifically, O_1 observations are randomly assigned to the first row with probability p_1, O_2 observations are randomly assigned to the second row with probability p_2, and so forth. With a fixed column total k, we also have that $\sum O_i - k$. Since each of the columns represents a multinomial experiment, the test of independence is equivalent to testing whether or not c multinomial proportions are the same.

Project 14-B: The Dating Strategies

a   To test if there has been a change from the online percentages in Quebec, we assume that the current responses should follow a 0.64:0.10:0.26 pattern. Our observed and expected counts are summarized below.

Quebec	A	B	C	Total
Observed	190	50	55	**295**
Expected	188.8	29.5	76.7	**295**

The expected counts are determined by multiplying the observed row total by the online percentages provided. For example, $188.8 = 295 \times 0.64$.

The test statistic is

$$\chi^2_{test} = \sum_{i=1}^{r} \frac{\left(O_i - \hat{E}_i\right)^2}{\hat{E}_i}$$

$$= \frac{\left(190 - 188.8\right)^2}{188.8} + \frac{\left(50 - 29.5\right)^2}{29.5} + \frac{\left(55 - 76.7\right)^2}{76.7}$$

$$= 20.39276$$

The critical χ^2 value obtained from Table 5 in Appendix I with $\alpha = 0.05$ and $(r-1) \times (c-1) = (2-1)(3-1) = 2$ degrees of freedom is 5.99147. Since our test statistic is greater than 5.99147, we reject the null hypothesis. There is sufficient evidence to suggest that there has been a change from the online percentages in Quebec.

b   To test whether the distribution of the response to the question "does not matter at all" agrees with the corresponding distribution from the online survey, we use the following null and alternative hypotheses:

H_0: $p_{AB} = 0.13/0.70$, $p_{BC} = 0.18/0.70$, $p_{ON} = 0.13/0.70$, $p_{QC} = 0.26/0.70$

versus

H_a: at least one of the probabilities is different

Note that in this case we have divided the online survey results for column C by the grand total for column C (i.e., we have determined the conditional probabilities). This is to ensure that the observed proportions sum to 1.

The test statistic is determined using the observed and expected values indicated in the table below.

Does not matter at all	AB	BC	ON	QC	Total
Observed	40	30	55	55	**180**
Expected	33.43	46.29	33.43	66.86	**180**

The test statistic is

$$\chi^2_{test} = \sum_{i=1}^{r} \frac{\left(O_i - \hat{E}_i\right)^2}{\hat{E}_i}$$

$$= \frac{\left(40 - 33.43\right)^2}{33.43} + \frac{\left(30 - 46.29\right)^2}{46.29} + \frac{\left(55 - 33.43\right)^2}{33.43} + \frac{\left(55 - 66.86\right)^2}{66.86}$$

$$= 23.04487$$

The critical chi-square value on $(2-1)(4-1) = 3$ degrees of freedom with $\alpha = 0.01$ is 11.3449. Since our test statistic is larger than the critical value, there is sufficient evidence to suggest that the distribution of the response "does not matter at all" does not agree with the distribution from the online survey. At least one of the proportions differs from the online survey.

c   To test whether or not the responses in category "A" follow the pattern of the online survey, we have the following observed and expected values:

Matter a bit	AB	BC	ON	QC	Total
Observed	140	130	270	190	**730**
Expected	191.2546	180.4797	185.8672	172.3985	**730**

The test statistic is
$$\chi^2_{test} = 67.73468$$
Comparing this to the critical value (with $\alpha = 0.025$ and 3 degrees of freedom) of 9.34840, we would reject the null hypothesis. There is sufficient evidence to suggest that the proportions in the "A" category have changed from what was found from the online survey.

d   i   The null and alternative hypotheses are
$$H_0: p_{AB} = p_{BC} = p_{ON} = p_{QC} = 0.25$$
versus
H_a: at least one of the probabilities is different

ii   The test statistic is based on the following observed and expected values:

Does not matter at all	AB	BC	ON	QC	Total
Observed	40	30	55	55	**180**
Expected	45	45	45	45	**180**

With this information, our test statistic is
$$\chi^2_{test} - 10$$

iii We would reject the null hypothesis in favour of the alternative if our test statistic exceeds the critical chi-square value (using 3 degrees of freedom and $\alpha = 0.05$) of 7.81473.

iv   Since our test statistic falls in the rejection region, we reject the null hypothesis. There is sufficient evidence to suggest that the proportions in category C across the provinces are not all the same.

e   To test if there is a relationship between the responses to the question "Would financial status affect your decision as to whether or not you would be interested in pursuing a relationship with someone" and the province of residence of the respondent, we employ the chi-square test on the contingency table of responses. Our null hypothesis is that the response to the question and the province of residence are independent. Our alternative assumes a relationship between response and province. The observed and expected counts within each of the cells are presented below.

Province	A	B	C	Total
Alberta	140 (135.81)	20 (30.70)	40 (33.49)	**200**
British Columbia	130 (129.02)	30 (29.16)	30 (31.81)	**190**
Ontario	270 (264.84)	65 (59.86)	55 (65.30)	**390**
Quebec	190 (200.33)	50 (45.28)	55 (49.40)	**295**
Total	**730**	**165**	**180**	**1075**

This gives us a chi-square test of
$$\chi^2_{test} = \sum_{i=1}^{r} \sum_{j=1}^{c} \frac{\left(O_{ij} - \hat{E}_{ij}\right)^2}{\hat{E}_{ij}}$$
$$= \frac{(140 - 135.81)^2}{135.81} + \frac{(20 - 30.70)^2}{30.70} + \cdots + \frac{(55 - 49.40)^2}{49.40}$$
$$= 9.085627$$

The critical value ($\alpha = 0.05$) on $(r-1)(c-1) = (4-1)(3-1) = 6$ degrees of freedom is 12.5916. Since the test statistic is less than the critical value, we would not reject the null hypothesis. There is insufficient evidence to suggest that there is a relationship between the response to the question and the province of resident of the respondent. The p-value for this test is greater than 0.10. Since the province of residence is not related to the response, one may wish to pool the data to provide a better estimate of the proportion of individuals who would respond A, B, or C to the question.

Chapter 15: Nonparametric Statistics

15.1 **a**   If distribution 1 is shifted to the right of distribution 2, the rank sum for sample 1 (T_1) will tend to be large. The test statistic will be T_1^*, the rank sum for sample 1 if the observations had been ranked from large to small. The null hypothesis will be rejected if T_1^* is unusually small.

b   From Table 7(a), Appendix I, with $n_1 = 6$, $n_2 = 8$, and $\alpha = 0.05$, H_0 will be rejected if $T_1^* \leq 31$.

c   From Table 7(c), Appendix I, with $n_1 = 6$, $n_2 = 8$, and $\alpha = 0.01$, H_0 will be rejected if $T_1^* \leq 27$.

15.3 **a** H_0: Populations 1 and 2 are identical
H_a: Population 1 is shifted to the left of population 2

b   The data, with ranks in parentheses, are given below.

Sample 1	Sample 2
1(1)	4(5)
3(3.5)	7(9)
2(2)	6(7.5)
3(3.5)	8(10)
5(6)	6(7.5)

Note that tied observations are given an average rank, the average of the ranks they would have received if they had not been tied. Then
$$T_1 = 1 + 3.5 + 2 + 3.5 + 6 = 16$$
$$T_1^* - n_1\left(n_1 + n_2 + 1\right) - T_1 - 5\left(10 + 1\right) - 16 = 39$$

c   With $n_1 = n_2 = 5$, the one-tailed rejection region with $\alpha = 0.05$ is found in Table 7(a) to be $T_1 \leq 19$.

d   The observed value, $T_1 = 16$, falls in the rejection region and H_0 is rejected. We conclude that population 1 is shifted to the right of population 2.

15.5   If H_a is true and population 1 lies to the right of population 2, then T_1 will be large and T_1^* will be small. Hence, the test statistic will be T_1^* and the large sample approximation can be used. Calculate
$$T_1^* = n_1\left(n_1 + n_2 + 1\right) - T_1 = 12\left(27\right) - 193 = 131$$
$$\mu_T = \frac{n_1\left(n_1 + n_2 + 1\right)}{2} = \frac{12\left(26 + 1\right)}{2} - 162$$
$$\sigma_T^2 = \frac{n_1 n_2 \left(n_1 + n_2 + 1\right)}{12} = \frac{12\left(14\right)\left(27\right)}{12} = 378$$

The test statistic is
$$z = \frac{T_1 - \mu_T}{\sigma_T} = \frac{131 - 162}{\sqrt{378}} = -1.59$$

The rejection region with $\alpha = 0.05$ is $z < -1.645$ and H_0 is not rejected. There is insufficient evidence to indicate a difference in the two population distributions.

15.7   The hypothesis of interest is

H_0: Populations 1 and 2 are identical

versus

H_a: Population 2 is shifted to the right of population 1

The data, with ranks in parentheses, are given below.

20s	11(20)	7(11)	6(7.5)	8(14)	6(7.5)	9(16.5)	2(2)	10(18.5)	3(3.5)	6(7.5)
65–70s	1(1)	9(16.5)	6(7.5)	8(14)	7(11)	8(14)	5(5)	7(11)	10(18.5)	3(3.5)

Then

$$T_1 = 20 + 11 + \cdots + 7.5 = 108$$

$$T_1^* = n_1\left(n_1 + n_2 + 1\right) - T_1 = 10\left(20 + 1\right) - 108 = 102$$

The test statistic is

$$T = \min\left(T_1, T_1^*\right) = 102$$

With $n_1 = n_2 = 10$, the one-tailed rejection region with $\alpha = 0.05$ is found in Table 7(a), Appendix I, to be $T_1^* \le 82$ and the observed value, $T = 102$, does not fall in the rejection region; H_0 is not rejected. We cannot conclude that this drug improves memory in mean aged 65 to 70 to that of 20-year-olds.

15.9   Similar to previous exercises. The data, with corresponding ranks, are shown in the following table.

Deaf (1)	Hearing (2)
2.75 (15)	0.89 (1)
2.14 (11)	1.43 (7)
3.23 (18)	1.06 (4)
2.07 (10)	1.01 (3)
2.49 (14)	0.94 (2)
2.18 (12)	1.79 (8)
3.16 (17)	1.12 (5.5)
2.93 (16)	2.01 (9)
2.20 (13)	1.12 (5.5)
$T_1 = 126$	

Calculate

$$T_1 = 126$$

$$T_1^* = n_1\left(n_1 + n_2 + 1\right) - T_1 = 9\left(19\right) - 126 = 45$$

The test statistic is

$$T = \min\left(T_1, T_1^*\right) = 45$$

With $n_1 = n_2 = 9$, the two-tailed rejection region with $\alpha = 0.05$ is found in Table 7(b), Appendix I, to be $T_1^* \le 62$. The observed value, $T = 45$, falls in the rejection region and H_0 is rejected. We conclude that the deaf children do differ from the hearing children in eye-movement rate.

15.11 The data, with corresponding ranks, are shown in the following table.

Lake 1	Lake 2
399.7 (12.5)	345.9 (2)
430.9 (16)	368.8 (6)
394.1 (10)	399.7 (12.5)
411.1 (14)	385.6 (7)
416.7 (15)	351.5 (3)
391.2 (8.5)	337.4 (1)
396.9 (11)	354.4 (4)
456.4 (18)	391.2 (8.5)
360.0 (5)	
433.7 (17)	
	$T_1 = 44$

Calculate

$$T_1 = 44$$

$$T_1^* = n_1(n_1 + n_2 + 1) - T_1 = 8(18+1) - 44 = 108$$

The test statistic is

$$T = \min(T_1, T_1^*) = 44$$

With $n_1 = 8$ and $n_2 = 10$, the two-tailed rejection region with $\alpha - 0.05$ is found in Table 7(b), Appendix I, to be $T \le 53$. The observed value, $T = 44$, falls in the rejection region and H_0 is rejected. We conclude that the distribution of weights for the tagged turtles exposed to the two lake environments were different.

15.13 **a** If a paired-difference experiment has been used and the sign test is one-tailed $(H_a: p > 0.5)$, then the experimenter would like to show that one population of measurements lies above the other population. An exact practical statement of the alternative hypothesis would depend on the experimental situation.

b It is necessary that α (the probability of rejecting the null hypothesis when it is true) take values less than $\alpha - 0.15$. Assuming the null hypothesis to be true, the two populations are identical and consequently, $p = P(\text{A exceeds B for a given pair of observations})$ is 1/2. The binomial probability was discussed in Chapter 5. In particular, it was noted that the distribution of the random variable x is symmetrical about the mean np when $p = 1/2$. For example, with $n = 25$, $P(X = 0) = P(X = 25)$.

Similarly, $P(X = 1) = P(X = 24)$ and so on. Hence, the lower tailed probabilities tabulated in Table 1, Appendix I, will be identical to their upper tailed equivalent probabilities. The values of α available for this upper tailed test and the corresponding rejection regions are shown below.

Rejection Region	α
$x \ge 20$	0.002
$x \ge 19$	0.007
$x \ge 18$	0.022
$x \ge 17$	0.054
$x \ge 16$	0.115

15.15   Similar to Exercise 15.14. The rejection regions and levels of α are given in the table for the three different values of n, and a one-tailed test.

$n=10$	$n=15$	$n=20$
$x \leq 0 \quad \alpha = 0.001$	$x \leq 2 \quad \alpha = 0.004$	$x \leq 3 \quad \alpha = 0.001$
$x \leq 1 \quad \alpha = 0.011$	$x \leq 3 \quad \alpha = 0.018$	$x \leq 4 \quad \alpha = 0.006$
$x \leq 2 \quad \alpha = 0.055$	$x \leq 4 \quad \alpha = 0.059$	$x \leq 5 \quad \alpha = 0.021$
		$x \leq 6 \quad \alpha = 0.058$
		$x \leq 7 \quad \alpha = 0.132$

For the two-tailed test, the rejection regions with $0.01 < \alpha < 0.15$ are shown below.

$n=10$	$n=15$	$n=20$
$x \leq 0; x \geq 10 \quad \alpha = 0.002$	$x \leq 2; x \geq 13 \quad \alpha = 0.008$	$x \leq 3; x \geq 17 \quad \alpha = 0.002$
$x \leq 1; x \geq 9 \quad \alpha = 0.022$	$x \leq 3; x \geq 12 \quad \alpha = 0.036$	$x \leq 4; x \geq 16 \quad \alpha = 0.012$
$x \leq 2; x \geq 8 \quad \alpha = 0.110$	$x \leq 4; x \geq 11 \quad \alpha = 0.118$	$x \leq 5; x \geq 15 \quad \alpha = 0.042$
		$x \leq 6; x \geq 14 \quad \alpha = 0.116$

15.17   **a**   If assessors A and B are equal in their property assessments, then p, the probability that A's assessment exceeds B's assessment for a given property, should equal 1/2. If one of the assessors tends to be more conservative than the other, then either $p > 1/2$ or $p < 1/2$. Hence, we can test the equivalence of the two assessors by testing the hypothesis
$$H_0: \quad p = 1/2 \quad \text{versus} \quad H_a: \quad p \neq 1/2$$
using the test statistic x, the number of times that assessor A exceeds assessor B for a particular property assessment. To find a two-tailed rejection region with α close to 0.05, use Table 1, Appendix I, with $n = 8$ and $p = 0.5$. For the rejection region $\{x = 0, x = 8\}$, the value of α is $0.004 + 0.004 = 0.008$, while for the rejection region $\{x = 0, 1, 7, 8\}$, the value of α is $0.035 + 0.035 = 0.070$, which is closer to 0.05. Hence, using the rejection region $\{x \leq 1 \text{ or } x \geq 7\}$, the null hypothesis is not rejected, since X = number of properties for which A exceeds B = 6. The p-value for this two-tailed test is
$$p\text{-value} = 2P(X \geq 6) = 2(1 - 0.855) = 0.290$$
Since the p-value is greater than 0.10, the results are not significant; H_0 is not rejected (as with the critical value approach).

   b   The t statistic used in Exercise 10.47 allows the experimenter to reject H_0, while the sign test fails to reject H_0. This is because the sign test used less information and makes fewer assumptions than does the t test. If all normality assumptions are met, the t test is the more powerful test and can reject when the sign test cannot.

15.19   Similar to Exercise 15.18. The hypothesis to be tested is
$$H_0: \quad p = 1/2 \quad \text{versus} \quad H_a: \quad p > 1/2$$
using the sign test with X, the number of "elevated" blood lead levels observed in $n = 17$ people, as the test statistic. Using the large sample approximation, the test statistic is
$$z = \frac{x - 0.5n}{0.5\sqrt{n}} = \frac{15 - 0.5(17)}{0.5\sqrt{17}} = 3.15$$
and the one-tailed rejection region with $\alpha = 0.05$ is $z > 1.645$. The null hypothesis is rejected and we conclude that the indoor firing range has the effect of increasing a person's blood lead level.

15.21 **a** H_0: Population distributions 1 and 2 are identical
versus
H_a: The distributions differ in location

b Since Table 8, Appendix I, gives critical values for rejection in the lower tail of the distribution, we use the smaller of T^+ and T^- as the test statistic.

c From Table 8 with $n = 30$, $\alpha = 0.05$ and a two-tailed test, the rejection region is $T \le 137$.

d Since $T^+ = 249$, we can calculate

$$T^- = \frac{n(n+1)}{2} - T^+ = \frac{30(31)}{2} - 249 = 216$$

The test statistic is the smaller of T^+ and T^- or $T = 216$ and H_0 is not rejected. There is no evidence of a difference between the two distributions.

15.23 Since $n > 25$, the large sample approximation to the signed-rank test can be used to test the hypothesis given in Exercise 15.21a. Calculate

$$E(T) = \frac{n(n+1)}{4} = \frac{30(31)}{4} = 232.5$$

$$\sigma_T^2 = \frac{n(n+1)(2n+1)}{24} = \frac{30(31)(61)}{24} = 2363.75$$

The test statistic is

$$z = \frac{T - E(T)}{\sigma_T} = \frac{216 - 232.5}{\sqrt{2363.75}} = 0.34$$

The two-tailed rejection region with $\alpha = 0.05$ is $|z| > 1.96$ and H_0 is not rejected. The results agree with Exercise 15.21d.

15.25 **a** The hypothesis to be tested is
H_0: Population distributions 1 and 2 are identical
versus
H_a: The distributions differ in location

and the test statistic is T, the rank sum of the positive (or negative) differences. The ranks are obtained by ordering the differences according to their absolute value. Define d_i to be the difference between a pair in populations 1 and 2 (i.e., $x_{1i} - x_{2i}$). The differences, along with their ranks (according to absolute magnitude), are shown in the following table.

d_i	0.1	0.7	0.3	−0.1	0.5	0.2	0.5
Rank $|d_i|$	1.5	7	4	1.5	5.5	3	5.5

The rank sum for positive differences is $T^+ = 26.5$ and the rank sum for negative differences is $T^- = 1.5$ with $n = 7$. Consider the smaller rank sum and determine the appropriate lower portion of the two-tailed rejection region. Indexing $n = 7$ and $\alpha = 0.05$ in Table 8, Appendix I, the rejection region is $T \le 2$ and H_0 is rejected. There is a difference in the two population locations.

b The results do not agree with those obtained in Exercise 15.16. We are able to reject H_0 with the more powerful Wilcoxon test.

15.27 **a** Similar to Exercise 15.26. The Wilcoxon signed-rank test is used, and the differences, along with their ranks (according to absolute magnitude), are shown in the following table.

d_i	−4	2	−2	−5	−3	0	1	1	−6
Rank $|d_i|$	6	3.5	3.5	7	5	--	1.5	1.5	8

The sixth pair has zero difference and is hence eliminated from consideration. Pairs 7 and 8, 2 and 3 are tied and receive an average rank. Then $T^+ = 6.5$ and $T^- = 29.5$ with $n = 8$. Indexing $n = 8$ and $\alpha = 0.05$ in Table 8, Appendix I, the lower portion of the two-tailed rejection region is $T \leq 4$ and H_0 is not rejected. There is insufficient evidence to detect a difference in the two machines.

b If a machine continually breaks down, it will eventually be fixed, and the breakdown rate for the following month will decrease.

15.29 **a** The paired data are given in the exercise. The differences, along with their ranks (according to absolute magnitude), are shown in the following table.

d_i	1	2	–1	1	3	1	–1	3	–2	3	1	0
Rank $\lvert d_i \rvert$	3.5	7.5	3.5	3.5	10	3.5	3.5	10	7.5	10	2.5	--

Let $p = P(\text{A exceeds B for a given intersection})$ and $X =$ number of intersections at which A exceeds B. The hypothesis to be tested is
$$H_0: \ p = 1/2 \quad \text{versus} \quad H_a: \ p \neq 1/2$$
using the sign test with x as the test statistic.

Critical value approach: Various two-tailed rejection regions are tried in order to find a region with $\alpha \approx 0.05$. These are shown in the following table.

Rejection Region	α
$x \leq 1; x \geq 10$	0.012
$x \leq 2; x \geq 9$	0.066
$x \leq 3; x \geq 8$	0.226

We choose to reject H_0 if $x \leq 2$ or $x \geq 9$ with $\alpha = 0.066$. Since $x = 8$, H_0 is not rejected. There is insufficient evidence to indicate a difference between the two methods.

p-value approach: For the observed value $x = 8$, calculate the two-tailed p-value:
$$p\text{-value} = 2P(X \geq 8) = 2(1 - 0.887) = 0.226$$
Since the p-value is greater than 0.10, H_0 is not rejected.

b To use the Wilcoxon signed-rank test, we use the ranks of the absolute differences shown in the table above. Then $T^+ = 51.5$ and $T^- = 14.5$ with $n = 11$. Indexing $n = 11$ and $\alpha = 0.05$ in Table 8, Appendix I, the lower portion of the two-tailed rejection region is $T \leq 11$ and H_0 is not rejected, as in part **a**.

15.31 **a** Since the experiment has been designed as a paired experiment, there are three tests available for testing the differences in the distributions with and without imagery: (1) the paired-difference t test; (2) the sign test; and (3) the Wilcoxon signed-rank test. In order to use the paired-difference t test, the scores must be approximately normal; since the number of words recalled has a binomial distribution with $n = 25$ and unknown recall probability, this distribution may not be approximately normal.

b Using the **sign test**, the hypothesis to be tested is
$$H_0: \ p = 1/2 \quad \text{versus} \quad H_a: \ p > 1/2$$
For the observed value $x = 0$, we calculate the two-tailed p-value:
$$p\text{-value} = 2P(X \leq 0) = 2(0.000) = 0.000$$
The results are highly significant; H_0 is rejected and we conclude there is a difference in the recall scores with and without imagery.

Using the **Wilcoxon signed-rank test**, the differences will all be positive ($x = 0$ for the sign test), so that

$$T^+ = \frac{n(n+1)}{2} = \frac{20(21)}{2} = 210 \quad \text{and} \quad T^- = 210 - 210 = 0$$

Indexing $n = 20$ and $\alpha = 0.01$ in Table 8, Appendix I, the lower portion of the two-tailed rejection region is $T \le 37$ and H_0 is rejected.

c   Answers will vary.

15.33   Similar to Exercise 15.32. The data with corresponding ranks in parentheses are shown below.

Treatment			
1	2	3	4
124 (9)	147 (20)	141 (17)	117 (4.5)
167 (26)	121 (7)	144 (18.5)	128 (10.5)
135 (14)	136 (15)	139 (16)	102 (1)
160 (24)	114 (3)	162 (25)	119 (6)
159 (23)	129 (12)	155 (22)	128 (10.5)
144 (18.5)	117 (4.5)	150 (21)	123 (8)
133 (13)	109 (2)		
$T_1 = 127.5$	$T_2 = 63.5$	$T_3 = 119.5$	$T_4 = 40.5$
$n_1 = 7$	$n_2 = 7$	$n_3 = 6$	$n_4 = 6$

The test statistic, based on the rank sums, is

$$H = \frac{12}{n(n+1)} \sum \frac{T_i^2}{n_i} - 3(n+1)$$

$$= \frac{12}{26(27)}\left[\frac{(127.5)^2}{7} + \frac{(63.5)^2}{7} + \frac{(119.5)^2}{6} + \frac{(40.5)^2}{6}\right] - 3(27) = 13.90$$

The rejection region with $\alpha = 0.05$ and $k - 1 = 3$ df is based on the chi-square distribution, or $H > \chi^2_{0.05} = 7.81$. The null hypothesis is rejected and we conclude that there is a difference among the four treatments.

15.35   Similar to Exercise 15.32. The data with corresponding ranks in parentheses are shown below.

Age			
10–19	20–39	40–59	60–69
29 (21)	24 (8)	37 (39)	28 (18)
33 (29.5)	27 (15)	25 (10.5)	29 (21)
26 (12.5)	33 (29.5)	22 (5.5)	34 (34)
27 (15)	31 (24)	33 (29.5)	36 (37.5)
39 (40)	21 (3)	28 (18)	21 (3)
35 (36)	28 (18)	26 (12.5)	20 (1)
33 (29.5)	24 (8)	30 (23)	25 (10.5)
29 (21)	34 (34)	34 (34)	24 (8)
36 (37.5)	21 (3)	27 (15)	33 (29.5)
22 (5.5)	32 (25.5)	33 (29.5)	32 (25.5)
$T_1 = 247.5$	$T_2 = 168$	$T_3 = 216.5$	$T_4 = 188$
$n_1 = 10$	$n_2 = 10$	$n_3 = 10$	$n_4 = 10$

a   The test statistic, based on the rank sums, is

$$H = \frac{12}{n(n+1)}\sum\frac{T_i^2}{n_i} - 3(n+1)$$

$$= \frac{12}{40(41)}\left[\frac{(247.5)^2}{10} + \frac{(168)^2}{10} + \frac{(216.5)^2}{10} + \frac{(188)^2}{10}\right] - 3(41) = 2.63$$

The rejection region with $\alpha = 0.01$ and $k-1 = 3\ df$ is based on the chi-square distribution, or $H > \chi_{0.01}^2 = 11.35$. The null hypothesis is not rejected. There is no evidence of a difference in location.

b   Since the observed value $H = 2.63$ is less than $\chi_{0.10}^2 = 6.25$, the *p*-value is greater than 0.10.

c   From Exercise 11.58, $F = 0.87$ with 3 and 36 *df*. Again, the *p*-value is greater than 0.10 and the results are the same.

15.37   Similar to previous exercises. The ranks of the data are shown below.

Campaigns		
1	2	3
11.5	6	1.5
7	15	8
1.5	13	4
10	14	11.5
3	5	9
$T_1 = 33$	$T_2 = 53$	$T_3 = 34$
$n_1 = 5$	$n_2 = 5$	$n_3 = 5$

a   The test statistic is

$$H = \frac{12}{n(n+1)}\sum\frac{T_i^2}{n_i} - 3(n+1)$$

$$= \frac{12}{15(16)}\left[\frac{(33)^2}{5} + \frac{(53)^2}{5} + \frac{(34)^2}{5}\right] - 3(16) = 2.54$$

With $k-1 = 2\ df$, the observed value $H = 2.54$ is less than $\chi_{0.10}^2 = 4.61$, and the *p*-value is greater than 0.10. The null hypothesis is not rejected and we cannot conclude that there is a difference in the three population distributions.

15.39   Similar to Exercise 15.38. The ranks of the data are shown below.

	Treatment			
Block	1	2	3	4
1	4	1	2	3
2	4	1.5	1.5	3
3	4	1	3	2
4	4	1	2	3
5	4	1	2.5	2.5
6	4	1	2	3
7	4	1	3	2
8	4	1	2	3
	$T_1 = 32$	$T_2 = 8.5$	$T_3 = 18$	$T_4 = 21.5$

a The test statistic is

$$F_r = \frac{12}{bk(k+1)}\sum T_i^2 - 3b(k+1)$$

$$= \frac{12}{8(4)(5)}\left[(32)^2 + (8.5)^2 + 18^2 + (21.5)^2\right] - 3(8)(5) = 21.19$$

and the rejection region is $F_r > \chi_{0.05}^2 = 7.81$. Hence, H_0 is rejected and we conclude that there is a difference among the four treatments.

b The observed value, $F_r = 21.19$, exceeds $\chi_{0.005}^2$, p-value < 0.005.

c–e The analysis of variance is performed as in Chapter 11. The ANOVA table is shown below.

Source	df	SS	MS	F
Treatments	3	198.34375	66.114583	75.43
Blocks	7	220.46875	31.495536	35.93
Error	21	18.40625	0.876488	
Total	31	437.40625		

The analysis of variance F test for treatments is $F = 75.43$ and the approximate p-value with 3 and 21 *df* is p-value < 0.005.

f The result is identical to the parametric result.

15.41 Similar to Exercise 15.38, with rats as blocks. The data are shown below along with corresponding ranks within blocks. Note that we have rearranged the data to eliminate the random order of presentation in the display.

Rat	A	B	C
		Treatment	
1	6 (3)	5 (2)	3 (1)
2	9 (2.5)	9 (2.5)	4 (1)
3	6 (2)	9 (3)	3 (1)
4	5 (1)	8 (3)	6 (2)
5	7 (1)	8 (2.5)	8 (2.5)
6	5 (1.5)	7 (3)	5 (1)
7	6 (2)	7 (3)	5 (1)
8	6 (1)	7 (2.5)	7 (2.5)
	$T_1 = 14$	$T_2 = 21.5$	$T_3 = 12.5$

a The test statistic is

$$F_r = \frac{12}{bk(k+1)}\sum T_i^2 - 3b(k+1)$$

$$= \frac{12}{8(3)(4)}\left[(14)^2 + (21.5)^2 + (12.5)^2\right] - 3(8)(4) = 5.81$$

and the rejection region is $F_r > \chi_{0.05}^2 = 5.99$. Hence, H_0 is not rejected and we cannot conclude that there is a difference among the three treatments.

b The observed value, $F_r = 5.81$, falls between $\chi_{0.05}^2$ and $\chi_{0.10}^2$. Hence, $0.05 < p$-value < 0.10.

15.43 Table 9, Appendix I, gives critical values r_0 such that $P(r_s \geq r_0) = \alpha$. Hence, for an upper-tailed test, the critical value for rejection can be read directly from the table.

a $r_s \geq 0.425$

b $r_s \geq 0.601$

15.45 For a two-tailed test of correlation, the value of α given along the top of the table is doubled to obtain the **actual** value of α for the test.

    a To obtain $\alpha = 0.05$, index 0.025 and the rejection region is $|r_s| \geq 0.400$.

    b To obtain $\alpha = 0.01$, index 0.005 and the rejection region is $|r_s| \geq 0.526$.

15.47   **a** The two variables (rating and distance) are ranked from low to high, and the results are shown in the following table.

Voter	x	y	Voter	x	y
1	7.5	3	7	6	4
2	4	7	8	11	2
3	3	12	9	1	10
4	12	1	10	5	9
5	10	8	11	9	5.5
6	7.5	11	12	2	5.5

Calculate $\sum x_i y_i = 442.5$ $\sum x_i^2 = 649.5$ $\sum y_i^2 = 649.5$

                $n = 12$ $\sum x_i = 78$ $\sum y_i = 78$

Then $S_{xy} = 422.5 - \dfrac{78^2}{12} = -84.5$ $S_{xx} = 649.5 - \dfrac{78^2}{12} = 142.5$ $S_{yy} = 649.5 - \dfrac{78^2}{12} = 142.5$

and $r_s = \dfrac{S_{xy}}{\sqrt{S_{xx} S_{yy}}} = \dfrac{-84.5}{142.5} = -0.593$

    b The hypothesis of interest is H_0: no correlation versus H_a: negative correlation. Consulting Table 9, Appendix I, for $\alpha = 0.05$, the critical value of r_s, denoted by r_0 is -0.497. Since the value of the test statistic is less than the critical value, the null hypothesis is rejected. There is evidence of a significant negative correlation between rating and distance.

15.49   **a** The data are ranked separately according to the variables x and y.

Rank x	7	6	5	4	1	12	8	3	2	11	10	9
Rank y	7	8	4	5	2	10	12	3	1	6	11	9

Since there were no tied observations, the simpler formula for r_s is used, and

$$r_s = 1 - \frac{6 \sum d_i^2}{n(n^2 - 1)} = 1 - \frac{6\left[(0)^2 + (-2)^2 + \cdots + (0)^2 \right]}{12(143)}$$

$$= 1 - \frac{6(54)}{1716} = 0.811$$

    b To test for positive correlation with $\alpha = 0.05$, index 0.05 in Table 9, Appendix I, and the rejection region is $r_s \geq 0.497$. Hence, H_0 is rejected, there is a positive correlation between x and y.

15.51 Refer to Exercise 15.50. To test for positive correlation with $\alpha = 0.05$, index 0.05 in Table 9, Appendix I, and the rejection region is $r_s \geq 0.600$. We reject the null hypothesis of no association and conclude that a positive correlation exists between the teacher's ranks and the ranks of the IQs.

15.53 The ranks of the two variables are shown below.

Leaf	1	2	3	4	5	6	7	8	9	10	11	12
Rank x	10.5	5.5	7.5	7.5	4	9	2	5.5	1	12	10.5	3
Rank y	12	7.5	9	6	4.5	10	3	4.5	1	11	7.5	2

Calculate $\qquad \sum x_i y_i = 636.25 \qquad \sum x_i^2 = 648.5 \qquad \sum y_i^2 = 649$

$\qquad\qquad\qquad n = 12 \qquad\qquad\quad \sum x_i = 78 \qquad\qquad \sum y_i = 78$

Then $S_{xy} = 636.25 - \dfrac{78^2}{12} = 129.25 \qquad S_{xx} = 648.5 - \dfrac{78^2}{12} = 141.5 \qquad S_{yy} = 649 - \dfrac{78^2}{12} = 142$

and $r_s = \dfrac{S_{xy}}{\sqrt{S_{xx}S_{yy}}} = \dfrac{129.25}{\sqrt{141.5(142)}} = 0.913$

To test for correlation with $\alpha = 0.05$, index 0.025 in Table 9, Appendix I, and the rejection region is $\left| r_s \right| \geq 0.591$. The null hypothesis is rejected and we conclude that there is a correlation between the two variables.

15.55   **a**   Define $p = P(\text{response for stimulus 1 exceeds that for stimulus 2})$ and $X =$ number of times the response for stimulus 1 exceeds that for stimulus 2. The hypothesis to be tested is
$\qquad H_0: \; p = 1/2 \quad$ versus $\quad H_a: \; p \neq 1/2$
using the sign test with x as the test statistic. Notice that for this exercise $n = 9$, and the observed value of the test statistic is $x = 2$. Various two tailed rejection regions are tried in order to find a region with $\alpha \approx 0.05$. These are shown in the following table.

Rejection Region	α
$x = 0; x = 9$	0.004
$x \leq 1; x \geq 8$	0.040
$x \leq 2; x \geq 7$	0.180

We choose to reject H_0 if $x \leq 1$ or $x \geq 8$ with $\alpha = 0.040$. Since $x = 2$, H_0 is not rejected. There is insufficient evidence to indicate a difference between the two stimuli.

   b   The experiment has been designed in a paired manner, and the paired difference test is used. The differences are shown below.
$\qquad d_i: \; -0.9 \quad -1.1 \quad 1.5 \quad -2.6 \quad -1.8 \quad -2.9 \quad -2.5 \quad 2.5 \quad -1.4$
The hypothesis to be tested is $H_0: \; \mu_1 - \mu_2 = 0 \quad$ versus $\quad H_a: \; \mu_1 - \mu_2 \neq 0$

Calculate $\bar{d} = \dfrac{\sum d_i}{n} = \dfrac{-9.2}{9} = -1.022 \qquad s_d^2 = \dfrac{\sum d_i^2 - \dfrac{(\sum d_i)^2}{n}}{n-1} = \dfrac{37.14 - 9.404}{8} = 3.467$

and the test statistic is

$\qquad t = \dfrac{\bar{d}}{\sqrt{\dfrac{s_d^2}{n}}} = \dfrac{1.022}{\sqrt{\dfrac{3.467}{9}}} = -1.646$

The rejection region with $\alpha = 0.05$ and 8 df is $\left| t \right| > 2.306$ and H_0 is not rejected.

15.57   **a**   Define $p = P(\text{school A exceeds school B in test score for a pair of twins})$ and $X =$ number of times the score for school A exceeds the score for school B. The hypothesis to be tested is
$\qquad H_0: \; p = 1/2 \quad$ versus $\quad H_a: \; p \neq 1/2$
using the sign test with x as the test statistic. Notice that for this exercise $n = 10$, and the observed value of the test statistic is $x = 7$.

Various two-tailed rejection regions are tried in order to find a region with $\alpha \approx 0.05$. These are shown in the following table.

Rejection Region	α
$x = 0; x = 10$	0.002
$x \leq 1; x \geq 9$	0.022
$x \leq 2; x \geq 8$	0.110

We choose to reject H_0 if $x \leq 1$ or $x \geq 9$ with $\alpha = 0.022$. Since $x = 7$, H_0 is not rejected. There is insufficient evidence to indicate a difference between the two schools.

p-value approach: For the observed value $x = 7$, calculate the two-tailed p-value:

$$p\text{-value} = 2P(X \geq 7) = 2(1 - 0.828) = 0.344$$

and H_0 is not rejected. There is insufficient evidence to indicate a difference between the two schools.

b   Consider the one-tailed test of the hypothesis as follows:

$$H_0: \quad p = 1/2 \quad \text{versus} \quad H_a: \quad p > 1/2$$

This alternative will imply that school A is superior to school B. From Table 1, Appendix I, the one-tailed rejection region with $\alpha \approx 0.05$ is $x \geq 8$ with $\alpha = 0.055$. The null hypothesis is still not rejected, since $x = 7$. (The one-tailed p-value $= 0.172$.)

15.59   The data, with corresponding ranks, are shown in the following table.

A (1)	B (2)
6.1 (1)	9.1 (16)
9.2 (17)	8.2 (8)
8.7 (12)	8.6 (11)
8.9 (13.5)	6.9 (2)
7.6 (5)	7.5 (4)
7.1 (3)	7.9 (7)
9.5 (18)	8.3 (9.5)
8.3 (9.5)	7.8 (6)
9.0 (1.5)	8.9 (13.5)
$T_1 = 94$	

The difference in the brightness levels using the two processes can be tested using the nonparametric Wilcoxon rank-sum test or the parametric two-sample t test.

1   To test the null hypothesis that the two population distributions are identical, calculate

$$T_1 = 1 + 17 + \cdots + 1.5 = 94$$

$$T_1^* = n_1(n_1 + n_2 + 1) - T_1 = 9(18 + 1) - 94 = 77$$

The test statistic is $T = \min(T_1, T_1^*) = 77$

With $n_1 = n_2 = 9$, the two-tailed rejection region with $\alpha = 0.05$ is found in Table 7(b), Appendix I, to be $T_1^* \leq 62$. The observed value, $T = 77$, does not fall in the rejection region and H_0 is not rejected. We cannot conclude that the distributions of brightness measurements are different for the two processes.

2   To test the null hypothesis that the two population means are identical, calculate

$$\bar{x}_1 = \frac{\sum x_{1j}}{n_1} = \frac{74.4}{9} = 8.2667$$

$$\bar{x}_2 = \frac{\sum x_{2j}}{n_2} = \frac{73.2}{9} = 8.1333$$

$$s^2 = \frac{(n_1-1)s_1^2 + (n_2-1)s_2^2}{n_1+n_2-2} = \frac{625.06 - \frac{(74.4)^2}{9} + 599.22 - \frac{(73.2)^2}{9}}{16} = 0.8675$$

and the test statistic is $t = \dfrac{\bar{x}_1 - \bar{x}_2}{\sqrt{s^2\left(\dfrac{1}{n_1}+\dfrac{1}{n_2}\right)}} = \dfrac{8.27-8.13}{\sqrt{.8675\left(\dfrac{2}{9}\right)}} = 0.304$

The rejection region with $\alpha = 0.05$ and 16 degrees of freedom is $|t| > 1.746$ and H_0 is not rejected.

There is insufficient evidence to indicate a difference in the average brightness measurements for the two processes.

Notice that the nonparametric and parametric tests reach the same conclusions.

15.61   Since this is a paired experiment, you can choose either the sign test, the Wilcoxon signed-rank test, or the parametric paired t test. Since the tenderizers have been scored on a scale of 1 to 10, the parametric test is not applicable. Start by using the easiest of the two nonparametric tests: the sign test. Define

$p = P(\text{tenderizer A exceeds B for a given cut})$ and $X =$ number of times that A exceeds B. The hypothesis to be tested is

$$H_0:\ p = 1/2 \quad \text{versus} \quad H_a:\ p \neq 1/2$$

using the sign test with x as the test statistic. Notice that for this exercise $n = 8$ (there are two ties), and the observed value of the test statistic is $x = 2$.

p-value approach: For the observed value $x = 2$, calculate

$$p\text{-value} = 2P(X \le 2) = 2(0.145) = 0.290$$

Since the p-value is greater than 0.10, H_0 is not rejected. There is insufficient evidence to indicate a difference between the two tenderizers.

If you use the Wilcoxon signed-rank test, you will find $T^+ = 7$ and $T^- = 29$, which will not allow rejection of H_0 at the 5% level of significance. The results are the same.

Student's t may not be appropriate here as the data are on a 10-point scale.

15.63   To test for negative correlation with $\alpha = 0.05$, index0 .05 in Table 9, Appendix I, and the rejection region is $r_s \le -0.564$. The null hypothesis is rejected and we conclude that there is a negative correlation between the two variables.

15.65   The hypothesis to be tested is

H_0: Population distributions 1 and 2 are identical

versus

H_a: The distributions differ in location

and the test statistic is T, the rank sum of the positive (or negative) differences. The ranks are obtained by ordering the differences according to their absolute value. Define d_i to be the difference between a pair in populations 1 and 2 (i.e., $x_{1i} - x_{2i}$). The differences, along with their ranks (according to absolute magnitude), are shown in the following table.

d_i	−31	−31	−6	−11	−9	−7	7
Rank $\|d_i\|$	14.5	14.5	4.5	12.5	10.5	7	7

d_i	−11	7	−9	−2	−8	−1	−6	−3
Rank $\|d_i\|$	12.5	7	10.5	2	9	1	4.5	3

The rank sum for positive differences is $T^+ = 14$ and the rank sum for negative differences is $T^- = 106$ with $n = 15$. Consider the smaller rank sum and determine the appropriate lower portion of the two-tailed rejection region. Indexing $n = 15$ and $\alpha = 0.05$ in Table 8, Appendix I, the rejection region is $T \le 25$ and H_0 is rejected. We conclude that there is a difference between math and art scores.

15.67 Similar to Exercise 15.38. The ranks within each block are shown below.

Varieties	1	2	3	4	5	6	T_i
A	4	2	3	3	3	3	18
B	1	3	2	2	2	2	12
C	5	4	4	4	4	5	26
D	3	5	5	5	5	4	27
E	2	1	1	1	1	1	7

a Use the Friedman F_r statistic calculated as

$$F_r = \frac{12}{30(6)}\left[18^2 + 12^2 + \cdots + 7^2\right] - 3(36) = 20.13$$

and the rejection region is $F_r > \chi^2_{0.05} = 9.49$. Hence, H_0 is rejected and we conclude that there is a difference in the levels of yield for the five varieties of wheat.

b From Exercise 11.66, $F = 18.61$ and H_0 is rejected. The results are the same.

15.69 **a–b** Since the experiment is a completely randomized design, the Kruskal–Wallis H test is used. The combined ranks are shown below.

Plant	Ranks					T_i
A	9	12	5	1	7	34
B	11	15	4	19	14	63
C	3	13	2	9	6	33
D	20	17	9	16	18	80

The test statistic, based on the rank sums, is

$$H = \frac{12}{n(n+1)}\sum \frac{T_i^2}{n_i} - 3(n+1)$$

$$= \frac{12}{20(21)}\left[\frac{(34)^2}{5} + \frac{(63)^2}{5} + \frac{(33)^2}{5} + \frac{(80)^2}{5}\right] - 3(21) = 9.08$$

With $df = k - 1 = 3$, the observed value $H = 9.08$ is between $\chi^2_{0.025}$ and $\chi^2_{0.05}$ so that $0.025 < p\text{-value} < 0.05$. The null hypothesis is rejected and we conclude that there is a difference among the four plants.

c From Exercise 11.64, $F = 5.20$, and H_0 is rejected. The results are the same.

15.71 **a** Neither of the two plots follow the general patterns for normal populations with equal variances.

b Use the Friedman F_r test for a randomized block design. The ***MINITAB*** printout follows.

Friedman Test: Cadmium versus Harvest blocked by Rate
```
S = 10.33   DF = 2   P = 0.006

                          Sum
                           of
Harvest   N  Est Median  Ranks
1         6      202.29   11.0
2         6      201.21    7.0
3         6      300.73   18.0
Grand median = 234.74
```

Since the *p*-value is 0.006, the results are highly significant. There is evidence of a difference among the responses to the three rates of application.

15.73 The data are already in rank form. The "substantial experience" sample is designated as sample 1, and $n_1 = 5, n_2 = 7$. Calculate

$$T_1 = 19$$

$$T_1^* = n_1(n_1 + n_2 + 1) - T_1 - 5(13) - 19 = 46$$

The test statistic is $T = \min(T_1, T_1^*) = 19$

With $n_1 = n_2 = 12$, the one-tailed rejection region with $\alpha = 0.05$ is found in Table 7(a), Appendix I, to be $T_1 \le 21$. The observed value, $T = 19$, falls in the rejection region and H_0 is rejected. There is sufficient evidence to indicate that the review board considers experience a prime factor in the selection of the best candidates.

15.75 Define $p = P($student exhibits increased productivity after the installation$)$ and $X =$ number of students who exhibit increased productivity. The hypothesis to be tested is

$$H_0: \quad p = 1/2 \quad \text{versus} \quad H_a: \quad p > 1/2$$

using the sign test with x as the test statistic. Using the large sample approximation, the test statistic is

$$z = \frac{x - 0.5n}{0.5\sqrt{n}} = \frac{21 - 0.5(35)}{0.5\sqrt{35}} - 1.18$$

and the one-tailed rejection region with $\alpha = 0.05$ is $z > 1.645$. The null hypothesis is rejected and we conclude that the new lighting was effective in increasing student productivity.

15.77 Similar to Exercise 15.32. The data with corresponding ranks in parentheses are shown below.

Training Periods (hours)			
0.5	1.0	1.5	2.0
8 (9.5)	9 (11.5)	4 (1.5)	4 (1.5)
14 (14)	7 (7)	6 (5)	7 (7)
9 (11.5)	5 (3.5)	7 (7)	5 (3.5)
12 (13)		8 (9.5)	
$T_1 = 48$	$T_2 = 22$	$T_3 = 23$	$T_4 = 12$
$n_1 = 4$	$n_2 = 3$	$n_3 = 4$	$n_4 = 3$

The test statistic, based on the rank sums, is

$$H = \frac{12}{n(n+1)} \sum \frac{T_i^2}{n_i} - 3(n+1)$$

$$= \frac{12}{14(15)} \left[\frac{(48)^2}{4} + \frac{(22)^2}{3} + \frac{(23)^2}{4} + \frac{(12)^2}{3} \right] - 3(15) = 7.4333$$

The rejection region with $\alpha = 0.01$ and $k - 1 = 3 \ df$ is based on the chi-square distribution, or $H > \chi_{0.01}^2 = 11.34$. The null hypothesis is not rejected and we conclude that there is insufficient evidence to indicate a difference in the distribution of times for the four groups.

15.79   **a**   The batsmen have already been ranked. Let x be the true ranking and let y be my ranking. Since no ties exist in either the x or y rankings.

$$r_s = 1 - \frac{6\sum d_i^2}{n(n^2 - 1)} = 1 - \frac{6\left[(-2)^2 + (1)^2 + \cdots + (1)^2\right]}{8(63)} = 1 - \frac{6(22)}{504} = 0.738$$

       b   To test for positive correlation with $\alpha = 0.05$, index 0.05 in Table 9, Appendix I, and the rejection region is $r_s \geq 0.643$. We reject the null hypothesis of no association and conclude that a positive association exists.

Case Study: How's Your Cholesterol Level?

1   The design is a randomized block design, with tasters as blocks and the three types of eggs as treatments.

2   Since the judges are only asked to provide a rating between 0 and 20, the resulting data are not likely to be normally distributed. The parametric assumptions are probably not satisfied in this case, and a nonparametric test should be used.

3   The Friedman F_r test should be used. The ranks within each block are shown below.

Tasters	H	S	E
Bowe	3	2	1
Carroll	3	1	2
Katzl	2	3	1
O'Connell	2	3	1
Passot	3	2	1
Totals	14	10	6

The Friedman F_r statistic is

$$F_r = \frac{12}{15(4)} \left[14^2 + 10^2 + 6^2 \right] - 3(20) = 66.4 - 60 = 6.4$$

and the rejection region is $F_r > \chi^2_{0.05} = 5.99$. Hence, H_0 is rejected and we conclude that there is a difference in the average scores for the three brands of egg substitutes.

Project 15-A: Air Conditioning Makes You Gain Weight

a   For this particular study, we wish to determine if the distribution of basal metabolic rate for females who use air conditioning is the same as for females who do not use air conditioning. Our null and alternative hypotheses are

> H_0: the distribution of basal metabolic rate for females from Vancouver who use air conditioning during the hours of night sleep is the same as for females from Vancouver who do not use air conditioning during the hours of night sleep.
>
> versus
>
> H_a: the distributions differ

The Wilcoxon rank-sum test begins by ordering all of the observations from smallest to largest. The observations are ranked, where the smallest observation is assigned a rank of 1, the second smallest is assigned a rank of 2, and so forth. Additionally, we label the observations based on whether they belong to Group A or Group B. We thus obtain the following list of ordered basal metabolic rates

950 (1, A), 987 (2, B), 998 (3, B), 1011 (4, B), 1027 (5, A), 1086 (6, B), 1088 (7, A), 1090 (8, A), 1099 (9, B), 1101 (10, B), 1125 (11, B), 1145 (12, A), 1150 (13.5, A), 1150 (13.5, A), 1199 (15, A)

Since the value 1150 appears twice, we have a tie. We accommodate the tie by finding the average of the ranks these observations would have been assigned (i.e., 13 and 14). In this case, each of these observations is assigned a rank of (13+14)/2=13.5.

Since Group A has 8 observations, and Group B has 7 observations, we set $n_1 = 7$ and $n_2 = 8$. Thus, when calculating T_1, we sum the ranks assigned to observations from Group B. Hence,

$$T_1 = 2 + 3 + 4 + 6 + 9 + 10 + 11 = 45$$
$$T_1{}^* = n_1(n_1 + n_2 + 1) - T_1 = 7(7 + 8 + 1) - 45 = 102 - 45 = 57$$

Our test statistic is the minimum of T_1 and $T_1{}^*$. In this case, we set $T_{test} = \min (45,57) = 45$. Note that since this is a two-tailed test, we need to look up a value associated with $\alpha/2 = 0.05/2 = 0.025$. The critical value when $\alpha/2 = 0.025$ (found in Table 7(b) in Appendix I) is $T_{crit} = 38$.

Our decision is to reject the null hypothesis in favour of the alternative if our test statistic is less than or equal to the critical value. In this case, since $T > T_\alpha$, we do not reject the null hypothesis. There is insufficient evidence to suggest that the distributions are different.

b   To test whether or not the metabolic rates for Group A are significantly higher than those for Group B, we update our null and alternative hypotheses.

> H_0: the distribution of basal metabolic rate for females from Vancouver who use air conditioning during the hours of night sleep is the same as for females from Vancouver who do not use air conditioning during the hours of night sleep.
>
> versus
>
> H_a: the distribution of basal metabolic rate for females from Vancouver who use air conditioning during the hours of night sleep is greater than for females from Vancouver who do not use air conditioning during the hours of night sleep.

While our alternative hypothesis has changed, the ranks and test statistic remain the same. We need only look up the appropriate critical value. Since our alternative is one-sided, we look up the critical value when $\alpha = 0.05$. In this case, we find $T_{crit} = 41$.

Our decision is to reject the null hypothesis in favour of the alternative if our test statistic is less than or equal to 41. Since $45 > 41$, there is insufficient evidence to suggest that the basal metabolic rate for females who use air conditioning during the hours of night sleep is higher than for females who do not use air conditioning during the hours of night sleep.

c   The normal approximation is generally valid when the sample sizes for both groups is 10 or larger. In this case, we have both sample sizes smaller than 10. For this reason, we do not use the normal approximation.

If we assume the data come from a normal distribution, we could use a t test to compare the mean basal metabolic rates. Of course, we would have to check whether or not we could assume that the group variances were equivalent in order to select the most appropriate t test statistic.

Project 15-B: Does Drinking Water Increase Metabolism?

a   Our null and alternative hypotheses are

H_0: the distribution of basal metabolic rate for females who drink the appropriate amount of water (A) is identical to the distribution of basal metabolic rate for females who do not drink the appropriate amount of water (B), and $P(A > B) = p = 0.5$.

versus

H_a: the distribution of basal metabolic rate for females who drink the appropriate amount of water is shifted to the right of the distribution of basal metabolic rate for females who do not drink the appropriate amount of water, and $p > 0.5$.

b   To determine the sign test statistic, we first determine the differences in our observations (before − after = $x - y$). The sign of the differences are identified (as indicated within the brackets).

-45 (−), -11 (−), -70 (−), -38 (−), -31 (−), -46 (−), -54 (−), -43 (−), -48 (−), -10 (−)

The test statistic is the number of positives observed. In this particular case, $T = 0$, since there are no positive differences.

c   Since our data are dependent (i.e., observations before and after treatment are related), the appropriate test for this situation is the sign test for a paired experiment. Here we assume under the null hypothesis that the probability that after values exceed before values is 0.5. The number of observational pairs where the difference is positive represents a binomial random variable.

d   Based on the alternative hypothesis, this is a one-tailed test. We reject the null hypothesis when $\alpha = 0.10$ if our observed test statistic is less than 3. This can be determined reviewing the cumulative binomial probabilities when $n = 10$ and $p = 0.5$. Note that $P(X \leq 3) = 0.172$ and $P(X \leq 2) = 0.055$. Hence, if we observed $X < 3$ we would reject the null hypothesis in favour of the alternative.

e   Since our test statistic falls within the rejection region, we can conclude at the $\alpha = 0.10$ level that drinking an appropriate amount of water was helpful in increasing metabolism.

f   The null hypothesis would be rejected if $\alpha > 0.000976525$. This value represents the p-value for our test statistic. That is, the probability of observing an observation as extreme or more extreme than that which was observed. In our case, the p-value is calculated using
$$p\text{-value} = P(X \leq 0) = {}_{10}C_0(0.5)^0(0.5)^{10} = 0.5^{10} = 0.000976525$$

g   Our large-sample z statistic for testing the hypothesis in part **a**, and given a sample size $n = 10$ and $x = 0$, is
$$z = \frac{x - 0.5n}{0.5\sqrt{n}} = \frac{0 = 0.5(10)}{0.5\sqrt{10}} = -3.162278$$
The critical value is $z_\alpha = -1.282$. Since our test statistic is less than our critical value, we reject the null hypothesis in favour of the alternative.

h   Our decisions are the same for both parts **e** and **g**. That is, there is sufficient evidence to suggest that an appropriate amount of water will increase the basal metabolic rate.

i   The null and alternative hypotheses for the Wilcoxon Signed-Rank test are

H_0: the relative frequency distribution of basal metabolic rate for females who drink the appropriate amount of water is identical to the relative frequency distribution of basal metabolic rate for females who do not drink the appropriate amount of water.

versus

H_a: the relative frequency distribution of basal metabolic rate for females who drink the appropriate amount of water is shifted to the right of the relative frequency distribution of basal metabolic rate for females who do not drink the appropriate amount of water.

j   To determine the test statistic for the Wilcoxon signed-rank test, we begin by calculating the differences (before − after) and then ranking the absolute values of the differences from smallest to largest as indicated by the values in the brackets.

$$-45 \ (6), \ -11 \ (2), \ -70 \ (10), \ -38 \ (4), \ -31 \ (3), \ -46 \ (7), \ -54 \ (9), \ -43 \ (5), \ -48 \ (8), \ -10 \ (1)$$

To determine the test statistic, we need to calculate T^- and T^+. T^- represents the sum of all ranks associated with a negative difference, while T^+ represents the sum of all ranks associated with a positive difference. Here we have

$$T^- = 1 + 2 + 3 + 4 + 5 + 6 + 7 + 8 + 9 + 10 = 55$$
$$T^+ = 0$$

Since our alternative hypothesis is one-sided (where our after distribution is hypothesized to fall to the right of the before distribution), we select T^+ as our test statistic.

k   The rejection region for our test can be found by looking up our critical value (Table 8 in Appendix I). For our particular study and given a one-tailed alternative hypothesis with $\alpha = 0.05$, we obtain a critical value of 11. That is, we reject the null hypothesis in favour of the alternative if our test statistic is less than or equal to 11.

l   Since our test statistic $T^+ = 0$ falls within the rejection region, we reject the null hypothesis in favour of the alternative. That is, there is sufficient evidence to suggest that drinking the appropriate amount of water will increase the basal metabolic rate.

m   The p-value for the Wilcoxon signed-rank test can be approximated by examining the values in Table 8 of Appendix I. Our observed test statistic of 0 given $n = 10$ for a one-tailed alternative hypothesis would be rejected even if $\alpha = 0.005$ (which would coincide with a rejection region such that you would reject the null hypothesis if $T^+ \leq 3$). Hence, we can state that the p-value for this test is p-value ≤ 0.005.

n   The large-sample Wilcoxon signed-rank test for testing the hypothesis in part **i** is calculated as
$$z = \frac{T^+ - E(T^+)}{\sigma_{T^+}} = \frac{0 - 27.5}{\sqrt{96.25}} = \ 2.803060$$
where $E(T^+) = n(n+1)/4 = 10(11)/4 = 27.5$, and $\sigma^2 = n(n+1)(2n+1)/24 = 96.25$. Our critical value for a one-tailed alternative hypothesis (with $\alpha = 0.05$) is -1.282. We would reject the null hypothesis if our test statistic is less than -1.282. Since our test statistic is -2.803060, we reject the null hypothesis in favour of the alternative. There is sufficient evidence to suggest that drinking the appropriate amount of water will increase the basal metabolic rate.

o   The results from parts **e**, **l**, and **n** all agree. That is, they all suggest that drinking the appropriate amount of water will increase basal metabolic rate.

p   To determine Spearman's rank correlation coefficient, we first rank each group, and then determine S_{xx}, S_{xy} and S_{yy}, as shown below.

Before (x):   1105(7), 1077(5), 1020 (4), 989 (3), 1120 (8), 1099 (6), 1145 (10), 907 (1), 1131 (9), 988 (2)
After (y):   1150(7), 1088(4), 1090 (5), 1027 (3), 1151 (8), 1145 (6), 1199 (10), 950 (1), 1179 (9), 998 (2)

$$S_{xx} = \sum_{i=1}^{n}(x_i - \overline{x})^2 = (7-5.5)^2 + (5-5.5)^2 + \cdots + (2-5.5)^2 = 82.5$$

$$S_{xy} = \sum_{i=1}^{n}(x_i - \overline{x})(y_i - \overline{y}) = (7-5.5)(7-5.5) + (5-5.5)(4-5.5) + \cdots + (2-5.5)(2-5.5) = 81.5$$

$$S_{yy} = \sum_{i=1}^{n}(y_i - \overline{y})^2 = (7-5.5)^2 + (4-5.5)^2 + \cdots + (2-5.5)^2 = 82.5$$

The Spearman rank correlation coefficient is calculated as

$$r_s = \frac{S_{xy}}{\sqrt{S_{xx}S_{yy}}} = \frac{81.5}{\sqrt{(82.5)(82.5)}} = 0.9878788$$

q The critical value for testing a correlation between the data given $\alpha/2 = 0.025$ (for a two-tailed hypothesis) is obtained from Table 9 in Appendix I. For our test, with $n = 10$, we have a critical value of 0.648. We will reject the null hypothesis if our test statistic exceeds this value. Since our test statistic is 0.9878788, we reject the null hypothesis in favour of the alternative. There is sufficient evidence to suggest that there is a relationship between x and y.

Project 15-C: Increase Your Overall Muscle Mass and Boost Your Metabolism

a   To use the Kruskal–Wallis H statistic, we first rank the observations from smallest to largest. Numbers inside the brackets represent ranks, S1 through S5 represent the strategy. We thus have

877 (1, S3)	890 (2, S3)	905 (3, S5)	955 (4, S2)	975 (5, S1)
981 (6, S4)	987 (7, S2)	993 (8, S5)	995 (9, S4)	998 (10, S1)
1001 (11, S2)	1009 (12, S5)	1012 (13, S4)	1034 (14, S4)	1055 (15, S1)
1074 (16, S1)	1089 (17, S3)	1098 (18, S4)	1099 (19, S2)	1101 (20, S1)
1123 (21, S1)	1129 (22, S4)	1134 (23, S2)	1143 (24, S5)	1151 (25, S3)
1159 (26, S5)	1173 (27, S3)	1188 (28, S3)	1191 (29, S5)	1195 (30, S2)

We sum the ranks for each of the treatments (S1 through S5). This gives us $T_1 = 87$, $T_2 = 94$, $T_3 = 100$, $T_4 = 82$ and $T_5 = 102$. Our test statistic is $H_{test} = 12/(30 \times 31) \times (1/6) \times (87^2 + 94^2 + 100^2 + 82^2 + 102^2) - 3(30 + 1) = 0.6193548$.

    Using $\alpha = 0.05$, we would obtain a critical χ^2 value (on $k - 1 = 5 - 1 = 4$ degrees of freedom) of 9.48773. We would reject the null hypothesis if our test statistic H exceeded 9.48773. Since our test statistic is less, we do not reject the null hypothesis. That is, there is insufficient evidence to suggest that there is a difference in location for at least two of the population distributions.

b   Using Table 5 in Appendix I, with 4 degrees of freedom, we can say that $P(\chi^2 > 0.6193548) > 0.10$.

c   Since our p-value is larger than α, we would fail to reject the null hypothesis.

d   Using the statistical package R (http://www.r-project.org/), we obtain the following output for analysis of variance:

	Df	Sum Sq	Mean Sq	F value	$P(>F)$
factor(strat)	4	2297	574	0.0587	0.9932
Residuals	25	244734	9789		

The approximate p-value for the F-statistic in testing equality of means is 0.9932. At the $\alpha = 0.05$ level, we would not reject the null hypothesis. There is insufficient evidence to suggest that any of the means differ from the others.

e   While the p-values are different, they both support the null hypothesis.

For the second experiment, we have the following solutions:

a   The experimental design is a randomized complete block design (RCBD).

b   The appropriate method for the analysis of an RCBD is the Friedman F_r test for randomized block designs. To calculate the F_r test statistic, we begin by ranking the observations within each block.

Age	S1	S2	S3	S4	S5
15–19	1187 (4)	1103 (3)	997 (1)	1029 (2)	1207 (5)
20–24	1310 (5)	1278 (3)	1251 (2)	1198 (1)	1305 (4)
25–29	1287 (4.5)	1191 (2)	1287 (4.5)	1121 (1)	1256 (3)
30–34	1223 (3)	1167 (2)	1234 (4)	1109 (1)	1245 (5)
35–39	1250 (4)	1289 (5)	1223 (1)	1244 (3)	1230 (2)
40–44	1312 (4)	11324 (5)	1288 (2)	1295 (3)	1159 (1)

Summing the ranks for each treatment we have
$T_1 = 4 + 5 + 4.5 + 3 + 4 + 4 = 24.5$
$T_2 = 20$
$T_3 = 14.5$
$T_4 = 11$
$T_5 = 20$

Our F_r test statistic is calculated as

$$F_r = \frac{12}{bk(k+1)} \sum_{i=1}^{k} T_i^2 - 3b(k+1) = \frac{12}{180}(24.5^2 + 20^2 + 14.5^2 + 11^2 + 20^2) - 108 = 7.433333$$

c   Since our $F_{r\ test} = 7.433333$, which is smaller than our critical χ^2 value of 9.48773, we do not reject the null hypothesis. We have sufficient evidence to suggest that the strategies are equally effective.

d   The observed significance level of this test can be determined as $1 - p$-value. Here our p-value exceeds 0.10, since $P(\chi^2 > 7.433333) > 0.10$ on 4 degrees of freedom. Thus, our significance level is less than 90%.

e   Using the statistical package R (http://www.r-project.org/) ,we obtain the following output for analysis of variance:

	Df	Sum Sq	Mean Sq	F value	$P_r(> F)$
factor(strat)	4	13470054	3367514	0.9964	0.4325
factor(age)	5	17880117	3576023	1.0581	0.4123
Residuals	20	67594925	3379746		

The approximate p-value for the F test associated with the strategies is 0.4325. At the 0.05 level, we would fail to reject the null hypothesis. There is sufficient evidence to suggest that all of the strategies result in similar BMR values.

f   While the p-values are different, they both support the null hypothesis.